D1597380

NASA AERONAUTICS BOOK SERIES

Unlimited Horizons

Design and Development of the U-2

Peter W. Merlin

Library of Congress Cataloging-in-Publication Data

Merlin, Peter W., 1964–
  Unlimited horizons : design and development of the U-2 / Peter W. Merlin.
    pages cm. — (NASA aeronautics book series)
  Includes bibliographical references and index.
  ISBN 978-1-62683-025-7
1. U-2 (Reconnaissance aircraft)—History. 2. U-2 (Reconnaissance
aircraft)—Design and construction. I. Title.
  UG1242.R4M4675 2015
  623.74'67—dc23
                                        2014045191

This publication is available as a free download at
http://www.nasa.gov/ebooks

ISBN 978-1-62683-025-7

90000>

9 781626 830257

National Aeronautics and Space Administration
Washington, DC

Table of Contents

A U-2 pilot gazes at the horizon from high altitude. (U.S. Air Force)

INTRODUCTION
A Cold War Necessity

"There is a certain feeling of courage and hope when you work in the field of the air. You instinctively look up, not down. You look ahead, not back. You look ahead where the horizons are absolutely unlimited."
– Robert E. Gross, Lockheed Chairman/CEO 1932–1961

On a summer day in 1955, ominous clouds darkened the skies over a remote desert valley in the Western United States, reflecting international tensions between the U.S. and the Union of Soviet Socialist Republics. In what had become known as the Cold War, the two superpowers vied for supremacy in the wake of World War II, waging a high-stakes game of brinksmanship as each strove to discover the other's strengths and weaknesses through overt and covert means. The next bold step for the U.S. involved a spindly silver airplane, innocuously designated U-2, undergoing preparations for its maiden flight in the skies above central Nevada. Although this event took place without fanfare and in utter obscurity, it heralded the beginning of an aeronautical technology program that spanned more than six decades and showcased innovative aircraft design and manufacturing techniques. Little did anyone realize at the time that what had begun as a tool of Cold War necessity would evolve into a versatile reconnaissance and research aircraft.

The U-2 program originated with a national requirement, an unsolicited proposal, and studies championed by a panel of notable scientists tasked with advising President Dwight D. Eisenhower on how the Nation might defend itself against the threat of a surprise Soviet nuclear attack. To do this required as much intelligence as possible on Soviet capabilities, but the Russian-dominated USSR was a closed society that was virtually inaccessible to the outside world.[1] British Prime Minister Winston Churchill once described Russia as "a riddle, wrapped in a mystery, inside an enigma."[2]

---

1. Chris Pocock, "Early History of the U-2 Dragon Lady," *Code One Online*, February 2002, *http://www.codeonemagazine.com/article.html?item_id=103*, accessed January 15, 2013.
2. Winston Churchill, *Maxims and Reflections* (Boston: Houghton Mifflin Company, 1949), p. 55.

The most promising avenue toward solving this riddle was through observation from high above. In a November 1954 memorandum to Allen W. Dulles, director of the Central Intelligence Agency (CIA), Dr. Edwin Land, founder of the Polaroid Company, advocated for development of a reconnaissance aircraft to be operated by the CIA with Air Force support. The vehicle, already under development by Lockheed Aircraft Company, was described as essentially a powered glider. It would accommodate a single pilot and require a range of 3,000 nautical miles. It would carry a camera capable of resolving objects as small as an individual person. To ensure survivability against Soviet surface-to-air missiles, the airplane would need to attain altitudes above 70,000 feet. Such a platform, he suggested, could provide locations of military and industrial installations, allow for a more accurate assessment of the Soviet order of battle, and allow estimates of Soviet ability to produce and deliver nuclear weapons. Land recognized that the airplane's apparent invulnerability was limited. "The opportunity for safe overflight may last only a few years," he wrote, "because the Russians will develop radars and interceptors or guided missile defenses for the 70,000-foot region."[3]

Designed as a stopgap measure to provide overhead reconnaissance capability during the early years of the Cold War, the versatile U-2 has since evolved to meet changing requirements well into the 21st century. Though many authors have documented the airplane's operational history, few have made more than a cursory examination of its technical aspects or its role as a NASA research platform. This volume includes an overview of the origin and development of the Lockheed U-2 family of aircraft with early National Advisory Committee for Aeronautics (NACA) and National Aeronautics and Space Administration (NASA) involvement, construction and materials challenges faced by designers and builders, releasable performance characteristics and capabilities, use of U-2 and ER-2 airplanes as research platforms, and technical and programmatic lessons learned.

---

3. Edwin H. Land, memorandum to Allen W, Dulles, November 5, 1954, *http://www.gwu. edu/~nsarchiv/NSAEBB/NSAEBB74/U2-03.pdf*, accessed January 23, 2013.

The Martin RB-57D was based on the B-57 light, twin-engine bomber, but with improved engines and a longer wingspan. (U.S. Air Force)

CHAPTER 1

Designing for High Flight

Air Force officials had been pursuing the idea of high-altitude reconnaissance since January 1953, when Bill Lamar and engine specialist Maj. John Seaberg of the Wright Air Development Center (WADC) in Ohio drafted a request for a design study to develop a highly specialized aircraft that would be produced in small numbers. Surprisingly, they recommended bypassing such prominent aircraft manufacturers as Lockheed, Boeing, and Convair and instead focusing on Bell Aircraft Corporation and Fairchild Engine and Airplane Corporation. Their superiors at Air Research and Development Command (ARDC) headquarters agreed that because a relatively small production run was envisioned, these smaller companies would likely give the project a higher priority. In order to provide an interim, near-term option, they also asked officials at the Martin Company to study the possibility of modifying the manufacturer's B-57 light jet bomber with a longer wingspan and improved engines. The three companies were asked to submit results by the end of the year. The study project, dubbed Bald Eagle, called for a subsonic aircraft with an operational radius of 1,500 nautical miles that would be capable of attaining an altitude of 70,000 feet and carrying a single crewmember and a payload of between 100 and 700 pounds. It was to be equipped with available production engines (modified, if necessary) and have as low a gross weight as possible.[1]

All three companies had submitted their respective studies by January 1954. Martin's modified B-57 (designated Model 294) featured lengthened wings, accommodations for cameras and sensors, and uprated twin engines. Fairchild's M-195 design was powered by a single engine and featured an over-the-fuselage intake and stub-boom mounting for the vertical and horizontal tail surfaces. Bell offered a delicate-looking, lightweight, twin-engine airplane called the Model 67.[2]

---

1. Chris Pocock, *50 Years of the U-2* (Atglen, PA: Schiffer Military History, 2005), pp. 10–11.
2. Jay Miller, *The X-Planes: X-1 to X-45* (Hinckley, U.K.: Midland Publishing, 2001), pp. 207–208.

Martin Model 294

In order to expedite construction and testing of an interim reconnaissance platform, the Model 294 was built using the standard Martin B-57 light, twin-engine bomber as a starting point. Under project Black Knight, designers at Martin replaced the stock J65-W-5 engines with two 10,000-pound-thrust Pratt & Whitney J57-P-9 turbojets. The airplane's wingspan was extended from 64 feet to 106 feet, expanding the gross wing area to 1,500 square feet. By April 1955, the Model 294 had been officially designated the RB-57D and an initial order for six airframes had been increased to 20. Three versions were built, including the first 13 airframes as a single-seat model equipped with several cameras and additional sensor gear located in a bay behind the pilot's station. Martin also built a single RB-57D-1 capable of carrying the AN/APQ-56 high-resolution, side-looking radar for both daylight and nighttime radar-mapping reconnaissance. The final six airframes, designated RB-57D-2, carried a second crewmember to operate sensors for gathering electronic intelligence (ELINT) and signals intelligence (SIGINT) data.[3]

Martin engineers designed an innovative aluminum honeycomb wing structure that was both strong and lightweight. Unfortunately, it proved vulnerable to water seepage and wing stress. An accelerated flight-test program in 1955 and 1956 revealed that the wing spar and some of the skin panels were prone to cracking and needed strengthening. The spar was not designed for long service life of high dynamic loads, and engineers initially estimated the fatigue life of the RB-57D to be fewer than 1,000 flight hours. In fact, several aircraft were retired after their wings separated following landing. Fortunately, no such incident occurred in flight.[4]

Fairchild M-195

During the General Configuration Study, designers at Fairchild initially considered a wide variety of possible configurations, from subsonic turboprop-powered airplanes with high-aspect-ratio wings to supersonic rocket and ramjet-powered vehicles. The supersonic configurations were quickly eliminated due to the projected length of time required for design and development. In a preliminary analysis, Fairchild engineers narrowed wing loading to between 10 and 30 pounds per square foot, and they studied configurations powered by two J57,

---

3. Jay Miller, *Lockheed U-2* (Austin, TX: Aerofax, 1983), p. 16.
4. Ibid., pp. 16–17.

J67, or J73 engines. This resulted in designs with straight, high-aspect-ratio wings and an operational ceiling between 65,000 and 67,200 feet.[5]

Taking into consideration overall structural weight versus aerodynamic gains, the design team ultimately chose a single-engine, J57-powered configuration. It was to be constructed from aluminum using conventional methods and as many off-the-shelf components as possible for use with internal electrical and environmental control systems. The M-195 featured a pressurized cockpit equipped with an ejection seat. A sensor bay was designed to accommodate two 36-inch equivalent-focal-length (EFL) oblique cameras and two 6-inch EFL oblique cameras. The two main landing gear wheels retracted into the wing roots in typical fashion, but instead of a nose wheel, the airplane was equipped with a steerable tail wheel. The wings, set low on the fuselage, were equipped with a gust relief system to elevate the flaps and ailerons when necessary. The powerplant installation was highly unconventional for the time, incorporating a dorsal inlet just behind and above the cockpit. This arrangement minimized intake and exhaust duct lengths to maximize use of available thrust, and at the same time, it permitted short pressurization ducts to the cockpit and sensor bay, reducing weight and improving efficiency.[6]

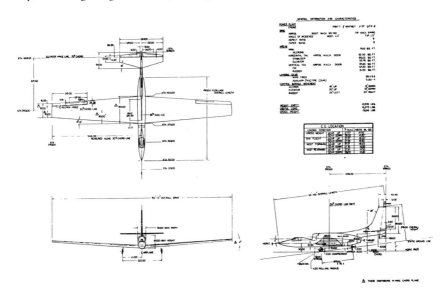

Fairchild M-195. (Jay Miller collection)

5. Ibid., p. 15.

6. Ibid.

Weight remained a critical factor. Fairchild engineers estimated the empty weight of the airframe, including payload and powerplant, to be 10,943 pounds. Including crew, fuel, and lubricants, the total gross takeoff weight was approximately 19,000 pounds. This would allow the M-195 to follow a mission profile that called for initial ascent to 61,100 feet at 150 knots indicated airspeed over a distance of 139 miles. The pilot would then climb to an operational cruising altitude of 65,000 feet over a distance of 161 miles. After leveling off and setting a cruise speed of 390 knots true airspeed, the airplane would have a range of 1,200 miles to its target. The return trip would be at cruising altitude, followed by a spiraling descent as close to home base as desired. The landing weight was projected to be approximately 12,106 pounds.[7]

Bell Model 67

The third entry in the design study was Bell's Model 67, which eventually came to be known as the X-16. Though the Martin RB-57D offered a rapid, low-risk response to the need for high-altitude reconnaissance, it was only intended to fill the gap until a more capable new design could be fielded. Fairchild's M-195 met the proposed requirements, but it was neither as capable as Bell's entry nor less risky than the RB-57D. The X-16 soon emerged as the leader of the pack.

Following official approval by the Air Force in May 1954 and the signing of a contract in September, Bell prepared to complete a prototype within 18 months, followed by production of 27 additional airframes. Led by the company's chief project engineer, Richard Smith, the Bell team designed the X-16 to cruise at 70,000 feet with an unrefueled range of 3,300 miles. A payload of two 12-inch EFL cameras or two 36-inch EFL cameras would permit photography of everything along a flight path 50 miles wide and up to 795 miles long. The extremely lightweight airframe featured high-aspect-ratio wings and was powered by two Pratt & Whitney J57-P-31 turbojet engines modified for enhanced performance at high altitudes. To reduce weight, the airplane had a centerline bicycle landing gear configuration with outrigger wheels to provide balance on takeoff and landing. Weight restrictions necessary to support altitude and range requirements further resulted in an extremely flexible airframe. This meant that the X-16 had an extremely low structural-dynamic envelope that was rated between +3 g's and −1 g during maneuvering flight. Due to structural flexibility, engineers predicted that the wings—spanning nearly 115 feet—would suffer aeroelastic divergence as they reached critical

---

7. Ibid., pp. 15–16.

A model of the Bell X-16 with an F-86 fighter for comparison. (Jay Miller collection)

Mach number.[8] The designers attempted to mitigate this concern by giving the wings a quarter-chord sweep angle of 15 degrees and moving the ailerons inboard from the wingtips. The pressurized cockpit was equipped with standard instruments, an ejection seat, a periscopic sextant for navigation, a control stick like in a fighter plane, and all necessary equipment for operating the reconnaissance systems. Empty weight was expected to be 23,330 pounds, with a gross takeoff weight of 36,200 pounds fully fueled.[9]

Construction of the X-16 prototype progressed smoothly for the first 12 months, but events in Washington, DC, and Burbank, CA, were about to have a profound effect on the airplane's future and that of Bell. First, CIA officials had learned of the Air Force study and argued that clandestine reconnaissance over denied territory should be a function of a civilian intelligence agency rather than of a military service. Second, Lockheed chief designer Clarence L. "Kelly" Johnson had also learned of the project and decided to submit an unsolicited proposal of his own.[10]

---

8. The lowest Mach number at which local airflow over some point on the airfoil reaches the speed of sound, even though the aircraft itself has an airspeed less than Mach 1.0.

9. Miller, *Lockheed U-2*, pp. 17–18.

10. Miller, *The X-Planes*, pp. 208–209.

Lockheed CL-282

Shortly after Lamar and Seaberg drafted their request, someone at the Pentagon informed Johnson of the Air Force study and Lockheed's exclusion from it. He managed to get a copy of the program requirements and quickly developed a concept for an airplane capable of attaining a maximum altitude of 73,000 feet with an operating radius of 1,400 miles from the beginning of a cruise climb starting at about 65,000 feet. Gross takeoff weight was to be just 13,768 pounds, including a 600-pound camera payload. To reduce weight, the airplane would have no undercarriage, taking off from a ground cart and landing on a skid attached to the lower fuselage. In December 1953, Johnson assigned engineers Phil Coleman and Gene Frost to develop procedures for lightening the airframe and increasing its wing area for maximum altitude capability.[11] They were soon joined by Henry Combs, a talented structural engineer and accomplished sailplane pilot.[12]

Johnson's new design, called the CL-282, was based on his XF-104 fighter interceptor. Although the fighter was optimized for high-speed flight in the Mach 2 range, Johnson realized that he could save time and expense by maximizing use of the original XF-104 design and manufacturing experience. He simply eliminated all unnecessary requirements such as fighter load factor, armament, and landing gear, while retaining the general fuselage and tail configuration. Johnson completely redesigned the wings and shortened the fuselage, but this resulted in only minor local changes to the loft lines, and it was possible to reuse all of the basic XF-104 tooling jigs as well as most of the detail jigs.[13]

The greatest challenge was reducing overall structural weight in order to allow the airplane to perform the desired mission while carrying a 600-pound, non-jettisonable payload. Structurally, the CL-282 fuselage was virtually identical to that of the XF-104 except for the deletion of a 62-inch section of the fuselage behind the cockpit. Since the CL-282 was designed for a maneuvering load factor of 2.5 g's as compared to 7.33 g's on the XF-104, fuselage strength requirements were reduced, allowing for reduced material gauges (i.e., aircraft

---

11. Kelly Johnson, "Log for Project X," Lockheed California Company, December 1953. This was the designer's personal diary of activities during design and development of the U-2. All information is from the author's copy, retyped from a copy in the Chris Pocock collection.

12. Pocock, *50 Years of the U-2*, pp. 11–12.

13. Jay Miller, *Lockheed Skunk Works: The First Fifty Years* (Arlington, TX: Aerofax, 1993), p. 213. Appendix I of Miller's book contains the entire text of Kelly Johnson's "CL-282 High Altitude Aircraft," Lockheed Report LR-9732, 1954.

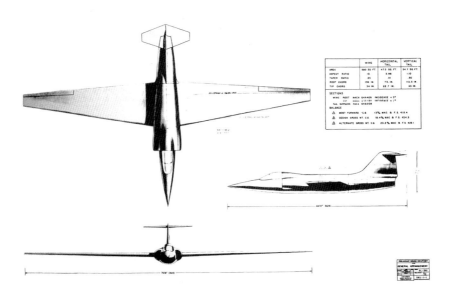

The Lockheed CL-282 was based on the F-104 Starfighter but had a significantly longer wing-span. (Lockheed Martin)

skin and structural members could be manufactured from thinner aluminum stock). Shortening the fuselage eliminated 3,990 pounds of fuel weight and, along with the removal of armament, necessitated moving the engine forward 562 inches to compensate for the change in the center of gravity. With the powerplant located in line with the wings (which also contained the fuel load), the 1-g bending moments of the fuselage were well below those of the XF-104, and tail loads were reduced. Elimination of landing gear bays also made it easier to shift the engine forward, but it was necessary to alter the shape and position of the inlet ducts to accommodate the change in engine position and improve airflow efficiency at lower airspeeds. The forward bulkhead of a 75-gallon sump tank between the inlet ducts also served to transfer fuselage shear loading to the outside contour of the duct assemblies. Basic fuselage joints, including those for mating the wings and tail, remained the same as on the XF-104, and the CL-282 retained the fighter's T-tail empennage configuration. The speed brakes were also retained. In place of landing gear, the airplane was equipped with an abrasion-resistant scuff strip approximately 15 inches wide and extending the full length of the bottom of the fuselage.

In the forward fuselage, the crew accommodations were radically revised. The original XF-104 cockpit included a downward ejection seat that, in the event of an emergency, could be jettisoned through an escape hatch. Because bailout velocities were expected to be low for the CL-282, the ejection seat

7

and escape hatch were eliminated altogether and replaced with a simple bucket seat. This meant that the pilot would have to open the hinged canopy and climb out. The cockpit was pressurized to provide an equivalent pressure altitude of 25,000 feet when the airplane was operating above 70,000 feet. Pressurization was supplied by bleed air from the engine. Since a cockpit altitude of 25,000 feet necessitated the pilot's use of a pressure-demand oxygen system throughout the flight, the pilot was equipped with a partial-pressure suit and a 7-hour supply of oxygen.[14]

Johnson conducted a limited study of wing configurations in search of the optimum planform. While considering the airplane's overall weight and balance characteristics, he sought to determine the minimum area and aspect ratio necessary for achieving a maximum altitude of 75,000 feet. The result was a configuration featuring thin, straight, high-aspect-ratio wings spanning 70 feet, with a total area of 500 square feet. Unlike in most conventional designs, the wings lacked a carry-through structure and were simply bolted onto the fuselage ring frames. This limited the airplane's maneuver load factor considerably, but Johnson included an innovative span-load distribution control system. When flying at higher speeds or in turbulent conditions at altitudes up to 35,000 feet, the wing control surfaces could be raised (4 degrees for flaps and 10 degrees for ailerons) to reduce bending moments and tail loads by moving the wing's center of pressure inboard. Otherwise, the wing was of a conventional two-cell construction with the beam located at approximately 48 percent of chord. It was designed to resist bending moment in each surface by way of spanwise stringers originating at the main fuselage frame joints. A structural rib in the wing root distributed wing torsion to the fuselage frames. The wings also contained nylon bladder fuel tanks with internal ties to prevent deformation of the airfoil with changes in vapor pressure. Small, replaceable wingtip skids provided protection for the ends of the wings, and the ailerons, during landing.

Three engine candidates were considered in lieu of the stock General Electric J79 turbojet. The General Electric J73-X-52 weighed 3,150 pounds and produced 8,920 pounds of thrust at sea level, with a specific fuel consumption (pounds per hour/pounds of thrust) of 0.917. At 75,000 feet and Mach 0.75, it would have provided 398 pounds of thrust and a specific fuel consumption of 1.377, giving the airplane a maximum speed of 495 knots at cruise altitude. The Rolls Royce Avon RA.14 weighed 2,897 pounds and produced 9,500 pounds of thrust at sea level, with a specific fuel consumption of 0.840. At maximum cruise conditions, it would have provided 385 pounds

---

14. Ibid.

of thrust and a specific fuel consumption of 1.372. Finally, the Wright TJ3B1 weighed 2,720 pounds and produced 7,800 pounds of thrust at sea level, with a specific fuel consumption of 0.880. At cruise, it would have provided 339 pounds of thrust and a specific fuel consumption of 1.340. Although the Rolls Royce engine demonstrated superior performance on the basis of sea level static ratings, Johnson selected the J73-X-52 because of its superior performance at altitude and ease of adaptation to the XF-104 fuselage.[15]

Johnson submitted his CL-282 design study to Col. Bernard Schriever at the Pentagon in March 1954. Schriever expressed great interest and requested a more specific proposal. A month later Johnson met with senior Pentagon officials, including several Air Force generals who were not particularly enthusiastic. ARDC Commander Lt. Gen. Donald Putt and his staff had completed an evaluation of industry studies that had been generated by the Bald Eagle project, and they agreed with Maj. Seaberg's recommendation that the proposed airplane be equipped with two engines. The CL-282 had only one, as did the Fairchild M-195. Shortly after the April meeting, Martin was given immediate approval to proceed with the RB-57D. In early June 1954, despite lobbying by advocates within the Air Force Development and Advanced Planning office, Air Force Headquarters rejected the Lockheed proposal because it was too unconventional and had only a single engine, and they were already committed to the Martin program.[16]

All was not lost, however. Trevor Gardner, assistant secretary of the Air Force for Research and Development, had been most impressed with Johnson's CL-282 presentation. In May 1954, Gardener and two colleagues briefed leading CIA intelligence analyst Philip Strong on the CL-282 and the Bald Eagle designs. They asked him if the CIA might be interested in the CL-282 even if the Air Force was not. Strong subsequently discussed the idea with members of the Intelligence Systems Panel of the Air Force Scientific Advisory Board, some of whom thought the RB-57D was too heavy and that a lighter, single-engine design might be better suited to the proposed mission. With Cold War tensions high, the Eisenhower administration commissioned a panel of top-level experts to study the Soviet threat. The intelligence subpanel chaired by Edwin Land included Jim Baker of Harvard University Observatory and physics Nobel Laureate Ed Purcell from Harvard. Strong briefed the Land Panel on the CL-282 and soon found allies.[17]

---

15. Ibid.

16. Pocock, *50 Years of the U-2*, p. 13.

17. Ibid., pp. 14–15.

In September, Bell Aircraft received a contract to build the X-16. During a visit to the Bell plant, Baker and Allen Donovan from Cornell Aeronautical Laboratory were not impressed. Donovan felt that, by comparison, the Lockheed design offered the same or better overall performance at almost one-third the gross weight. Meanwhile, Land lobbied aggressively for the CL-282 while encouraging innovative ideas for reducing payload weight. Every extra pound meant 2 feet of altitude lost.[18]

Donovan briefed members of the Intelligence Systems Panel on the merits of the CL-282 and defined three requirements for a high-altitude spy plane: a single engine, a sailplane-type wing, and low structural load factors. Air Force proponents of the X-16 had argued that a second engine would allow the pilot to keep the plane aloft in the event of a single engine failure, but Donovan argued that it could only do so at an altitude that made it vulnerable to hostile ground fire. Single-engine aircraft were both lighter and historically more reliable than multi-engine aircraft. Stressing the absolute need to fly above 70,000 feet in order to avoid intercept, he noted that in the thin upper atmosphere, the power curve of a jet engine would fall off to about 6 percent of its sea-level thrust. The solution, he said, was to incorporate a high-aspect-ratio, low-induced-drag wing of the type used on sailplanes. Finally, he added that low structural load factors would reduce the airplane's overall gross weight. Donovan explained that aircraft built to military standards were engineered for combat maneuvers. Strengthening wings and other structures to withstand high speeds and sharp turns would add extra weight to the airframe and would be unnecessary considering the proposed mission profile. In short, a successful design required a delicate balance of thrust, lift, and weight. The Air Force study had resulted in designs that were altogether too conventional to meet the necessary requirements. The only viable candidate, Donovan insisted, was Lockheed's CL-282.[19]

Donovan's arguments won support for the CL-282, but that did not generate funds for Lockheed to pursue the concept. The Air Force was already committed to the Martin and Bell programs, so funding for Lockheed had to come from another source. The Land Panel offered a solution.[20]

Land and Gardner met with CIA Director Allen Dulles in late October in an effort to convince him that not only was it imperative that the CL-282 be built, but that its development and operation should not be entrusted to the

---

18. Ibid., p. 16.
19. Gregory W. Pedlow and Donald E. Welzenbach, *The CIA and the U-2 Program*, 1954–1974 (Washington, DC: CIA, 1998), pp. 25–26.
20. Ibid., p. 26.

Air Force. Dulles was initially skeptical that the agency should involve itself with such a major technical development effort, but Land insisted that the CIA had a right to pioneer scientific techniques for intelligence collection. Further, he emphasized that the civilian agency would be better suited to conducting covert reconnaissance missions. Land noted the urgency of proceeding swiftly, since "the opportunity for safe overflight may last only a few years, because the Russians will develop radars and interceptors or guided missile defenses for the 70,000-foot region."[21]

Next, Land and Presidential science advisor James Killian met with President Eisenhower. Despite knowing of the Air Force commitments, the president approved development of the CL-282. Eisenhower agreed that the new reconnaissance program should be controlled by the CIA and stipulated that it should be handled in an unconventional way so as to avoid bureaucratic entanglements and interservice rivalries. The strong advocacy of Killian and the distinguished scientists of the various advisory committees, combined with Eisenhower's support, ultimately won over Dulles, but some Air Force officials feared the decision to build the CL-282 put both the RB-57 and X-16 in jeopardy. The Air Force had already rejected Lockheed's design because of its single engine and because the X-16 offered a more conventional configuration as well as a more versatile platform that could be used in multiple military roles. Following additional discussions with Allen Donovan, Gen. Putt met with 15 scientists from the Technological Capabilities Panel and Maj. Seaberg from WADC, who briefed the group on all four aircraft proposals. Comparing their capabilities, Seaberg noted that the Bell, Fairchild, and Lockheed designs were comparable aerodynamically and that Martin's modified airframe was somewhat less capable overall. He stated that in his opinion, the CL-282's General Electric J73 engine would be insufficient for attaining the necessary altitude. Replacing the J73 with the Pratt & Whitney J57, however, would make the CL-282 competitive with both the Bell and Fairchild entries. One significant advantage of Lockheed's design was that Kelly Johnson had promised that his airplane would be flying by August 1955. Bell was not expected to deliver the first X-16 until the spring of 1956. Ultimately, Johnson was authorized to go ahead with the CL-282, but the Air Force did not abandon the X-16 until Lockheed's airplane completed its first flight.[22]

---

21. Chris Pocock, *The U-2 Spyplane: Toward The Unknown* (Atglen, PA: Schiffer, 2000), p. 17.

22. Pedlow and Welzenbach, *The CIA and the U-2 Program*, pp. 33–35.

Building the Team

On November 26, 1954, Allen Dulles assigned his special assistant, Richard Bissell, to take charge of the CL-282 development effort, which was designated Project Aquatone. Among Bissell's first tasks were arranging for money from the CIA's Contingency Reserve Fund to get the project started and finding ways to divert Air Force materiel to the program. Because security was paramount, he made the Aquatone project staff self-sufficient with its own contract management, administrative, financial, logistical, communications, and security personnel. Col. Osmond J. Ritland was assigned as Air Force liaison to the project and worked closely with Bissell. With Ritland's help, a number of J57 engines procured by the Air Force for use in the B-52, KC-135, F-100, and RB-57 were diverted for use in the CL-282 in order to prevent a separate contract with Pratt & Whitney from jeopardizing program security.[23] Kelly Johnson had promised Bissell that he could deliver the first airplane in just 8 months, but he had also been pressured into

The CIA placed Richard Bissell in charge of the Aquatone program. (CIA)

making significant design changes. The final configuration had been scaled up from the original CL-282 and now included landing gear. The sharply pointed XF-104 nose had been blunted and the XF-104's T-tail replaced with a more conventional arrangement. The new design eventually received a deceptive designation identifying it as a utility aircraft: U-2.[24]

In early December, Johnson began assembling a team of engineers and manufacturing personnel. He assigned Dick Boehme to assist him as project engineer and supervisor, and together they selected two dozen engineers for specialized design work. The task was made more difficult because they had to pull these workers from other Lockheed projects without being able to tell

23. Ibid., p. 40.
24. Pocock, *50 Years of the U-2*, p. 18.

their former supervisors why.[25] Each worker was selected for a particular specialty. Chan Engelbry worked out the aerodynamics while Carl Allmon and Alvin Jensen drafted the airplane's loft lines. Henry Combs, Ray McHenry, and Richard Hruda were tasked with calculating stress, and Lorne Cass calculated loads. Bob Wiele, Bill Bissell, Robert Kelly, and Royal Dow designed the wing structure. Two men were assigned to design the tail assembly, Herb Nystrom (vertical stabilizer) and Rod Kreimendahl (horizontal stabilizer). Ed Baldwin, Leroy English, Jack Painter, and Ray Kirkham designed various parts of the fuselage with additional help from Dave Robertson, who also developed the fuel system. Dan Zuck designed the cockpit. Cornelius Gardner designed the airplane's unique landing gear. The systems group included Vern Bremberg (hydraulics), Cliff Rockel and Sam Murphy (electrical), Vic Sorenson and George Ellison (controls), Ed Martin (reconnaissance systems), Doug Cone (air conditioning), and Elmer Gath (propulsion). Pete Gurin, John Henning, and Richard Lutz performed static testing. Leon Gavette designed various ground handling equipment, and Bob Charlton wrote the first technical manuals. Art Vierick was in charge of the manufacturing group, which included assembly foreman John Wanamaker, Bob Hunter, Charles Van Der Zee, and Tommy McCoy.[26] Johnson's team initially toiled 45 hours per week, but even after the staff grew to more than 80 people, work increased to 65 hours per week.[27]

Due to the need for extreme secrecy, the original U-2 manufacturing team worked within Lockheed's Advanced Development Projects division, informally known as the Skunk Works.[28] This elite organization had been established during World War II to develop the P-80 Shooting Star, one of the Nation's first jet aircraft, and eventually served as the company's rapid prototyping and development unit. Its early success was due in large part to Kelly Johnson's insistence that his engineers and draftsmen be located not more than 50 feet from the assembly floor. Construction difficulties and other problems could then be immediately brought to the attention of the appropriate design or manufacturing personnel. Paperwork was kept to a minimum, with no emphasis on neatly typed memorandums. In order to keep the project moving quickly, engineers simply made pencil notations directly on their original drawings. As a result,

25. Pedlow and Welzenbach, *The CIA and the U-2 Program*, p. 43.

26. Henry G. Combs, "U-2 Design and Fabrication," in *Proceedings of the U-2 Development Panel*, the U-2 History Symposium, National Defense University, Fort McNair, DC, September 1998, pp. 3–5.

27. Pedlow and Welzenbach, *The CIA and the U-2 Program*, p. 43.

28. The Skunk Works was named after the Kickapoo Joy Juice factory known as the Skonk Works in Al Capp's *Lil' Abner* cartoon strip. The nickname, coined by Lockheed engineer Irv Culver, was altered slightly to avoid copyright infringement.

Kelly Johnson, center, believed that managers, engineers, and shop personnel should interact as closely as possible in order to solve problems quickly. (Lockheed Martin)

Manufacturing crews assemble U-2 components. For security reasons, staffing was kept to a minimum. (Lockheed Martin)

problems could be resolved in a matter of hours rather than days or weeks.[29] This management technique was ideally suited to the U-2 design effort and became a hallmark of Lockheed's future programs.

Performance and payload were the driving factors behind the U-2 design. To ensure that the airplane would meet required specifications, for example, Al Robinson had to address challenges of reducing airframe and equipment weight. The U-2 configuration's higher gross weight compared to that of the original CL-282 threatened altitude performance. Lamenting this problem, Johnson once told his engineering staff that he would trade his grandmother for a 10-pound weight reduction. Subsequently, Robinson and the other engineers started referring to pounds as "grandmothers," as they struggled to eliminate unnecessary weight from the airframe and systems.[30] The desired gross weight needed to be 1.5 times the weight of the powerplant. Ultimately, even with the addition of a drag chute for landing, a 300 percent increase in the oxygen supply capacity, improved brakes, and an autopilot, the final gross takeoff weight was within 10 pounds of the original proposal.[31]

Henry Combs was impressed by the skill and efficiency demonstrated by various team members. To keep things moving, estimates were used when firm data were unavailable. As soon as more accurate data became available, work based on the estimates was modified as necessary. Staffing was kept to the absolute minimum necessary to accomplish any given task, and workers were allowed to do their jobs with as little interference as possible. Combs also admired the supervisory skills of Johnson's "backup genius," Dick Boehme, noting that his "engineering judgment was excellent and his ability to keep everyone in harmony with Kelly was extremely important."[32]

Building the Plane

Having promised delivery of 20 flyable airframes to the CIA at a cost of $22.5 million, Johnson next addressed challenges posed by the need for secrecy and the logistics involved in constructing the revolutionary airplane. Program security was ensured through various means. First, the original U-2 manufacturing

---

29. Pedlow and Welzenbach, *The CIA and the U-2 Program*, p. 45.

30. Pocock, *50 Years of the U-2*, p. 18.

31. Don Downie and Jim Jarboe, *The Inquisitive Angel*, a 16-millimeter film documentary produced by Hycon Mfg. Co. for the CIA in April 1957. Declassified in 2006, Roadrunners Internationale collection.

32. Combs, "U-2 Design and Fabrication," pp. 3–5.

The first 20 airframes were built at Lockheed's plant at Burbank Airport. (Lockheed Martin)

and development team was segregated in a remote corner of the Lockheed plant in Burbank, CA. Production facilities there were limited, so when the Air Force ordered 25 airframes, a second manufacturing plant was established at Oildale, near Bakersfield. Security constraints meant that normal subcontracting procedures were virtually impossible. Procurement of materials involved using sterilized drawings (with certain information redacted) and purchase orders; deliveries were routed to various inconspicuous locations.[33] Financing was handled under a special account separate from normal Lockheed channels. Dummy company names were established for use when dealing with outside vendors. Depending on what was being purchased, vendors might sign a contract with C&J Manufacturing Company (using Kelly Johnson's initials), J.E. Ramsey Company (named for Lockheed's purchasing manager), or B.V. Ward (named for Dick Boehme, Art Vierick, and George Welty). Only a senior executive from each vendor had been briefed to know the real identity of the customer. Specially cleared drivers picked up items from vendors using

---

33. Ibid., pp. 2–5.

unmarked trucks, delivering them to Burbank or Oildale. Correspondence was handled through a post office box outside of Burbank, and all communications with the customer took place via secure comlink.[34]

Approximately 87 percent of each airframe built in Burbank was fabricated within a single building. Metal components were fed through the company's main presses at night and on Sundays, then hidden from day-shift workers not cleared into the program. At peak production of the first 50 airframes, only 600 people were involved at both the Burbank and Oildale plants.[35] The designers and builders employed unorthodox methods with regard to engineering drawings and procedures. Typical company standards were abandoned—sometimes resulting in oversize drawings more than 20 feet long—and military specifications (Mil-Spec) served only as a design guide, but were not strictly followed. If a part had to be sent to an outside machine shop, accompanying drawings were sanitized of any information revealing the airplane's configuration. Personnel had access only to the minimum knowledge necessary to do their jobs. At the lowest level, vendor employees knew only that they were building an airplane, but they knew nothing about its configuration or mission. The midlevel included those who assembled partial or complete airframes and saw them loaded aboard cargo planes bound for unknown destinations. At the highest access level, there were only a few people who knew the identity of the customer, the test location, operational capabilities, and the overall mission. Workers were briefed to tell no one, not even family members, what they were doing. At Johnson's direction, no paperwork or blueprints were ever marked SECRET lest the label call attention to the documents in the event they fell into the hands of unauthorized persons. According to one former worker, "Kelly said that marking a document Top Secret was telling the enemy exactly what was most important to steal. Documents and drawings had no company or security markings. Everything was done within physically secured areas. We *never* talked about the program away from work."[36]

Every morning, Johnson met with each member of his team to discuss any problems from the previous day and take any necessary corrective action.[37] In order to streamline manufacturing operations, there was no formal configuration control board. Engineering drawings were released directly to assembly or functional system supervisors who were responsible for planning any necessary

---

34. Ray Passon, "The Early Days of the U-2: How They Did It," *Star Dusters Newsletter*, September 2003, p. 9.

35. Downie and Jarboe, *The Inquisitive Angel.*

36. Passon, "The Early Days of the U-2: How They Did It," pp. 9–10.

37. Downie and Jarboe, *The Inquisitive Angel.*

Lockheed established a second U-2 production line in Oildale to build airframes for the Air Force. (Lockheed Martin)

work and making a bill of material (a list of raw materials, subassemblies, intermediate assemblies, subcomponents, parts, and quantities of each needed to manufacture an end product). Each supervisor followed the design process from the beginning and maintained close contact with designers, thus ensuring that each component or assembly could be produced in volume (known as a producibility function) and providing greater opportunity to review or check engineering drawings before final release. As a result of schedule pressure and philosophical differences, engineering and manufacturing personnel often engaged in heated discussions, but always with mutual respect. Tooling and assembly supervisors coordinated an informal system for tool design. Throughout the manufacturing process, mockup and development mechanics were responsible for fabricating parts as well as assembling them. One noted that, "Some may say that this can only work for a prototype or small number of aircraft, but this was successful for production of more than 50 of the original U-2s."[38]

Johnson's U-2 design, finalized by January 1955, was a model of simplicity and innovation. The airframe was constructed primarily of aluminum alloys machined to the thinnest gauges allowable within structural strength requirements. Skin thickness varied from just 0.020 to 0.063 of an inch. Structural stiffening consisted of the fewest possible number of ribs, stringers, and doubler

---

38. Passon, "The Early Days of the U-2: How They Did It," p. 10.

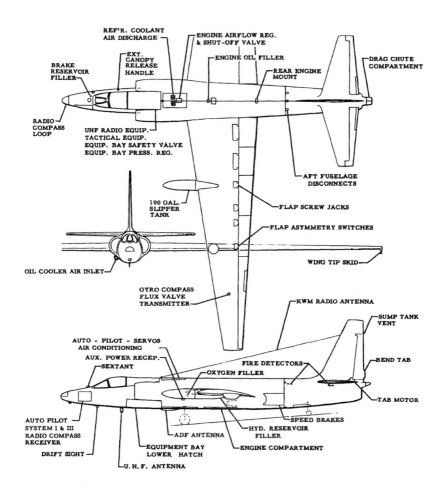

GENERAL CONFIGURATION

The final U-2 design configuration was a study in elegant simplicity and technical innovation. (CIA)

plates. All skin panels were flush riveted and the control surfaces aerodynamically balanced, with virtually no gaps at any of the hinge points. All aerodynamic control surfaces were cable operated. To further reduce weight, the hydraulic system was simplified and none of the primary flight controls were hydromechanically boosted. Johnson spent 2 days designing lightweight landing gear consisting of a bicycle arrangement with a double-wheel main gear and a small tail wheel,

U-2 forward fuselage assemblies under construction. (Lockheed Martin)

both mounted along the centerline.[39] The landing gear assembly weighed just 257 pounds. By comparison, conventional tricycle gear on a comparable aircraft would typically weigh about 750 pounds and occupy valuable space inside the wings that, on the U-2, was used to increase fuel capacity. This careful engineering of weight and space considerations resulted in an extra 1,500 feet of altitude capability and an additional 100 miles of cruising radius.[40] To maintain lateral balance during takeoff, the wingtips were equipped with mid-span outriggers, or pogos—small rubber wheels on the ends of curved steel legs that dropped away as soon as the plane became airborne. Skid plates on the wingtips protected the airfoils during landing.

The single J57 engine received air through a bifurcated inlet system. With the engine located at mid–wing chord for balance, the main gear well had to be placed between the air intake ducts, which was further forward than desirable. Engineers faced a challenge in designing the ducts because at cruise altitude the engine needed near perfect ram-air distribution in order to function. After trying a variety of options, the final duct configuration provided airflow comparable to that of a ground-based engine test cell.[41]

---

39. Pocock, *50 Years of the U-2*, p. 19.
40. Downie and Jarboe, *The Inquisitive Angel*.
41. Ibid.

To expedite flight testing, early U-2 flights were made with a 10,500-pound-thrust J57-P-37 engine designed for use in the B-52. Pratt & Whitney engineers spent 12 months developing the 11,500-pound-thrust J57-P-31 specifically for the U-2 in an accelerated program that normally would have taken up to 3 years. The new engine had a 16-stage compressor and operated at full power for the duration of flight. Fuel consumption was 9,000 pounds per hour at sea level, dropping to 700 pounds per hour at 70,000 feet cruising altitude. The J57-P-31 was designed to operate at up to nearly 74,600 feet before succumbing to oxygen starvation. With the earlier J57-P-37, the U-2 sometimes experienced as many as six flameouts at cruise altitude in a single flight. Louis Setter, one of the first U-2 instructor pilots, recalled that, "There were literally hundreds of high-altitude flameouts with the P-37 engine during early test and pilot training flights, but nearly all of these culminated in successful airstarts." Setter also observed that on one memorable day, "I had two students coming in with flameouts and one Lockheed test pilot still at altitude with a flameout, all at the same time."[42]

With the improved fuel system and turbine design of the J57-P-31, the flameout problem virtually ceased. An improved ignition system also allowed for restart at high altitude, eliminating the need to descend to a lower altitude, where the U-2 would be vulnerable to hostile fire. Even with the J57-P-37, there were only two forced landings due to engine failure in the first 20 months (more than 5,000 flight hours) of U-2 operations.[43]

The fuselage interior was plain and uncluttered. A pressurized compartment just forward of the main gear, known as the Q-bay, contained reconnaissance equipment. Ed Martin devised a system for installing and removing payloads using pallets mounted on interchangeable hatches that fitted flush to the bottom of the Q-bay. A second hatch on top of the Q-bay allowed access for maintenance and installation/removal activities. With the Q-bay consisting largely of empty space, only the mid-fuselage spar supported the cockpit and nose section. The small, cramped crew station looked like a fighter cockpit—a holdover from the XF-104/CL-282 design—but featured a control yoke of the type used in bombers and transports. Cables and pulleys linked the yoke to the ailerons, and a similar arrangement connected the rudder to two pedals. The instrument panel contained an assortment of conventional dials and switches, but it was dominated in the center by a hooded driftsight—a downward-looking periscope that allowed the pilot to see beneath the aircraft.[44] Designed by

42. Louis C. Setter, correspondence with author, March 22, 2014.
43. Downie and Jarboe, *The Inquisitive Angel*.
44. Pocock, *50 Years of the U-2*, pp. 19–20.

Workers assemble U-2 wings in Oildale. (Lockheed Martin)

James Baker and built by Walter Baird of Baird Associates, this optical system served as a navigational aid, enabling pilots to spot and recognize landmarks on the ground.[45] By turning a knob on the instrument panel, the pilot could flip a mirror and convert the periscope to a sextant, viewing the sky through a small glass hemisphere on the airplane's nose, just ahead of the cockpit. Celestial navigation was routinely used by U-2 pilots and was quite accurate at high altitudes, as long as the autopilot was operational.[46] The lightweight canopy (stressed to handle a pressure differential of 5 pounds per square inch [psi]) was hinged on the left side and operated manually. There was no ejection seat or canopy jettison system. In the event of emergency, the pilot was expected to manually unlatch the canopy and bail out. The airplane's empennage was built as a single unit that included the aft fuselage, vertical tail with rudder, and two horizontal stabilizers. For ease of assembly, the entire setup was joined to the forward fuselage using just three ⅝-inch tension bolts.[47]

When Johnson calculated new specifications for the wings, including a 2.5-g load limit and an aspect ratio of 10.67, it resulted in a wingspan of 80 feet and a total area of 600 square feet, a 20-percent increase over the original CL-282 specifications. The new wing featured three-spar construction and

45. Pedlow and Welzenbach, *The CIA and the U-2 Program*, p. 56.
46. Setter, correspondence with author.
47. Pocock, *50 Years of the U-2*, p. 20.

retained Johnson's gust control feature, but Bob Wiele replaced conventional rib stiffeners with an unusual latticework of aluminum tubing. The gust control system, which allowed the flaps to tilt upward 4 degrees and the ailerons to tilt 10 degrees, was designed to reduce tail loads and wing bending in turbulent conditions by completely changing the airfoil characteristics.[48] The long, thin wings were among the most efficient in the world, with a lift-to-drag ratio of 25.6:1, better than many competition sailplanes. From an altitude of 70,000 feet, the U-2 could glide approximately 300 miles.[49]

Four integral fuel tanks—two leak-proof compartments in each wing—carried a total of 1,335 gallons, which fed into a fuselage sump tank before reaching the engine. The outer 6 feet of wing was not used for fuel storage. In 1957, the U-2 was equipped with two 100-gallon slipper tanks that could be installed on the wings when a mission called for additional range capability. Weight and balance during flight were among the most important considerations when designing the fuel system. A complex system of feed lines and valves enabled the pilot to transfer fuel to maintain aircraft trim as fuel was consumed. Unfortunately, this made it impossible to provide the pilot with a standard full-to-empty type of quantity gauge in the cockpit. Instead, the first 49 U-2 aircraft came equipped with a mechanical fuel totalizer/counter. Prior to engine start, counters were set to indicate the amount of fuel in each wing, and a flow meter then subtracted the actual number of gallons of fuel consumed during the flight. A warning light came on when the quantity was down to 50 gallons in the sump tank. As standard practice, the pilot maintained a plot of fuel and oxygen remaining versus elapsed time.[50]

Proper fuel was also critical. Ordinary jet fuel, JP-4, had such a low vapor pressure that it would boil off during operation at high altitudes. Fortunately, help came from retired Air Force Lt. Gen. Jimmy Doolittle, a vice president of Shell Oil Company and also a member of the Technological Capabilities Panel. Thanks to Doolittle's intervention, Shell set to work to develop a low-volatility, low-vapor-pressure, kerosene-based fuel that met specifications.[51] The result, known variously as LF-1A and as JP-TS, was a broad mixture of aliphatic and aromatic hydrocarbon compounds with an initial boiling point of 315 degrees Fahrenheit (°F) at sea level and a freezing

---

48. Ibid.
49. Downie and Jarboe, *The Inquisitive Angel*.
50. Norman Polmar, *Spyplane: The U-2 History Declassified* (Osceola, WI: MBI Publishing Company, 2001), pp. 61–62.
51. Ibid., p. 62.

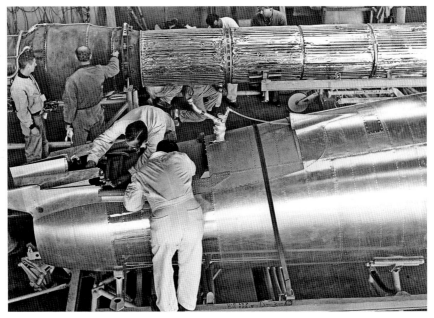

Two workers prepare to attach the vertical tail, foreground, while others inspect the engine and tailpipe assembly. (Laughlin Heritage Foundation)

point of 164 °F.[52] Production of LF-1A had an unintended consequence to U.S. consumers in the spring and summer of 1955. Manufacturing the special fuel required the use of petroleum products that Shell normally used to make the company's Flit insect repellent spray. In order to supply the U-2 program with several hundred thousand gallons of LF-1A, Shell had to limit production of Flit, causing a nationwide shortage.[53]

The tendency of liquids to boil at high altitudes also had a significant effect on the design of life-support systems for the U-2. Fluids in the human body will vaporize at altitudes above 63,000 feet unless the body is kept under pressure. Without special life-support garments, reduced atmospheric pressure at typical cruise altitudes also threatened to place considerable stress on the pilot's cardiovascular system and prevent adequate oxygenation of the blood. During cruise, the U-2 cockpit was pressurized to the equivalent of 28,000 feet above sea level. Since symptoms of hypoxia can be experienced when as low as 12,000 feet, the pilot was required to wear a partial-pressure suit (i.e., a garment that only

52. E.R. Kinkead, C.L. Gaworski, C.D. Flemming, et al., "Tumorigenic Evaluation of Jet Fuels JP-TS and JP-7," U.S. Air Force, AL-TR-1991-0020, April 1991, pp. 11–12.

53. Pedlow and Welzenbach, *The CIA and the U-2 Program*, p. 62.

A C-124 transport ferried the U-2 to the test site for final assembly. (Laughlin Heritage Foundation)

pressurizes certain critical parts of the body) that provided oxygen to the helmet at all times and inflated if cockpit pressure altitude increased to above 28,000 feet.[54]

By the third week of May 1955, the fuselage assembly was out of the jigs, but the wings were way behind schedule. Johnson was worried about instability due to bending, and Bob Kelly had not yet completed his design for the ailerons. In an effort to make up for lost time, Johnson drove his people harder than ever and had shifts working round the clock. By early June, the static test article was complete. Stress analysis of the fuselage, landing gear, and wings indicated that predicted critical load limits were fairly accurate. The horizontal tail required strengthening, but otherwise Johnson's design had passed the first test. In July, after the wings were completed and installed, Johnson spent 3 days inspecting the prototype, which was known simply as Article 341.[55] Workers then removed the wings and tail, carefully packed the various components, and loaded them into a C-124 transport.[56] The Article was nearly ready to fly.

---

54. Ibid., pp. 62–63.

55. Lockheed gave each airframe a three-digit production serial number, known as the Article number. This was completely separate from Air Force serial numbers or civilian registration numbers.

56. Pocock, *50 Years of the U-2*, pp. 24–25.

After being completely reassembled, Article 341 was ready for testing. (Lockheed Martin)

CHAPTER 2
Aquatone and Oilstone

While the airplane was being built, key personnel sought to establish a secure test site. In April 1955, Lockheed test pilot Tony LeVier flew Johnson, Richard Bissell, and Ritland to a dry lakebed adjacent to the Atomic Energy Commission's (AEC) proving ground north of Las Vegas, NV. With its remote location, excellent year-round flying weather, and the fact that the airspace overhead was already governed by AEC security restrictions, it was ideally suited to the U-2 project. Upon returning to Washington, Bissell and Ritland took immediate steps to have the lakebed and its environs added to the proving ground. Johnson drew up a plan for a small, temporary facility with a 5,000-foot asphalt runway, a control tower, three hangars, an aircraft parking apron, miscellaneous support facilities, and rudimentary personnel accommodations. Construction of what became known as Watertown Airstrip began the following month and, shortly thereafter, Lockheed, CIA, and Air Force personnel began moving in. Arrangements were made to acquire a C-47 transport and two T-33 jet trainers as support aircraft.[1]

Early development and operation of the U-2 was a joint effort. Lockheed was exclusively responsible for construction and developmental testing. The CIA had overall control of the program, which was codenamed Aquatone, as well as responsibility for developing security protocols and paying for airframes and camera equipment. The Air Force provided support in myriad ways, including supplying engines, ground support equipment, maintenance and training personnel, air traffic controllers, and transportation for workers to the test site. Air Force officials chose to name their part of the program Oilstone.[2] This was but a foreshadowing of the future. Throughout its service life, the U-2 program would have many different nicknames and codenames.

---

1. Pedlow and Welzenbach, *The CIA and the U-2 Program*, pp. 56–57.
2. Ibid., pp. 60–61.

First Flights

Kelly Johnson assigned Skunk Works foreman Dorsey Kammerer to over-see preparations at the test site and Frank "Red" Harvey to supervise the various personnel. Ernie Joiner served as chief of flight testing, assisted by flight-test engineer Glen Fulkerson. Others included instrumentation specialist Paul Deal, analysis engineers Mich Yoshii and Bob Klinger, and radio technician Jack Reedy. Tony LeVier was the first test pilot assigned to the project. Maintenance personnel responsible for Article 341 included crew chief Fritz Frye, mechanics Leroy Flynn and Bob Murphy, and electrician Vernon Buckner. If any special components needed to be manufactured, the test site had a metal shop staffed by Carl Herman, Bob Johnson, and Pop Christman. Any work on the airplane was thoroughly checked by inspectors Dick Padjet and Pete Wilkerson. Radioman Frank Cruz was in charge of communications. Gene Cuthbert oversaw supply stock. Paul Smith did double duty as both clerk and photographer. Utility electrician Dick Hough and painter Frank Harvey rounded out the shop personnel.[3]

As Johnson had promised, the disassembled components of the first U-2 arrived at the test site on July 25, less than 8 months after Lockheed received a go-ahead on the contract. After reassembly, the airplane was subjected to ground vibration testing to measure structural modes and frequencies for three different fuel load configurations. To undergo these tests, Article 341 was mounted on a ground transport dolly and shaken at various frequencies, some as low as a half-cycle per second. To prevent deformation of engine bearings during ground vibration tests, the engine was motored by blowing compressed air directly onto the front compressor with a hose and by blowing air into the starter to turn the rear compressor. The results were satisfactory and no problems were noted with coupling of structural modes.[4] Next, technicians prepared the prototype for its first engine run. At first, the J57 would not start with the special fuel, so the ground crew improvised. Someone found several 5-gallon drums of conventional JP-4, linked them together, and ran a hose to a fuel valve on the J57. Technicians got the engine running with the JP-4, then disconnected the hose and ran the remainder of the test using LF-1A. Mechanics later traced the problem to the spark plugs, which were too short.[5]

---

3. "Original U-2 Flight Test Crews - 1955," Nevada Aerospace Hall of Fame historical collection, courtesy of author.

4. Robert T. Klinger, "Flight Test Development of the Lockheed U-2 Airplane," Lockheed Aircraft Corp. paper SP-109, November 4, 1958, p. 29.

5. Pocock, *50 Years of the U-2*, p. 25.

Final assembly took place in a hangar at the test site. (Laughlin Heritage Foundation)

Once this discrepancy was corrected, the Lockheed crew was able to complete engine testing and prepare for taxi trials.

On August 1, 1955, Article 341 was towed onto the dry lakebed. Tony LeVier got the engine running well on his second attempt then began a low-speed taxi run to the north. At about 45 miles per hour (mph), the wingtips began to lift but the pogos were locked into place and remained attached, although they were no longer touching the ground. LeVier found that he needed to apply a little rudder to keep the nose straight. He noted that the pogo wheels trailed satisfactorily and absorbed small lateral loads very smoothly. Maximum speed was about 50 knots, just sufficient to make the ailerons slightly effective. LeVier found the performance of the wheel brakes to be very poor. At the end of the 2-mile run, he made full 90-degree deflections of the tail-wheel steering system in both directions before turning 180 degrees and coming to a stop.[6]

Ernie Joiner inspected the brakes prior to the second taxi test. This time, LeVier made his run to the south—accelerating to 70 knots in about a quarter mile—and then pulled the throttle to idle. "It was at this point that I became aware of being airborne," he wrote in his post-test report, "which left me with utter amazement, as I had no intentions whatsoever of flying."[7] He immediately started back toward the ground but had difficulty judging his altitude because there were no markings on the lakebed. LeVier gunned the throttle in an effort to accelerate and avoid stalling, but the J57 engine was slow to respond. From a height of approximately 35 feet, the U-2 dropped and made contact with the ground in a 10-degree left bank. The impact was hard enough that Article 341 bounced back into the air. The second touchdown was gentler, allowing LeVier to regain control, but he found the brakes ineffective in slowing the aircraft. After rolling for some distance and finally veering to the left, the U-2 came to a stop with the main wheel tires on fire directly beneath the fuel sump tank. The chase crew promptly extinguished the blaze. LeVier later noted that it would have been best to remain airborne, but with the throttle in idle, he felt that he probably would not have been able to accelerate to full power in time to avert the hard landing.[8] The unplanned flight hinted at the plane's airworthiness, foreshadowing its tendency at low speeds to remain in ground effect while gliding for great distances above the runway.

To prevent delays, the brakes and tires were replaced that same afternoon. An inspection revealed no significant damage from the fire so another taxi test

---

6. Skip Holm, "Article Airborne," *Air Progress Aviation Review*, June 1986, p. 25.

7. Ibid., p. 26.

8. Ibid.

was scheduled for the following day. In the meantime, LeVier and Bob Murphy painted some black stripes on the lakebed surface north of the asphalt runway to provide a visual reference. "Although this runway was far from adequate in regards to markings," LeVier noted, "it was a big improvement."[9]

In the morning, Article 341 was towed back onto the lakebed and LeVier climbed into the cockpit. "Engine start, OK." A few minutes later, he radioed, "Rolling." To preclude a repetition of the inadvertent takeoff, he held the control yoke forward and attempted to raise the tail. At 55 knots, the tail wheel lifted off the ground, and he completed a 1-mile run to evaluate directional and lateral control. The results were satisfactory, and with the tail up, the airplane reached 85 knots without taking off. LeVier eased off a bit on the yoke, and felt the airplane become very light, and it might well have lifted off had he not pulled the throttle to idle. He then activated the gust controls, allowing the tail to settle back to the ground. As the airplane slowed to 70 knots, he applied light wheel braking with little or no effect. Approximately 3 miles down the runway, rapidly approaching the edge of the lakebed, he chopped the power and the U-2 rolled to a stop. The brakes were extremely hot and might have caught fire again if not for quick action by the chase crew.[10]

While allowing the brakes to cool down, LeVier told Ernie Joiner that he had been bothered by unsatisfactory reflections on the windscreen from some light-colored material forward of the instrument panel. He felt it might have contributed to the visibility problems he experienced during previous tests. He also noted that the cockpit was extremely hot and recommended installing some sort of sunshade inside the canopy. After the ground crew had turned the airplane around, he made a low-speed run to the south with the flaps set at 35 degrees. This time the U-2 attained a maximum speed of 50 knots, and LeVier didn't bother with the wheel brakes. He simply allowed the airplane to coast to a stop. Afterward, he concluded that tail-wheel steering was of little use and might even be prone to inducing a ground loop. He and Kelly Johnson both agreed that the wheel brakes should not be used at speeds above 30 knots until the airplane's overall gross weight had been considerably reduced. LeVier's final comment in the postflight debriefing was, "I believe the aircraft is ready for flight."[11]

The test team spent the morning and early afternoon of August 4 preparing for the maiden flight. Johnson kept a close watch as Ernie Joiner, Glen Fulkerson, Bob Murphy, and several others readied the airplane while LeVier

---

9. Ibid.
10. Ibid.
11. Ibid., p. 27.

checked his test plan. In earlier conversations with the test pilot, Johnson insisted that the U-2 should be landed with the main gear making initial contact with the runway, followed by the tail wheel. "I disagreed," LeVier later recalled, "and told him it should be stalled-in with the tail wheel touching first."[12] Otherwise, he believed, the airplane would bounce. Johnson, however, felt that the U-2's high-aspect-ratio wing would have a significant effect on its landing characteristics, differentiating it from other bicycle-gear-equipped airplanes like the B-47. LeVier had, in fact, interviewed a number of B-47 pilots in preparation for his U-2 flight, but he agreed to make the first attempt using Johnson's suggested method.

For the final preparations, Article 341 was towed to the north end of the lakebed and aligned with the runway. As during taxi tests, the pogos were

Chase cars follow the U-2 as it rolls across the dry lakebed. (Laughlin Heritage Foundation)

locked in place to provide balance during touchdown. There was a flurry of activity as support personnel and equipment were moved into place. LeVier—using call sign Angel 1—climbed into the cockpit and began preflight checks. Bob Matye took off in the C-47 with Johnson and Henry Combs on board as observers. Their first task was to check local weather conditions and winds aloft because a storm was moving in. Ernie Joiner (call sign Ground Hog) prepared to monitor the test from his position on the lakebed. Apparently no one had

---

12. Miller, *Lockheed Skunk Works: The First Fifty Years*, p. 79.

thought to secure the airspace in advance of the test flight. A few minutes after the C-47 departed, he observed an Air Force F-86 making a fairly close gunnery pass overhead. Ray Goudey took off in a T-33 to serve as safety chase, and a fire truck was positioned 1 mile to the south, adjacent to the runway. All of the months of preparation had led to this moment. LeVier initiated engine start. Nothing happened.[13]

After two failed attempts to start the engine with LF-1A, Joiner decided they should refuel the airplane with JP-4 and try again. Nearly an hour was lost during this delay, and the observation and chase airplanes had to land to conserve fuel. Rain was already falling north of the lakebed and a crosswind blew in from the southwest, forcing LeVier to taxi the U-2 to a new starting point further to the east than originally planned. Finally, it was time, and he began his takeoff roll using approximately 85 percent revolutions per minute (rpm). He held the nose down until the airplane reached 100 knots, at which point it lifted off the ground. "The initial climb out felt very good," he reported later, "with what appeared to be satisfactory longitudinal stability and control." He noted that the right wing felt heavy, and Johnson told him to hold the wing up to balance the fuel. As he circled the lakebed at an altitude of 5,000 feet and a speed of around 160 knots with the landing gear still down, LeVier declared, "This thing flies like a baby buggy."[14]

"Try gear up if you want," Johnson suggested. LeVier raised the gear, climbed to 8,000 feet, and continued to explore the airplane's handling qualities through a variety of gentle maneuvers, including stalls. "Yaws right slightly, very sensitive at 100 knots. Right wing still heavy at 90. Aileron input at 85 knots. Lots of stall warning. Recovering." LeVier activated the speed brakes at approximately 140 knots, resulting in moderate tail buffet. He made six stalls, beginning in a clean (flaps up) configuration and gradually increasing the flap angle. He concluded that the airplane had normal buffet characteristics prior to full stall, with a very mild downward pitch. He noted that the wings were bowed slightly upward and that he was picking up a little bit of rain on the windscreen. After 15 minutes of flight, he descended, lowered the gear and flaps, and started his landing approach from 5,000 feet. "It wasn't difficult to realize that this was no ordinary aircraft," he later recalled. "With the power lever in almost idle, the wing flaps partially down and dive brakes extended, the aircraft had a very flat glide angle and a long float on flaring out."[15]

---

13. Holm, "Article Airborne," p. 28.

14. Ibid.

15. Ibid., pp. 28–29.

A summer storm flooded the lakebed minutes after Article 341 landed. (Lockheed Martin)

Attempting to touch the main wheels down first while pushing forward on the control yoke to lower the nose produced an erratic and uncontrollable porpoise maneuver. As the U-2 bounced into the air, Johnson yelled, "Go around!" LeVier added power and circled around for another attempt. He made a shallower approach this time, but the airplane just floated in ground effect approximately 10 feet above the lakebed. "Boy, for more drag," he lamented. After several more approaches and go-arounds with similar results, LeVier finally achieved a two-point landing with both the main gear and tail wheel touching down simultaneously. He also activated the gust control system to further reduce lift.[16] Johnson was forced to agree that LeVier had been right. It was best to land with the tail wheel touching the ground at the same time or just ahead of the main gear. The entire flight lasted less than 40 minutes. The storm broke 10 minutes later, flooding the lakebed with 2 inches of water.[17]

LeVier worked to perfect his landing technique during a second flight 2 days later, with Bob Matye flying chase in a T-33. Rolling north across the lakebed, the U-2 lifted off at 70 knots and immediately began to porpoise. LeVier added power and pulled up, resulting in a mild stall buffet, but this

16. Ibid., p. 29.
17. Johnson, "Log for Project X."

was less alarming than the porpoising. Matye thought a slight tailwind might have been a factor. After climbing to nearly 7,000 feet, LeVier began the first of several touch-and-go landings. His first approach was long and shallow, but he aborted when it began to seem hazardous. On the second approach, he employed the speed brakes and 10 degrees of flap, with the engine at 70 percent rpm. At 5 feet above the ground, he established the landing attitude in mild stall buffet and let the airplane settle in. This resulted in a two-point touchdown with a forward lunge and mild porpoising. He later described this second attempt as "successful and a reasonably good landing. I used the gust control and except for being awful slow, it certainly is a useful aid to [flying] this aircraft." LeVier then raised the flaps, set power to 85 percent rpm, and held the control yoke forward. The plane started porpoising again on takeoff, and he attributed this motion to low pressure in the main landing gear shock strut.[18] The third and final landing was about the same.

Following the flight, LeVier had several recommendations. First, he suggested adjusting the shock strut pressure. He also speculated that using the gust controls during takeoff might reduce the porpoise motion, as well as pitching and stall buffet during the initial climb. He further recommended that some method be devised to allow the pilot to establish a proper landing attitude that would result in a two-point touchdown every time. Finally, he recommended fitting the seat with a back cushion. "I'm still using a regular bed pillow," he fumed. "I believe we should make up a few slightly tapered back cushions of two or three-inch thickness."[19]

Having proven the basic airworthiness of the U-2, and having solved the difficult challenge of developing a successful landing technique, Johnson scheduled the official first flight for August 8. This time, representatives of the CIA and Air Force had been invited, along with high-ranking Lockheed executives. After briefing his guests on the day's schedule, Johnson donned a parachute and climbed into the back of Matye's T-33.[20] The U-2 was readied for flight, remaining in the same configuration as during the previous tests, with the pogos locked into the wings.

Matye and Johnson took off first, circling the lakebed while LeVier taxied into position for departure to the north. They caught up as the U-2 started its roll. Takeoff was smooth this time, probably as a result of adjustments mechanics had made to shock strut pressure. LeVier made a gentle climb to the left, raising the gear when he had attained a speed of 130 knots. He brought

18. Holm, *Article Airborne*, pp. 30–31.

19. Ibid., p. 96.

20. Johnson, "Log for Project X."

Tony LeVier completed the first phase of contractor testing in the U-2. (Lockheed Martin)

the plane around in a wide circle and made a pass at moderate altitude—around 8,000 feet—over the spectators before starting a series of planned test maneuvers. Johnson recorded airspeed calibration data during a climb to 30,500 feet, but Matye had difficulty keeping up with the U-2 even though LeVier reported that his engine was practically idling. Soon, the U-2 was nearly 1,000 feet above the T-33. During the climb, LeVier noted that his cabin pressure fluctuated as much as 500 feet in 2-second cycles. After leveling off, he accelerated to 260 knots and detected some aileron buzz and possibly a slight rumble in the air intake ducts. The roughness was noticeable even with the engine in idle, so LeVier increased rpm, lowered the landing gear, and extended the wing flaps. Johnson informed him that the right pogo was shaking a little and advised terminating the speed run.[21]

The tail wheel failed to come down on the first attempt. Descending at a rate of 1,500 feet per minute, LeVier took a moment to perform a stall using 30 degrees of flap. He began to feel slight buffeting at around 80 knots, and the airplane stalled at 72 knots, pitching down and to the left. "It sort of crabs around," he noted. "You can feel it." He recovered quickly and actuated the speed brakes, at which time the tail wheel finally extended. The duct rumble began to ease at 20,000 feet. He had no difficulty setting up his approach angle, but judging the airplane's height above the lakebed remained a problem. As touchdown seemed imminent, he actuated the gust control mechanism and set power to idle, but he was still a bit too high. The aileron lost effectiveness, causing the left wing to drop suddenly. LeVier realized too late that he should have waited until touchdown to activate the gust controls. The left wingtip struck the ground fairly hard, but with sparing application of the wheel brakes, he managed to bring the airplane to a halt directly in front of the viewing

---

21. Holm, *Article Airborne*, pp. 96–97.

area.[22] The VIP guests were then allowed to inspect the airplane, and Johnson declared that he had successfully achieved his self-imposed 8-month deadline.[23]

Developmental Testing

Over the next several weeks LeVier completed 16 additional flights, exploring the airplane's stall characteristics, taking the U-2 to its maximum stress limits (+2.5 g's and –1.5 g's) and expanding the performance envelope. He flew the U-2 to its maximum speed of Mach 0.85, or around 560 miles per hour (487 knots), and in preparation for cruising at altitudes never previously reached in sustained flight, the 42-year-old LeVier became the oldest test pilot to complete Air Force partial-pressure-suit training. He expanded the low and medium altitude flight envelopes and by August 16, he had reached an altitude of 52,000 feet. He then left Project Aquatone and returned to Burbank to serve as the company's director of flying.[24] Before LeVier left, he checked out two more pilots, Bob Matye and Ray Goudey, who began making at least one flight nearly every day. As the pace of testing increased, Robert Sieker and Robert Schumacher joined the team to help expand the airplane's performance capabilities and test the reconnaissance systems. Goudey performed in-flight structural tests, and Schumacher was instrumental in clearing the U-2 for maximum altitude operation as well as for testing sensor systems. Kelly Johnson paid Sieker a $25,000 bonus for performing an intentional deadstick landing during one test flight.[25] By September 8, the U-2 had been flown to 65,600 feet (approximately 12 miles above the ground), but engine flameouts at high altitude were becoming a significant problem.

The second and third airframes were delivered in September and October, and the test program was proceeding fairly smoothly. On December 1, Johnson noted, "We have built four flying airplanes, have the ninth airplane in the jig, and have flown over our design altitude any number of times."[26] By March 31, 1956, the U-2 fleet consisted of nine airplanes with a combined total of 1,042 flight hours. The pilots were routinely flying at altitudes that would have been considered incredible in 1955. Three consecutive flights by Matye exceeded, by significant margins, the world altitude record of 65,890 feet that had been set

22. Ibid.
23. Johnson, "Log for Project X."
24. Pedlow & Welzenbach, *The CIA and the U-2 Program*, p. 71.
25. Miller, *Skunk Works*, p. 80.
26. Ibid.

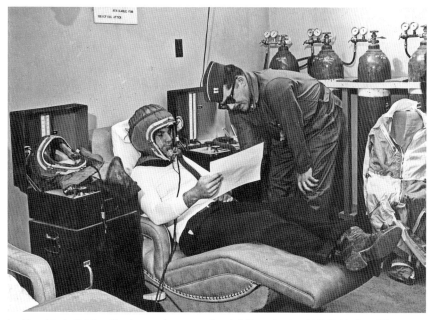

Lockheed test pilot Ray Goudey receives a weather briefing prior to a U-2 flight. (Laughlin Heritage Foundation)

in August 1955 by British pilot Walter Gibb in an English Electric Canberra (the original version of the Martin B-57).[27] The test pilots devoted a great deal of effort to studying the problems of engine performance. The J57-P-31 powerplant was still not available, and the J57-P-37 had significantly poorer combustion characteristics and a tendency to flame out at cruising altitude. Combustion problems most often manifested at altitudes between 57,000 and 65,000 feet, within a portion of the performance envelope that the pilots called the "badlands." In one typical example, the airplane was cruising at 64,000 feet when flameout occurred. The pilot briefly restarted the engine, but it quit again at 60,000 feet. He was ultimately forced to descend to 35,000 feet before regaining successful engine operation.[28] During a test flight this was merely an inconvenience, but if a similar event occurred in the course of an operational mission over hostile territory it would place the pilot in deadly peril.

As engineers struggled with the flameout problem, logistical difficulties threatened to slow Lockheed's production progress. Pratt & Whitney announced that the J57-P-31 engines would not be available until the spring

---

27. Ibid.
28. Pedlow & Welzenbach, *The CIA and the U-2 Program*, p. 71.

A U-2A climbs to altitude during a test flight. (U.S. Air Force)

of 1956, and even the interim J57-P-37 was becoming scarce because the company had committed its full production capacity for these engines to the Air Force for use in F-100 fighters and KC-135 tankers. In order to keep U-2 production on schedule, Col. Leo Geary (who had replaced Ritland) arranged for the diversion of a number of engines that had been destined for Boeing's KC-135 production line to the U-2 production line.[29] This kept the program running until the first J57-P-31 engines arrived, at which point the airplane's performance increased significantly. The new engine had greater thrust, lower weight, and consumed very little oil. Most important, flameout at altitude was almost impossible.[30] By June 1, 1956, the J57-P-31 engine had propelled the U-2 to 74,500 feet.[31]

Structural demonstrations, initially conducted with the aircraft restricted to 80 percent of design limit loads, included wind-up turns to 3 g's. A camera mounted atop the fuselage was used to measure wingtip deflections. Flight data

---

29. Ibid.
30. Benedict J. Koziol, "The U-2 Aircraft Engine," in *Proceedings of the U-2 Development Panel*, U-2 History Symposium, National Defense University, Fort McNair, DC, September 1998, pp. 7–8.
31. Johnson, "Log for Project X."

were then correlated with static test data prior to extending static testing to ultimate loads using the ground-test article. Ray Goudey tested the structural limit loads in an orderly fashion despite schedule pressures, and Lockheed engineers were pleased to learn that the airframe proved stronger than many had thought. Although Lockheed engineers measured ultimate loads of as much as 4 g's, flight limit loads remained at 2.5 g's, as originally specified, so as not to overstress any of the airplanes.[32]

Since the beginning of the project, the U-2 prototype had served as the flagship of the test fleet, and it was the most extensively instrumented airframe. Technicians installed strain gages in Article 341, using the same locations where measurements had been taken on the structural test article. The developmental test program lasted 7 months and included basic aircraft and engine performance assessments, stability and control evaluations, structural demonstrations, and operational testing of aircraft systems. By February 29, 1956, Article 341 had made 83 flights and logged 150 flight hours. Subsequently, this airplane was used primarily for testing modifications to the J57-P-37 engine and development of the improved J57-P-31 engine, as well as for other miscellaneous tests. Article 342 was also instrumented for testing, although not as extensively as Article 341, and was primarily dedicated to testing various reconnaissance camera systems. This airplane was flown 22 times (logging 33 flight hours) during this demonstration then released for use in the pilot training program. Instrumentation used in Article 342 was transferred to Article 344, and the majority of camera testing was accomplished with the latter. Article 344 was also used for autopilot development testing and weather research flights, eventually accruing 250 flight hours over the span of 85 sorties before being released for use in pilot training. A fourth airplane, Article 351, was used for testing System I, a radar detection and recording system; System II, an advanced high-frequency navigation and communication system; System III, a VHF radio transmission recording system; and the AN/APQ-56 radar mapping system, as well as the J57-P-31 engine.[33]

Lockheed engineers in Burbank subjected the ground-test article to static loading to destruction in order to establish safe flight limitations for a series of structural demonstrations. During five sorties with Article 341, the airplane underwent pull-ups, pushovers, stalls, and roll and yaw maneuvers at gross weights between 15,900 and 16,800 pounds. Tests were conducted with gust controls and flaps faired and extended, landing gear down, and speed brakes retracted and extended. The pilot performed the aileron roll test by starting

32. Pocock, *50 Years of the U-2*, p. 29.
33. Klinger, "Flight Test Development of the Lockheed U-2 Airplane," p. 4.

from a 45-degree left bank and rolling into a 45-degree right bank at a speed of 150 knots. Wingtip deflection was measured during level and maneuvering flight, and researchers found that upward deflection could be reduced as much as 5 inches by shifting the flaps and ailerons up for gust control. The most difficult aspect of measuring wing deflection turned out to be the need for very precise piloting technique. It was found that g-loading had to be increased as gradually as possible while maintaining the planned test airspeed. Otherwise, if g-loading increased too rapidly, dynamic overswing resulted in erroneous measurements, particularly at high negative-g conditions where pilots had a tendency to maneuver rapidly.[34]

Prior to in-flight structural demonstrations, technicians made reinforcements to portions of the airplane's structure. These changes were based on the results of the ultimate static load tests performed earlier. Subsequent flight-testing proved these modifications airworthy and all U-2 airplanes were strengthened accordingly. Other reinforcements were implemented in response to incidents that occurred during flight-test and training operations. During one sortie with Article 342, the pilot slowed the airplane by extending the speed brakes in level flight at 260 knots. As the plane decelerated to 250 knots (Mach 0.56) at 20,000 feet, an elevator tab support bracket failed and tore loose from the web of the rear stabilizer beam. To prevent reoccurrence of this type of failure, the bracket was redesigned to be tied into the top and bottom beam caps. This modification was incorporated into the entire U-2 fleet and no further trouble was experienced. Another modification resulted from discovery of fuselage skin wrinkles at the aft end of the tail wheel well. These wrinkles were only evident when the airplanes were sitting on the ground with a heavy fuel load. Although this was not considered a flight hazard, doubler plates were installed to alleviate load concentration while on the ground.[35]

Lockheed engineer Robert T. Klinger remarked in a November 1958 report that "The U-2 project was unique in practically all aspects; the design, testing, production, pilot training and service deployment [were] conducted on a 'crash' basis, by a relatively few number of people, while maintaining the highest order of security." In fact, the entire developmental flight-test program was conducted by just four engineers and five test pilots, assisted by a small cadre of about 20 maintenance, supply, and administrative personnel. Unlike in conventional aircraft procurement programs, the U-2 was not subjected to the formal eight-phase test program then in use by the Air Force. Instead, the

---

34. Ibid., pp. 152–156.
35. Ibid., pp. 156–161.

airplane's operational suitability, reliability, and other factors were evaluated concurrently with the developmental testing and pilot training programs.[36]

In the spring of 1957, two decades before the advent of what has come to be known as low observable—or stealth—technology, the CIA sought to make the U-2 less vulnerable to radar detection. For this pioneering effort, known as Project Rainbow, Lockheed engineers Luther McDonald, Mel George, and Ed Lovick teamed up with Harvard physics professor Ed Purcell and Frank Rodgers, associate head of the Radar Division at MIT's Lincoln Laboratory, to reduce the airplane's radar signature through two vastly different approaches. One method, nicknamed "trapeze," involved stringing copper-plated steel wires with ferrite beads across the aircraft's outer skin at specific distances from the fuselage, wings, and tail. As applied to Article 343, the wires were strung across laminated wood stand-offs that bristled from the fuselage, tail, and the leading and trailing edges of the wings.[37] In the second approach, Article 341 received a coating of high-frequency radar-absorbent material (RAM) on the underside of the fuselage. The RAM, varying in thickness from a quarter-inch to about 1 inch, consisted of a fiberglass honeycomb topped by layers of Salisbury Screen, a conductive graphite grid on canvas sheets. It was nicknamed "wallpaper" because of the circuit grid pattern on its surface. Additionally, the RAM coating prevented the dissipation of engine heat through the aircraft's skin, earning it the nickname "thermos." With the addition of RAM or wires, the U-2 suffered from excess weight and drag, making it aerodynamically "unclean." Hence Article 343 and Article 341 were known as "Dirty Birds." These modifications reduced the airplane's maximum altitude by as much as 5,000 feet and cut its range by 20 percent.[38]

During one of Robert Sieker's Rainbow test flights in Article 341, the insulating properties of the coating surrounding the engine bay caused the hydraulic system to overheat and reduce pressure to the fuel boost pump motor. The result was a flameout at 72,000 feet and loss of cabin pressure. Ordinarily, this would not have been a serious problem because the pilot was wearing his partial-pressure suit. Unfortunately, as his suit inflated, the clasp on his faceplate failed, causing loss of consciousness when the air rushed out of his helmet. The airplane stalled and entered a flat spin. Descending into the lower atmosphere, Sieker finally regained his senses and attempted to bail out. It took search teams several days to locate the wreckage, which was

---

36. Ibid., pp. 6–7.

37. Pocock, *50 Years of the U-2*, p. 50.

38. Peter W. Merlin and Tony Moore, *X-Plane Crashes* (North Branch, MN: Specialty Press, 2008), p. 84.

Engineers attempted two very different approaches to reducing the airplane's radar signature. One involved stringing ferrite beads on wires along the fuselage and wings while the other required coating parts of the aircraft with radar-absorbent material. (CIA)

Article 341 crashed in a flat spin following a flameout at 72,000 feet. Lockheed test pilot Robert Sieker was killed. (CIA)

largely intact. Sieker's body was found nearby with his parachute only partially deployed.[39] Investigators determined that had his life-support system not malfunctioned, he would have most likely been able to bring the plane home safely. Kelly Johnson called for a redesign of the faceplate latch, a dual oxygen regulator, and an ejection seat that could be used interchangeably with the existing bucket seat.[40]

Testing continued despite the loss of Article 341 and a valued member of the team. Several months later, the entire test operation was moved to the North Base auxiliary airfield at the edge of Rogers Dry Lake on Edwards Air Force Base. "I hesitate to say that this was an easy flight test program," recalled Ernie Joiner during a presentation in 1998, "for there were some challenging elements. It must be said, though, that the U-2 program was unique in that we overlapped flight test development with training and with deployment. This was historic and would have been impossible without a good airplane and a reliable engine."[41]

---

39. Ibid.

40. Pocock, *50 Years of the U-2*, p. 51.

41. Ernie L. Joiner, "Testing the U-2," in Proceedings of the U-2 Development Panel, p. 21.

Pilot Training

Even as developmental testing continued, the time had come to begin training CIA and Air Force U-2 pilots. Members of the Air Force training cadre began arriving in early November 1955. Col. William R. Yancey, handpicked by Gen. Curtis Lemay, chief of Strategic Air Command (SAC), was tasked with representing SAC's interests in the program. He had been specifically instructed to evaluate the Lockheed flight-test effort, verify that the airplane and reconnaissance equipment performed as expected, and report his findings directly to Lemay as soon as possible. Should the results prove satisfactory, Yancey was to train a specified number of pilots for operational missions. Shortly after delivery of the third U-2, the Air Force activated the 4070th Support Wing with Yancey as commander. His staff included deputy commander Col. Herbert Shingler, navigator and classroom instructor Maj. Robert E. Mullin, navigation officer and mission planner Jack Delap, logistics and supply officer Maj. Art Lien, development and flight-test officers Maj. Louis A. Garvin and Lt. Col. Phillip O. Robertson, flight instructors Capt. Hank Meierdierck and Capt. Louis Setter, and three airmen. Ray Goudey and Bob Matye gave the pilots ground instruction and checkout before allowing them to make familiarization and proficiency flights around the local area.[42]

Teaching Yancey's group how to fly the U-2 was particularly challenging because there was as yet no two-seat model of the U-2. The unique handling characteristics of the single-seat plane could only be experienced firsthand in solo flight. The student pilot first underwent extensive ground training, as well as practice in the T-33. For his initial U-2 flights, the student took off with an instructor pilot flying chase in the T-33 and providing instructions and encouragement over the radio. Each U-2 was built by hand, and slight variations in construction contributed to differences in aircraft behavior. This was especially noticeable when stalling the airplane during landing approach. One airplane might regularly fall off to the right and another to the left. Lockheed flight-test engineers took note of this and added small fixed metal strips to the leading inboard edge of the wing to modify the airplane's stall characteristics as necessary.[43]

All CIA and Air Force U-2 pilots were initially selected from veterans of SAC F-84 fighter squadrons scheduled to be disbanded and to have their personnel reassigned. Those chosen for the CIA program had to resign their Air Force

42. William R. Yancey, undated letter (circa 2007) to Hank Meierdierck regarding early U-2 training operations, Roadrunners Internationale historical reference collection.

43. Pocock, *50 Years of the U-2*, p. 31.

commissions, effectively becoming civilians for the duration of their assignment. The selection process was rigorous. Because U-2 pilots were expected to endure the stress of flying at extremely high altitudes for extended periods of time, every effort was made to exclude those who might be unable to handle the claustrophobic conditions of the pressure suit and the airplane's cramped cockpit. In preparation for high-altitude operations, each man underwent thorough physical and psychological examinations at the Lovelace Clinic in Albuquerque and fitting for partial-pressure suits at the David Clark Company in Worcester, MA. Another challenge involved teaching the pilots the proper way to handle the delicate U-2. Former fighter pilots accustomed to flying fast and making abrupt maneuvers needed to understand the limitations of a lightweight airframe not designed to handle the stresses of loops, barrel rolls, or even a hard pull-up.[44]

The first group of pilot trainees arrived at Watertown Airstrip on January 11, 1956. Two more classes soon followed, resulting in a total of 28 student pilots. Yancey's flight instructors devised a syllabus consisting of ground school and flight checkout. Before being allowed to solo in the U-2, each student first flew a number of analog sorties in the T-33 to simulate high-altitude flameouts and restarts, practice U-2 landing approach techniques, and demonstrate near-stall landings. An instructor pilot shadowed the U-2 when each student made his first solo, a flight to 20,000 feet followed by five practice landings on the lakebed. Students didn't wear the pressure garment until the third solo flight, which was typically a 3-hour flight to 60,000 feet. The next nine sorties introduced trainees to high-altitude navigation and photography, long-duration flight (upward of 8 hours), night flying, and landings on the paved airstrip. Each pilot was declared mission qualified after logging at least 58 flight hours in the U-2 and completing a final 8-hour check ride.[45] Francis G. "Frank" Powers, who was assigned to the second group of trainees, was most impressed by the attention paid to the flying portion of the syllabus. "While at Watertown we flew the U-2 far more than we would have if we'd been in the Air Force and checking out in a new aircraft," he wrote in his memoir. "As a result, on completing our training we had the utmost confidence in its reliability."[46]

Once a sufficient number of pilots had completed training, they were tasked with an operational checkout of the U-2, including the planes, ground and flight crews, navigation systems, life-support systems, cameras, and other

44. Pedlow & Welzenbach, *The CIA and the U-2 Program*, pp. 74–75.

45. Pocock, *50 Years of the U-2*, p. 32.

46. Francis Gary Powers and Curt Gentry, *Operation Overflight* (New York: Holt Rinehart and Winston, 1970), p. 36.

Ground crews prepare U-2s for training flights. (Laughlin Heritage Foundation)

equipment. During a 5-day training exercise in April 1956, U-2s took off from Watertown on eight cross-country sorties for the purpose of testing various camera systems. The entire exercise was conducted in the manner of a standard Air Force Operational Readiness Inspection, with Col. Yancey and his detachment serving as observers. They carefully examined all aspects of the U-2 unit's performance, including that of maintenance personnel, flight crews, camera technicians, and mission planners. When the exercise was over, Yancey reported that the detachment was ready for deployment. He then briefed a high-level Pentagon panel that included the Secretary of the Air Force and the Chief of Air Staff. These officials concurred with Yancey's determination that the U-2 was ready to become operational.[47] As the CIA detachments began departing for overseas duty, Air Force pilot training began in earnest.

By mid-1956, the U-2 had been flown on several missions lasting more than 10 hours and covering over 5,000 statute miles. Airplanes equipped with the J57-P-31 engine had attained altitudes up to 74,500 feet.[48] Not surprisingly, the intensive training program resulted in a number of mishaps, some fatal. In his March 21, 1956, diary entry, Kelly Johnson noted that Article 342 had

---

47. Pedlow & Welzenbach, *The CIA and the U-2 Program*, pp. 77–78.
48. Johnson, "Log for Project X."

been "wrecked" when Carmine Vito made a rough landing.[49] This apparently sounded much worse than it actually was, as the airplane was soon repaired and flying. But there were more serious mishaps to come.

One incident with deadly results was a consequence of the unusual landing gear arrangement. As originally designed, the pogo outriggers were to be dropped during or shortly after takeoff using a manual release system. "We soon learned that any delay by the pilot in dropping them would often cause them to hang up," Ernie Joiner recalled. "When that happened, it was wise to stay clear of the airplane's flight path." On May 15, CIA pilot Wilburn S. "Billy" Rose had just taken off for a training flight in Article 345 when he noticed that one of the outriggers had failed to separate. He tried to shake it loose while flying low over the lakebed but the airplane, heavy with fuel, stalled and crashed. Rose became the first CIA fatality of the program. To prevent a reoccurrence of the problem, the pilot actuation system was removed so that the pogos would fall away automatically as soon as the wings started to lift, while the airplane was still on the runway. A spring was installed on the upper end of the pogo to push it away from the wing as soon as the weight of the aircraft was lifted.[50]

The trainees continued to suffer a variety of landing mishaps. On June 1, Bill Strickland somehow allowed Article 344 to run out of fuel. He landed 392 yards short of the lakebed, miraculously without damaging the airplane. Another pilot was not so lucky, damaging Article 355 in a rough landing just shy of 8 weeks after the airplane had been delivered. Fortunately, it was repairable.[51]

Takeoff could be equally hazardous. During a night training flight in Article 354 on August 31, Frank G. Grace, Jr., tried to climb too steeply during takeoff. Apparently failing to maintain a proper climb angle, he stalled with insufficient altitude for recovery. Grace died when his airplane plummeted 50 feet to the ground, cartwheeled on its left wing, and struck a power pole near the runway.[52]

On September 17, 1956, Article 346 lost part of its right wing shortly after Howard Carey took off from Lindsey Air Force Base in Wiesbaden, Germany. The aircraft disintegrated in flight, killing the pilot. The exact cause was never determined. Kelly Johnson believed it resulted from overpressure in the wing tanks during a steep climb, but it was also noted that the U-2 might have been caught in the jet wash from a flight of four Canadian F-86 fighters that had just passed by. The U-2 airframe was not stressed to withstand severe turbulence. One of Carey's fellow pilots theorized that the accident could have been caused

---

49. Ibid.
50. Joiner, "Testing the U-2," p. 22.
51. Johnson, "Log for Project X."
52. Pedlow & Welzenbach, *The CIA and the U-2 Program*, pp. 79–80.

Some of the most challenging aspects of the U-2 resulted from the airplane's unusual landing gear configuration. (Laughlin Historical Foundation)

by an unintentional extension of the flaps. The flap switch was located alongside the throttle, where it could be easily bumped to the down position during the climb. As long as the gust alleviation system was activated—as it routinely was during takeoff—this would have no adverse effect, but once the pilot deactivated the gust controls, the flaps would revert to the commanded position.[53]

The loss of Article 357 on December 19, 1956, resulted from pilot hypoxia after Robert Ericson took off from Watertown on a cross-country flight over northern Arizona. As the U-2 climbed to altitude, a small leak slowly depleted his oxygen supply. Hypoxia gradually set in, impairing the pilot's judgment. As his reaction time slowed and he lost track of the aircraft's speed, the U-2 exceeded the placarded 190-knot maximum. The delicate airframe quickly approached its load limits and finally disintegrated when it reached 270 knots. Ericson somehow managed to jettison the canopy and was sucked out of the aircraft at an altitude of 28,000 feet. Fortunately, his chute opened automatically at 15,000 feet, and he touched down without injury.[54] The aircraft was a total loss, its wreckage strewn across part of the Navajo Indian Reservation south of Ganado.

---

53. Pocock, *50 Years of the U-2*, p. 338.
54. Pedlow & Welzenbach, *The CIA and the U-2 Program*, p. 80.

A U-2A is slowed by a drag chute during landing. (Laughlin Historical Foundation)

Training continued unabated despite these mishaps. The first operational mission occurred just 18 months after program go-ahead and was conducted over Soviet-occupied Eastern Europe on June 20, 1956. By mid-June 1957, three CIA detachments had been deployed around the world, Air Force U-2 personnel were assigned to the 4080th Strategic Reconnaissance Wing and based in Del Rio, TX, and test operations were transferred to Edwards Air Force Base. As director of Project Aquatone, Richard Bissell was very pleased with the outcome. "The active participation and support of the Air Force continued throughout the life of the program," he wrote in his memoirs, "and without its many contributions the project could not have been carried through."[55]

---

55. Richard M. Bissell, Jr., Jonathan E. Lewis, and Frances T. Pudlo, *Reflections of a Cold Warrior: From Yalta to the Bay of Pigs* (New Haven, CT: Yale University Press, 1996), p. 97.

The U-2C had fluted inlets to accommodate increased airflow to the J75 engine and a dorsal spine housing additional equipment. Note the 100-gallon slipper tanks on each wing. (Lockheed Martin)

CHAPTER 3
Design Evolution

Over the years, the U-2 family of aircraft spawned two major design variants and a host of specialized models. These changes enhanced survivability and increased operational effectiveness. The basic design parameters and performance characteristics have remained largely unchanged except for those resulting from improvements in propulsion and avionics technology. Despite its planned short-term obsolescence, the airplane's versatility ensured that descendants of the original U-2 would remain in service well into the 21st century.

The First Upgrade

Beginning in late 1958, Lockheed embarked on a program to retrofit the CIA fleet with more powerful engines to increase operational altitudes. This first major upgrade to the airplane was dubbed U-2C. It featured a new powerplant and larger inlets for improved performance. Kelly Johnson selected Article 342 to serve as the prototype, and Lockheed technicians replaced its J57-P-31 engine with a Pratt & Whitney J75-P-13 axial-flow turbojet weighing 4,900 pounds and providing 15,800 pounds of thrust at sea level. Seven years later, the U-2C fleet would be equipped with more powerful J75-P-13B engines with a 17,000-pound-thrust rating. In order to improve airflow to the engine's compressor face, the inlets were widened and fluted, allowing a greater mass of air to enter.[1] Greater thrust meant that the airplane reached operational altitudes more quickly and reduced time spent in the tropopause (the atmospheric band between 45,000 and 55,0000 feet), where contrails typically formed. This reduced the chances of visual detection. Use of the more powerful J75 also enabled the U-2 to carry a larger payload. The J75 engines were in short supply in 1959 due to Pratt & Whitney's commitments to the Air Force for F-105 production, but the CIA managed to obtain an initial supply of 12 engines. The Air Force never equipped its U-2 fleet with the J75.[2]

---

1. Pocock, *50 Years of the U-2*, p. 399.
2. Pedlow & Welzenbach, *The CIA and the U-2 Program*, pp. 149–152.

Developmental testing of the U-2C was expedited to meet operational requirements for the airplane. Article 342 was thoroughly instrumented for airplane and powerplant performance evaluations, autopilot development, stability and control, and operational systems testing. Ray Goudey made the maiden flight of the U-2C on May 13, 1959, at Edwards. Soon thereafter, Article 358 and Article 351 joined the program as the second and third U-2C models. These airframes were used primarily for testing aircraft systems and reconnaissance equipment. All three were used for accelerated service testing to demonstrate operational reliability and collect cruise performance data. All testing was complete by July 24, 1959, just 10 weeks after the first flight. The three airplanes completed 106 sorties totaling 381 flight hours. Articles 351 and 358 were deployed with an operational detachment on August 12, but Article 342 remained at Edwards for further performance testing and development of an electrical power system and the System IX Granger Deceptive Repeater installation.[3]

Designers made a number of significant changes to the basic airplane. The U-2C was approximately 1,450 pounds heavier than the U-2A, with the new J75 engine accounting for 1,100 pounds of the increase. The landing gear and associated structure had to be strengthened, and heavy-duty tires installed, to accommodate the heavier gross takeoff weight. The fuselage sump tank was slightly larger, holding 95 to 100 gallons of fuel—about a 10-pound increase. The total area of the engine air inlets was increased to accommodate the greater airflow requirements of the new powerplant. Lockheed engineers redesigned the leading edge of the horizontal stabilizer, making it more rounded and increasing the camber. The operating speed of the gust control system was reduced 50 percent to provide a smoother response. Numerous internal systems were modified to improve engine and hydraulic oil cooling, autopilot performance, fuel flow, electrical power, and environmental controls. Much attention was devoted to improving heat shielding around the engine to provide adequate aircraft structural cooling.[4]

Based on lessons learned with the U-2A, Lockheed engineers made several changes to improve U-2C controllability. The elevator trim tab operating speed was doubled, downward elevator travel was increased from 11.5 to 20 degrees to offset a nose-up pitching tendency resulting from a rapid increase in power, and gust control system response was slowed by half to decrease the rate of change in elevator stick force. The modified airplane demonstrated improved

---

3. Robert T. Klinger, "Flight Test Development of the Lockheed U-2C Airplane," Lockheed Aircraft Corp., SP-179, July 1, 1960, pp. 6–7.

4. Ibid., pp. 14–18.

altitude performance, but its center-of-gravity limits were significantly narrower. On one early test flight, Bob Schumacher reported that the center of gravity was so far forward that the airplane might become uncontrollable if the autopilot disconnected before the fuel supply from auxiliary slipper tanks on the wings was exhausted. In order to mitigate this problem, the horizontal stabilizers were subsequently modified to balance the aerodynamic load with increased camber and more rounded leading edges. For most operational configurations, ballast had to be added to the tail. The U-2C upgrade initially raised the airplane's maximum altitude to more than 74,600 feet (and later to 75,000 feet with the J75-P-13B) and improved the compressor stall margin. Unfortunately, increased altitude capability corresponded with a decrease in range from 4,000 to 3,300 nautical miles when the pilot flew a maximum-power cruise profile. Mission planners favored this profile because the U-2C entered cruise climb at 67,000 feet, and nearly two-thirds of the entire mission was flown at altitudes above 70,000 feet.[5]

A combination of higher thrust and greater compressor stall margin gave the U-2C more operational flexibility at high altitudes than had the U-2A. The engine could be operated anywhere between minimum fuel flow and maximum power, increasing maximum altitude capability and providing the pilot with a wide range of reduced power cruise altitudes as desired. Range could be increased with the addition of two 100-gallon slipper tanks on the wings, but the additional weight resulted in an altitude penalty of 500 to 1,200 feet. At maximum power, use of slipper tanks gave the U-2C a range of 3,350 nautical miles to zero fuel. The U-2 pilot could achieve a more economical relationship between gross weight and altitude by leveling off and cruising at constant altitude and airspeed. For a level 70,000-foot-cruise mission with slipper tanks, the range was 3,800 nautical miles. Reducing the level cruising altitude to 68,000 feet increased the range to 4,050 miles, and the maximum slipper tank range was estimated to be 4,600 nautical miles.[6]

A U-2 Built for Two

In early 1957, Lockheed received a contract to modify a U-2A with an infrared sensor mounted in one of two configurations. When installed below the fuselage just aft of the cockpit, it could be used to detect the heat signatures of jet aircraft flying at lower altitudes. From atop the fuselage, it would be

5. Pedlow & Welzenbach, *The CIA and the U-2 Program*, p. 152.
6. Klinger, "Flight Test Development of the Lockheed U-2C Airplane," pp. 24–25.

used to scan for rocket and missile exhaust plumes. The sensor, designated AN/AAS-8, was co-developed by Lockheed and Baird Atomic. In December 1957, the sensor package was installed on the lower fuselage of Article 389 in what became known as the AIRSearch configuration. The equipment was housed in a rotating barrel that was pressurized by nitrogen gas. Immediately aft of this cylindrical assembly, an aerodynamic fairing was installed to smooth the airflow around the sensor package. The cylinder contained mirrors that could be tilted as necessary to focus the infrared energy onto a lead sulfide detector. The optical path for the navigational sextant was modified to include an infrared oscilloscope, combining one display into two so that additional instruments did not need to be added to the already cramped cockpit. In order to allow the U-2 pilot to identify aircraft detected at lower altitudes, driftsight magnification was doubled. The modified airplane was delivered to Edwards in March 1958. As originally envisioned, this technology would have supplemented airborne early warning aircraft and ground-based Ballistic Missile Early Warning System (BMEWS) radar stations in detecting inbound enemy aircraft. But U-2 reconnaissance missions over the Soviet Union had produced information that diminished fears that Russian long-range bomber fleets posed a significant threat. On the other hand, the Soviets were making great progress in the development of intercontinental ballistic missiles. Fears of a U.S.-Soviet "missile gap" spurred military leaders at the Pentagon to develop plans for a Missile Defense and Alarm System (MIDAS) early warning satellite, but it was not expected to be operational before 1961 at the earliest.[7]

The AN/AAS-8 was first tested in the spring of 1958 during Project Low Card. Capt. Hugh "Pat" Hunerwadel flew Article 389 to Ramey Air Force Base, Puerto Rico, to assess the sensor's performance during observations of test launches of U.S. ballistic missiles from Cape Canaveral, FL. These tests ended prematurely in early June when the U-2 ran off the runway, badly damaging the downward protruding sensor. Article 389 was airlifted back to Edwards for repairs and since the priority had shifted to missile detection, the sensor package was moved to the upper fuselage. Project Low Card resumed in September with another pilot. By the end of this deployment, the AN/AAS-8 had been used to track 11 of 12 launches over the Atlantic Missile Range between April and November, despite the 4-month interruption caused by the runway mishap.[8]

In light of the spectacular success of the AN/AAS-8, which detected missile plumes at ranges in excess of 1,000 miles, Lockheed and Baird Atomic

---

7. Pocock, *50 Years of the U-2*, p. 362.
8. Ibid., pp. 362–363.

The final configuration of what came to be known as the U-2D. Note the cylindrical sensor housing between the canopies. (Lockheed Martin)

produced two separate reports. Kelly Johnson and Walter Baird presented these documents at the Pentagon along with a proposal that a fleet of as many as 15 sensor-equipped U-2 aircraft should be kept on constant airborne patrol around the borders of the Soviet Union to provide early warning of missile attacks against the U.S. or its allies. Johnson recommended building 84 additional U-2 airframes with provisions for the AN/AAS-8 as well as a second crew position behind the cockpit. The new model, designated U-2B, would have been equipped with an astroinertial navigation system and a UHF data link for line-of-sight communication between the aircraft and monitoring stations on the ground. The U-2B was expected to be at least 1,500 pounds heavier than the standard U-2A, cutting the airplane's range by 25 percent but without significantly reducing altitude capability. To mitigate the risk of losing an airplane due to engine failure, Johnson provided an option to install a small Pratt & Whitney JT12 turbojet for emergency return-to-base capability if the primary engine could not be restarted. The inlet and exhaust ducts for the JT12 were to have been covered by jettisonable aerodynamic fairings when not in use. A final notification called for replacing the bicycle landing gear with a conventional tricycle arrangement. Although this added 884 pounds to the

A second crew station had to be built to accommodate the sensor operator. (Lockheed Martin)

airframe, Lockheed's reported noted, "the expected gain in overall operations by lessening landing accidents outweighs this."[9]

Although Pentagon officials liked the concept, they had doubts about the reliability of the communications links and navigational accuracy, especially since the aircraft would be operating within the Arctic Circle. Johnson was subsequently authorized to modify three additional prototypes for further testing. Capitalizing on lessons learned from project Low Card, Skunk Works engineers designed a compartment behind the cockpit to accommodate a sensor operator. It had become clear that the pilot could not effectively fly the airplane and operate the sensor equipment simultaneously. The first airframe to receive this modification was Article 377. Technicians converted the Q-bay into a crew station with sensor control panels, an entry hatch on top of the fuselage, and a downward ejection seat similar to those used in early model F-104 Starfighters. The sensor barrel was mounted between the pilot's canopy and the observer's hatch, which itself was topped with the aerodynamic fairing that fit just behind the sensor. Bob Schumacher made the maiden flight on January 7, 1958, with flight-test engineer Glen Fulkerson in the observer's

---

9. Ibid., pp. 363.

seat. Unfortunately, this airplane was lost 8 months later in a crash that took the life of Pat Hunerwadel. A second prototype was ready by early 1959. Article 394 was the first U-2 purpose-built in the two-seat configuration. In an improvement over the first version, the downward ejection seat was replaced with a more conventional upward-firing escape system.[10]

As the early warning panel of the Presidents Science Advisory Committee (PSAC) reviewed progress on MIDAS and BMEWS, it was clear that operational deployment of a satellite system was still a long way off. Johnson had promised to have the three squadrons of U-2B aircraft operational within 2 years, with the first in service just 18 months after start of production. The PSAC panel recommended immediate procurement of the U-2B as a complement to the BMEWS, but critics were skeptical that the Soviets were indeed planning to launch a preemptive nuclear strike against the U.S. and felt that there were already other, more reliable technologies for early detection of missile launches. The U-2B proposal did not immediately receive approval as Johnson had hoped, but testing of the infrared sensor system continued with a second two-place airframe, Article 388, which joined the test fleet in late 1959. In time, senior Government officials downgraded the Soviet missile threat, and the BMEWS radar sites became operational. Johnson's U-2B proposal was eventually discarded, but the two test bed aircraft, officially designated U-2D in 1961, continued to be used for sensor technology development and a variety of other test projects. In at least one instance, the U-2D was flown parallel to the flightpath of NASA's X-15 in order to track the rocket plane's exhaust plume as it soared to the edge of space.[11] Article 394 was eventually converted into a single-seat U-2C and transferred to SAC. Article 388 remained at Edwards until its retirement in 1978.[12]

Increased Range

Anticipation of long-duration sorties highlighted the need to increase the airplane's operational range beyond that which could be obtained with the addition of external fuel tanks. The logical solution was to give the U-2 in-flight refueling capability. This merely required the addition of a dorsal receptacle to accommodate the extendable refueling boom of a KC-135 Stratotanker. Although this modification promised a useful capability, many feared it could

---

10. Ibid., pp. 363–364.
11. Ibid., p. 366.
12. Ibid., p. 368.

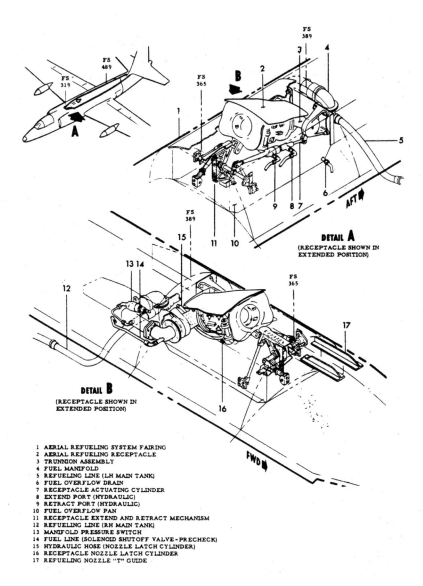

FS 389
FS 489
FS 319
FS 365
B
A
AFT
DETAIL A
(RECEPTACLE SHOWN IN EXTENDED POSITION)
FS 389
FS 365
DETAIL B
(RECEPTACLE SHOWN IN EXTENDED POSITION)
FWD

1 AERIAL REFUELING SYSTEM FAIRING
2 AERIAL REFUELING RECEPTACLE
3 TRUNNION ASSEMBLY
4 FUEL MANIFOLD
5 REFUELING LINE (LH MAIN TANK)
6 FUEL OVERFLOW DRAIN
7 RECEPTACLE ACTUATING CYLINDER
8 EXTEND PORT (HYDRAULIC)
9 RETRACT PORT (HYDRAULIC)
10 FUEL OVERFLOW PAN
11 RECEPTACLE EXTEND AND RETRACT MECHANISM
12 REFUELING LINE (RH MAIN TANK)
13 MANIFOLD PRESSURE SWITCH
14 FUEL LINE (SOLENOID SHUTOFF VALVE-PRECHECK)
15 HYDRAULIC HOSE (NOZZLE LATCH CYLINDER)
16 RECEPTACLE NOZZLE LATCH CYLINDER
17 REFUELING NOZZLE "T" GUIDE

An aerial refueling receptacle was installed in a dorsal spine on U-2E and U-2F models. (U.S. Air Force)

A U-2F during refueling trials. (U.S. Air Force)

not significantly extend overall mission length, which was a function of human endurance. For operational purposes, pilot fatigue constraints limited mission duration to a maximum of approximately 10 hours. Upon approval of the project in May 1961, Lockheed began modifying six CIA airframes into what became known as the U-2F configuration.[13] Air Force interest in the U-2F resulted in a decision to convert six SAC airplanes for refueling. This order was eventually reduced to three, which were delivered in the fall of 1962 under the designation U-2E.[14]

Article 342 was once again selected to serve as prototype for a new configuration. It was equipped with a pressurized dorsal fairing atop the mid fuselage to house the refueling receptacle along with a 400-watt single-side-band radio that permitted voice communications at ranges of more than 3,000 miles. Bob Schumacher conducted the first simulated refueling trials, easing in behind a KC-135 and closing to the requisite distance without actually hooking up. Initial tests indicated that refueling rendezvous could be easily accomplished at an altitude of 35,000 feet and indicated air speed of 220 knots. For the low-altitude rendezvous trial, Schumacher had been wearing a standard flight suit and helmet. Later pilots discovered that wearing the partial-pressure suit and its specialized helmet resulted in significantly reduced visibility while maneuvering

---

13. Pedlow & Welzenbach, *The CIA and the U-2 Program*, pp. 198–199.

14. Pocock, *50 Years of the U-2*, pp. 153 and 190.

The view from the tanker boom operator's station while refueling a U-2F. (Lockheed Martin)

toward the refueling boom. Another challenge was posed by the fact that the in-flight refueling capability meant missions could be extended beyond the imposed 10-hour limit. Even without concern for pilot fatigue, practical mission endurance was inherently limited by the onboard oxygen supply. Eventually, an extra oxygen bottle was added, extending the pilot's air supply for a 14-hour mission if required.[15]

Refueling trials began with dry hook-ups followed by the first transfer of fuel from the KC-135 to the U-2. Testing was completed over the span of several weeks, and two more airframes were already undergoing modification. Soon, operational pilots began practicing the delicate art of in-flight refueling. The KC-135 could transfer as much as 900 gallons to the U-2 in just 5 minutes. The main tanks were fed first, followed by sump tanks, and finally the slipper tanks (if attached). Center-of-gravity requirements necessitated development of a cross-transfer system between the tanks. This consisted of a series of motorized and solenoid-operated valves that operated automatically. A manual override was provided and the pilot had to keep an eye on transfer rates and

---

15. Ibid., pp. 146–147.

valve operations so as to prevent structural failure resulting from overpressure of displaced air if the tanks filled too fast. This, however, was only one of the potential hazards of in-flight refueling.[16]

Ordinarily, the aircraft receiving fuel closes on the tanker from behind, but because the U-2 had such a narrow speed envelope, the KC-135 had to make adjustments during rendezvous. First, the U-2 pilot stabilized his aircraft at the proper altitude and airspeed. It was then overtaken by the tanker about a quarter-mile off the right side and at the same altitude. After passing the U-2, the KC-135 pilot reduced speed as the U-2 moved down and left to take its position below the refueling boom. After the boom was lowered, the U-2 pilot slowly climbed into final position, careful to avoid the tanker's wake vortex or jet-wash from the tanker's engines, either of which could flip the U-2 into a deadly roll. After refueling, the pilot had to reset the fuel counter and delicately disengage from the tanker. The U-2 pilot achieved separation by decreasing power and descending approximately 100 feet below the tanker before sliding away to the left or right. Only when completely clear of the tanker's vortices was it safe to climb away.[17] These hazards were not to be taken lightly. On March 1, 1962, Capt. John Campbell perished during a nighttime refueling mission over Edwards. As he maneuvered his U-2F behind the KC-135 at an altitude of 35,000 feet, it flipped and tumbled out of control. Campbell apparently attempted to eject, but his seat never left the plane. Aerial refueling operations were suspended as Lockheed engineers once again evaluated the loads imposed on the U-2 airframe while maneuvering behind the KC-135. Some suggested that if jetwash were the problem, it might be safer to refuel from the prop-driven KC-97, though this would require rendezvous at lower altitudes and slower speeds. The KC-135 was ultimately retained as the primary tanker for the U-2.[18]

The U-2 Goes to Sea

Early in the development program, some had suggested operating the U-2 from an aircraft carrier to provide additional mission flexibility. This idea was even briefed to President Eisenhower in May 1957, but critics rejected the idea because the carrier capability would add little to the coverage of Soviet Bloc countries reachable by the U-2 from land bases. Acting CIA Director

---

16. Ibid., p. 347.

17. Ibid.

18. Ibid., pp. 156–157.

The U-2G fit easily inside the hangar deck of the USS *Kitty Hawk*. (Lockheed Martin)

Lt. Gen. Charles P. Cabell acknowledged that flexibility and independence of foreign jurisdiction would generally enhance U.S. reconnaissance capability with respect to areas outside the Soviet Bloc, but he felt the benefits would be too limited to justify the expense of modifying the aircraft. Additionally, since the CIA and Air Force jointly administered the U-2 program, any such modification required the concurrence of both for final approval. The Air Force chief of staff decided that there was no need to develop a carrier capability, and he disapproved of the proposal. Navy officials attempted on several occasions over the next 3 years to obtain a joint agreement between the CIA and Air Force, but development of a carrier-based U-2 did not gain impetus until 1963, when deputy CIA Director Lt. Gen. Marshall S. Carter became interested in the idea.[19]

Carter discussed the concept with Kelly Johnson, who assured him that the aircraft could be modified with relatively minor engineering changes and at reasonable cost. Carter then directed Col. Jack Ledford, assistant director of the Office of Special Activities, to investigate the feasibility of U-2 carrier operations and determine how to implement such a program. To begin, Ledford's deputy, James A. Cunningham, Jr., assembled a team of representatives from

---

19. CIA, "U-2 Aircraft Carrier Operation: Project Whale Tale," CIA-RDP75B00446R000100210015-3, December 1964, approved for release September 30, 2003, pp. 1–3.

Lockheed and the office of the Chief of Naval Operations to visit several aircraft carriers and naval air stations. The purpose of these survey trips was to identify and resolve any potential problems that might affect development and operational deployment of the U-2G. Cunningham then assembled the team's findings and recommendations into a report for Gen. Carter in which he addressed the question of whether the U-2G could be economically adapted to operate from carriers within acceptable safety parameters, with sufficient frequency to be effective, and without adversely affecting the Navy's operational commitments. Cunningham concluded that "present engineering analyses confirm that the aircraft can be so operated theoretically as to produce a viable carrier capability for reconnaissance purposes."[20]

As soon as Carter approved Cunningham's recommendations, on July 23, 1963, Lockheed began working to modify the first of several airframes to the new configuration. Adapting the U-2 to its new environment posed multiple challenges. The types of aircraft typically flown from carriers required a catapult to launch from the deck and arresting gear to bring the aircraft to a halt upon landing. These operations imposed structural stresses on the airframe and landing gear beyond those the U-2 had been designed to withstand. Necessary changes to the U-2 would undoubtedly affect the airplane's range and altitude characteristics. The addition of an arresting hook, beefed up landing gear, and other equipment promised unavoidable weight penalties, but there were no significant aerodynamic changes. Concurrently, the CIA coordinated with the Navy to arrange for U-2 carrier suitability tests and to develop a pilot training program. There were a great many questions regarding the airplane's behavior during approach and landing. The U-2 normally landed tail-high, which would make snagging the arresting cable with the hook nearly impossible without a skillful power-on approach just above stall speed. Additionally, wind patterns over the stern of a fast-moving carrier typically produced a downdraft immediately to the rear of the stern, followed by an updraft from 1,000 to 1,500 feet aft of the carrier. Specialized landing techniques had to be developed to overcome the adverse effects of these phenomena.[21]

In designing the U-2G, Lockheed engineers made several major changes to the basic airframe. The most obvious external difference was the addition of an arresting hook installed beneath the aft fuselage and covered with a plastic aerodynamic fairing that would be jettisoned in preparation for landing. A reinforced main landing gear strut more than doubled the original design specification for maximum deceleration speed. The tail wheel strut was also

---

20. Ibid., p. 3.
21. Ibid., pp. 3–6.

reinforced and protected by the addition of a metal plate to deflect the arresting cable. Engineers added thicker pressure bulkheads in the landing gear bay and augmented longerons in the fuselage at the wing's trailing edge to enable the aircraft to withstand the added stresses of arresting-hook engagement. With a full fuel load, the U-2G would necessarily be above its maximum gross landing weight at takeoff. In order to quickly reduce aircraft weight in the event of an emergency requiring immediate landing, the U-2G was equipped with a mechanically operated fuel jettison system. Because of the critical need to reduce lift at touchdown, mechanical spoilers were added to the outboard trailing edge of the wings. Activated by a simple switch on the throttle quadrant at touchdown, these caused the wing to stall almost immediately, enabling the pilot to make a precision landing. For obvious structural reasons, catapult launch of the U-2G was not feasible, but the airplane's normal takeoff characteristics were deemed more than sufficient.[22]

There were, of course, logistical challenges involved in loading the U-2 aboard a carrier and handling the airplane on deck. Using a standard fuselage-handling cart as a starting point, Lockheed manufactured a special sling for lifting the airplane to place it on board or remove it from the ship. The hangar deck offered adequate space for maintenance work or fueling, but moving the airplane up to the flight deck required Lockheed engineers to design a specialized handling cart because the ship's elevator was not large enough to easily accommodate the U-2.[23] James Cunningham noted that "the handling, launching, and retrieval will always be a special operation, requiring considerable technical skill from both ground support personnel and pilots."[24]

Carrier suitability trials began in August 1963. These preliminary tests, dubbed Project Whale Tale, used an unmodified U-2C flown by Bob Schumacher from the USS *Kitty Hawk* approximately 50 miles off the coast of California. Although security was considered paramount, it was impossible to conceal the airplane from the multitude of personnel at the Navy port in San Diego and onboard the carrier itself. Schumacher had flown Article 352 into Naval Air Station North Island under cover of darkness, and the U-2 was hoisted aboard the *Kitty Hawk* after midnight. Navy personnel involved in the loading operation included firefighters, security guards, crane operators, and numerous others.[25] Despite the most stringent precautions by both Navy and CIA security personnel to prevent unwitting persons gaining knowledge of the

22. Ibid., pp. 6–7.
23. Ibid., p. 5.
24. Pocock, *50 Years of the U-2*, p. 201.
25. CIA, "U-2 Aircraft Carrier Operation: Project Whale Tale," p. 9.

U-2 pilot attempts to snag the arresting cable during landing aboard the *Kitty Hawk*.
(Lockheed Martin)

operation, Kelly Johnson was horrified to see unexpected crowds of spectators. As he later noted in his diary, "I don't think more than 2,000 or 3,000 people saw the aircraft go aboard, as they kept coming back all night from a carnival that was held adjacent to the loading docks!"[26]

After dawn, the *Kitty Hawk* steamed westward into the Pacific Ocean to a point approximately 20 miles south of San Clemente Island. The ship was under way at 20 knots into a 10-knot headwind. The combined 30-knot wind across the flight deck posed a challenge for the deck crew as they positioned the lightweight airplane for takeoff. When given clearance, Schumacher advanced the throttle and began rolling down the deck. He was airborne within a mere 321 feet, the pogos dropped to the deck, and by the time the U-2 cleared the carrier's bow it had already climbed 1,000 feet. After initially making a steep climb, Schumacher circled around and made several low approaches to the flight deck at speeds between 75 and 78 knots to evaluate the airplane's handling qualities in the crosswinds and turbulence surrounding the carrier. On the third approach, he briefly touched down but bounced, striking the right wingtip against the steel deck plating before reapplying power and

26. Pocock, *50 Years of the U-2*, p. 201.

going around. After a final pass that allowed observers to check for damage, Schumacher flew the U-2 to Lockheed's facility in Burbank. The test was considered a complete success that furnished Lockheed engineers with valuable data for use in further developing the U-2G design changes.[27]

Kelly Johnson and his team mulled over many questions still not fully answered. They briefly considered using a parachute and speed brakes to arrest the airplane on landing instead of the tailhook and cable system, because repeated arrested landings might overstress the tail-mounting bolts. There was concern that shock effects of carrier landings and associated twisting moments might eventually cause wing fatigue or fuel leaks or even damage sensitive reconnaissance and navigational equipment. Most carrier-based aircraft were designed for landing deceleration speeds of 15 to 20 feet per second, but Johnson was only confident that he could beef up the landing gear to withstand a 10-foot-per-second deceleration. All the while, Johnson worked to keep modification costs as low as possible. One cost-saving innovation was his recommendation to transfer two Air Force U-2A airframes to the project since they had already been scheduled for overhaul and conversion to U-2C standards. Accordingly, articles 348 and 362 were converted to G models along with articles 382 and 385. After Article 362 was lost in July 1964, it was replaced with Article 349, which had been transferred from the Air Force. Originally built as a U-2A, Article 349 now received the J75 engine, the carrier landing modifications, and in-flight refueling capability, and it was designated the sole U-2H model. It seemed like the perfect combination of characteristics for mission flexibility. Unfortunately, the excess weight considerably reduced maximum altitude. Consequently, the refueling receptacle was removed less than a year later, returning the airplane to the standard U-2G configuration.[28]

For the arresting gear, Johnson ultimately settled on a modified version of the tailhook used on the T-2A. On the U-2, it was mounted ahead of the tail wheel and attached to the same structural framework that included the wing attach points and engine mounts. Small fairings surrounded the hook to reduce aerodynamic drag, and although the jettisonable fairing had been eliminated, there was provision for a plastic cover to hide the hook from view when it was not in use. A shield assembly ahead of the tail-wheel doors was installed to deflect the arresting cable in the event that the hook failed to connect. Johnson studied several lift-reduction systems before settling on the spoilers. Fixed slots in the flaps offered the simplest solution and the least weight penalty but would have required a much steeper angle of attack on final approach. A proposed

27. CIA, "U-2 Aircraft Carrier Operation: Project Whale Tale," p. 11.

28. Pocock, *50 Years of the U-2*, pp. 201–206.

leading-edge slat would have required borrowing space from the fuel tanks to accommodate actuators, resulting in a 400-nautical-mile loss in range. With the addition of the spoilers and fuel-dump system, the total weight penalty resulting from the modifications was around 350 pounds.[29]

CIA project staff and Naval Training Command personnel formulated a three-phase training syllabus known as Whale Tale II. Phase One of the short but comprehensive carrier qualification course included initial flight checkout in the Navy's T-2A and simulated carrier landings under the supervision of a highly qualified landing signals officer (LSO) at Naval Air Station Monterey, CA. In Phase Two, trainees completed additional practice landings at Naval Air Station Pensacola, FL, followed by actual carrier landings aboard the USS *Lexington* in the Gulf of Mexico. Phase Three consisted of carrier-type approaches and landings in the U-2G on a specially prepared lakebed runway at Edwards and, finally, actual carrier landings in the U-2.[30]

The first four pilots began Phase One training in November 1963 under the supervision of Lt. Cdr. John Huber. After 2 weeks, the group moved to Pensacola for Phase Two and completed initial carrier qualification. A second group of four CIA pilots plus Schumacher and Detachment G Comm. Bill Gregory began training in January 1964 and completed Phase Two on February 15. Phase Three commenced with the delivery of the first U-2G to the Edwards detachment. Bob Schumacher tested the spoiler system during initial field carrier-landing practice sorties, discovering a variety of minor problems that included airframe buffeting, tail vibration, and a rolling tendency at stall. Once these minor problems were resolved, each detachment pilot had the opportunity to fly numerous practice sorties. In developing landing techniques based on experience with both the T-2A and U-2G, they agreed that an ideal carrier landing required approximately 40 knots wind speed across the deck. Since the U-2 typically landed at 70 knots this resulted in an actual touchdown speed of about 30 knots. The ultimate key to success was complete trust in the LSO. Observing from the deck, Huber signaled the U-2 pilot with regard to last-minute altitude adjustments and the precise moment for chopping the throttle to idle.[31]

With simulated carrier-landing practice completed, the stage was now set for Whale Tale III deployment aboard the USS *Ranger*. Like the previous training project, this effort was divided into three parts. Phase One was devoted exclusively to Lockheed testing of U-2G carrier-landing characteristics and operational

---

29. Ibid., p. 202.

30. CIA, "U-2 Aircraft Carrier Operation: Project Whale Tale," p. 11.

31. Pocock, *50 Years of the U-2*, pp. 202–203.

Lockheed test pilot Bob Schumacher makes a successful arrested landing on March 2, 1964. (Air Force Flight Test Museum)

suitability. As soon as these tests were completed, the airplane was turned over to Detachment G personnel for Phase Two, which consisted entirely of carrier takeoff and landing practice. In Phase Three, the Edwards detachment evaluated the airplane's operational capabilities. The results provided valuable lessons with regard to piloting techniques and operational procedures.[32]

On February 29, 1964, Bob Schumacher began Phase One with a series of touch-and-go landings in Article 362, which had been specially instrumented for the tests. This part of the testing went well, but he reported turbulence on approach requiring significant throttle adjustments. When Schumacher attempted his first arrested landing, he approached too fast and a little high. The airplane bounced and the hook engaged the cable while the U-2G was still airborne, causing it to slam back to the deck and nose over. Minor damage to the nose section was easily repaired aboard ship, but afterward Schumacher flew the plane to Burbank so engineers could study the instrument readings and add a steel skid beneath the forward fuselage to prevent a similar mishap. Once carrier-landing techniques had been perfected, this additional modification was no longer required. In order to solve the turbulence problem, the carrier's

32. CIA, "U-2 Aircraft Carrier Operation: Project Whale Tale," pp. 11–12.

speed had to be reduced until the wind over the deck dropped to 25 knots and the updraft behind the ship flattened out below the U-2's approach path.[33]

Schumacher returned on March 2 in Article 348 and completed Phase One with four successful arrested landings. The airplane was then turned over to Gregory's detachment for Phase Two. That same day, Robert Ericson made several touch-and-go landings but was unable to successfully perform an arrested landing. His plane ran short of fuel while the USS *Ranger* maneuvered away from a foreign vessel that had entered the operational area, and he eventually had to land at North Island. Jim Barnes flew Article 348 back to the carrier on March 3, but on his first touch-and-go, he allowed the right wing to drop. The right wing skid became entangled with the arresting cable and tore off. Barnes gunned the throttle, gained some altitude, and flew the airplane to Edwards for repairs. These incidents delayed completion of Phase Two by another week, which allowed project pilots to refine their approach techniques based on experience gained up to that point. Once flight operations resumed, all pilots qualified for carrier operations without further incident. The end of Phase Three signaled the detachment's operational readiness.[34]

The U-2's carrier capability was put to the test a few months later during Operation Fishhawk. This called for a flight over the French nuclear test site at Mururoa Atoll in the middle of the Pacific Ocean. So remote was the test site that the USS *Ranger* and her escort had to sail more than 3,000 miles just to get within range for the U-2 mission. All necessary support equipment and personnel and one of three pilots were aboard the carrier when it departed San Diego. On May 12, two additional pilots ferried their U-2G aircraft to the ship from Edwards via Hawaii. One week later, when the *Ranger* was within 800 nautical miles of Mururoa, one of the airplanes took off on a maximum-range sortie covering more than 1,000 miles. Since additional photographic coverage was required, a second mission was launched on May 22.[35]

Detachment G pilots continued to receive carrier qualification in the T-2A and perform practice touchdowns in the U-2 at Edwards. Over time, the pilots discovered that each of the airplanes had unique flying qualities. Article 382, for example had a tendency to drop off to the left in a stall. On April 26, 1965, Buster Edens, a 9-year veteran of the U-2 program, was briefed on this phenomenon before taking the airplane up for a series of simulated carrier landings. After taking off and climbing to 13,000 feet to check stall characteristics, which appeared normal, he returned to the landing pattern and made

33. Pocock, *50 Years of the U-2*, pp. 202–203.
34. CIA, "U-2 Aircraft Carrier Operation: Project Whale Tale," pp. 13–15.
35. Pocock, *50 Years of the U-2*, p. 204.

an approach to the runway. At touchdown, the left wing dropped, dragging the skid for about 50 feet as Edens added power and struggled to get aloft. He managed to level the wings and become airborne, making a left turn to reenter the downwind leg. A ground observer advised him to check the wing balance again, which he apparently did at an altitude of 3,000 feet. At this point, the airplane dipped to the left into a descending spiral. Edens extended the speed brakes to arrest the spin but never regained control. He ejected at extremely low altitude and was killed because his parachute did not fully open.[36]

Accident investigators recommended that in the future, stall checks be conducted with sufficient altitude available for spin recovery or, at the very least, safe egress. They also suggested that efforts be made to ensure symmetrical stall characteristics for all U-2 aircraft and that necessary modifications be made to prevent fuel from moving from one wing to the other when the pump was not operating.[37] In his diary, Kelly Johnson lamented the stall and trim problems and the stall strips on the wings that had to be hand tailored for each aircraft individually. "If we put the stall strips where they give us good landing and takeoff characteristics," he wrote, "then we run into buffeting and pitching at altitude."[38]

Although the overall results of the Whale Tale effort were highly successful, there was substantial Navy opposition to conducting additional U-2 carrier missions. Operation and deployment of an aircraft carrier was extremely expensive and required an entire flotilla of support vessels. Moving an entire carrier battle group quickly or in secret was virtually impossible, and senior Navy leadership complained that the U-2 operation was interfering with other fleet priorities.[39] In 1969, all surviving U-2G airframes were placed in flyable storage, but this was not the end of U-2 operations at sea.

The First Trainer

Other than the U-2D, there had never been a two-seat U-2. Unlike most military airplanes, there was no trainer model with provisions for an instructor pilot and trainee. Student pilots received instruction and checkout in the T-33 before making their first solo flight in the U-2. Although the idea of building a U-2 trainer had been raised many times, the idea failed to gain traction until

---

36. Ibid., p. 207.
37. Ibid.
38. Ibid., p. 208.
39. Pedlow & Welzenbach, *The CIA and the U-2 Program*, p. 251.

The U-2CT had an instructor's station above and behind the student's cockpit. (U.S. Air Force)

the early 1970s. In the wake of several landing accidents, 15th Air Force commander Gen. Paul K. Carlton sent the SAC U-2 unit operations officer, Col. Tony Martinez, to Lockheed to discuss the possibility of modifying one of the damaged airframes into a two-place trainer. Kelly Johnson offered to rebuild the U-2C for $1 million but estimated it would cost $5 million to $6 million to convert it into a trainer. Air Force officials approved the expenditure and Johnson assigned Ed Baldwin to lead the conversion team at the Skunk Works facility in Palmdale, CA. Maj. George Worley of the 100th Strategic Reconnaissance Wing advised Baldwin on what controls and instruments would be needed for the instructor's cockpit.[40]

Baldwin began with Article 393, which had been badly damaged during a landing accident in May 1972. Using parts of other crashed airframes, his team installed a second cockpit for the instructor pilot above and directly behind the student's cockpit. The conversion was completed just 5 months after receiving the go-ahead. Lockheed chief test pilot Bill Park made the maiden flight of the U-2CT on February 13, 1973. He found that the odd-looking configuration handled well and apparently had no adverse effect on the airplane's aerodynamics. Eleven days later, after the U-2CT had been painted gloss white with SAC markings, Worley flew the trainer to Davis-Monthan Air Force Base near Tucson, AZ. Crew chief TSgt. Jose Ortiz rode

---

40. Pocock, *50 Years of the U-2*, p. 349.

in the front cockpit during the ferry flight, becoming the first enlisted crew-man to fly in a U-2.[41]

Based on a new training syllabus written by Worley, new U-2 pilots first received an hour of taildragger experience in a Bellanca Decathlon. They would then need to make five flights with an instructor in the U-2CT before being allowed to solo. The new trainer soon proved its worth and was very popular with student pilots. A second U-2CT was built from Article 359 in the summer of 1975 and delivered in January 1976. Both trainers remained in service until 1987.[42]

Second Generation

The number of U-2s operated by the CIA fluctuated over the course of the airplane's first decade of service. By 1963, nearly half of the 55 airframes built had been lost to attrition and others were swapped back and forth between the agency and the Air Force. Although Kelly Johnson recognized the need to put the U-2 back into production, he was reluctant because the Government was already heavily invested in the airplane's successor, the A-12, and variants including the YF-12 and R-12 (later redesignated SR-71). So, rather than restart the production line, Johnson assigned several of his engineers to develop a simple modification to improve the U-2's capabilities. Merv Heal and his team proposed adding two 30-inch fuselage plugs, one aft of the Q-bay and one aft of the wings, adding 60 inches to the airframe. This would give the airplane more room for equipment, a refueling receptacle, and carrier arresting gear. Johnson was so enthusiastic about the improved capabilities that in September 1963 he recommended building a new batch of 25 aircraft, designated U-2L, at a cost of approximately $1 million apiece.[43]

Air Force and Navy officials expressed interest in the basic U-2L, but the CIA requested a capability for installing an upward-facing optical sensor to take images of Soviet satellites. Johnson subsequently sought a 240-inch focal length camera that could fit in the nose of the U-2, pointed upward. He then proposed a rotating nose assembly that would allow the camera to take pictures of the ground as well. This version of the airplane was dubbed U-2M. But getting approval for production was no longer as easy as it once had been. The National Reconnaissance Office (NRO), established in 1960, now had

---

41. Ibid.
42. Ibid.
43. Ibid., p. 236.

procurement approval authority for all overhead reconnaissance programs, and despite the fact that the NRO was a joint organization between the CIA and military services, there was a significant amount of bureaucratic infighting. In September 1964, the NRO rejected Lockheed's U-2L and U-2M proposals in favor of less costly upgrades to the existing fleet.[44]

In March 1965, NRO Director Brockway McMillan directed the Air Force and CIA to study future requirements for the U-2. He also asked for comparison of U-2 intelligence collection capabilities versus the A-12/SR-71 and reconnaissance satellites, as well as an estimate of the future role of airborne reconnaissance platforms in the face of improved hostile air defense systems. Three months later, McMillan received a recommendation to procure more U-2 airplanes. This gave Kelly Johnson the opportunity to propose yet another improvement. Up to this point, he had yet to alter the U-2's wing configuration, but he began investigating new high-lift NASA airfoils, swept wings, and changes in aspect ratio. In July, he pitched a proposal for building 27 U-2N airframes with a longer wingspan and increased lifting surface. Unimpressed, McMillan rejected the proposal on the basis that "Although a new version would have somewhat improved performance, it would still be highly vulnerable to both ground and air missiles."[45]

Johnson's team continued to work despite this setback. In an effort to improve the wing configuration, Lockheed spent $250,000 on designing and wind tunnel testing a new wing with a NASA-developed flap, designed by Richard Whitcomb of Langley Research Center, that would increase critical Mach number, the lowest Mach number at which airflow over some point of the aircraft reaches the speed of sound. Initial test results were disappointing. Although the new flap arrangement delayed the onset of transonic drag rise, the airplane's overall profile drag increased by 30 percent. As Johnson noted in his diary, "When we combined this with the extremely heavy weight of the new wing and its controls we obtained a very discouraging outcome."[46]

In the meantime, Pratt & Whitney engineers were working on improvements to boost climb performance. The result was the J75-P-13B with 17,000 pounds of thrust at sea level. The NRO ordered 24 of the new engines to upgrade the existing U-2 fleet, but flight testing demonstrated a clear need for widening the air inlet to optimize performance. Johnson saw this as an opportunity to press his case for a wholly revised U-2 design, and he directed Merv Heal to conduct another design study. The U-2R featured an enlarged

44. Ibid., pp. 236–237.
45. Ibid., p. 237.
46. Ibid.

fuselage with additional equipment space and provisions for interchangeable nose assemblies to carry a variety of cameras and sensors, depending on mission requirements.[47] As Johnson later wrote, "We made a complete circle and ended up merely enlarging the present U-2 to take advantage of a 20 percent power increase…. Going back to the original concept, where we can fly with a lift coefficient of 0.6 to 0.7, gives us an airplane with a 7,000 mile range unrefueled and a few thousand feet more altitude."[48] As it turned out, Johnson's range estimate was overly optimistic, but there was significant improvement.

He pitched his proposal in January 1966, offering to build the first two aircraft for just $12.5 million. The Air Force expressed little interest at the time, giving higher priority to the SR-71 program, but the CIA funded a 3-month study contract for basic engineering. Lockheed spent a nearly equivalent sum of company money on wind tunnel–model testing. Additional testing was undertaken to determine the airplane's vulnerability to radar tracking and surface-to-air missiles.[49] By August 1966, the original U-2 fleet had dwindled to 15, and several of these were undergoing repairs at Lockheed. To increase the number of available aircraft and lengthen the fleet's service life, Director of Central Intelligence Richard Helms initially approved an order for eight airframes. Within 6 months, he and Secretary of Defense Robert McNamara jointly placed an order for another four.[50]

Johnson assigned Ed Baldwin and Fred Cavanaugh to spearhead the engineering effort, and he gave their 30-person team 12 months to refine the design, build the aircraft, and fly the prototype. Apart from enhanced performance, design goals included a better electrical system along with improved maintainability and servicing provisions. The enlarged fuselage not only offered substantially increased internal volume for additional equipment but also achieved better overall weight distribution. Other improvements included the elimination of protruding oil cooler intakes (to reduce drag), enlarged horizontal and vertical tail surfaces, hydraulically actuated roll and lift spoilers, enlarged retractable leading-edge stall strips, strengthened landing gear, a zero-zero ejection seat, proper stressing for arresting gear, and folding wingtips for ease of storage on the ground or inside an aircraft carrier. A mockup review on November 29, 1966, resulted in very few recommendations for design changes. Johnson's engineering team had taken thorough advantage of prior experience and lessons learned from the earlier U-2 production program. One problem

---

47. Ibid., pp. 237–238.
48. Miller, *Lockheed Skunk Works: The First Fifty Years*, p. 89.
49. Pocock, *50 Years of the U-2*, p. 238.
50. Pedlow & Welzenbach, *The CIA and the U-2 Program*, p. 251.

With its lengthened fuselage and wings, the U-2R, right, was significantly larger than the U-2C. (Lockheed Martin)

that had been addressed was that the first-generation U-2 had become so heavy that the margin between stall buffet and compressibility at high altitudes was only 6 knots. With improved wings and engine, the U-2R had a comparatively generous 20-knot window, greatly improving the airplane's flying qualities.[51]

The original U-2 had an 80-foot span with 600 square feet of wing area. By contrast, the U-2R had a 103-foot span with 1,000 square feet of lifting surface. Bob Wiele, who led the wing design team, retained the original NACA 64A airfoil and reduced wing loading to the values attained with the U-2A. The airplane's lift-to-drag ratio was 27:1, its lift coefficient was 0.6 to 0.7, and the aspect ratio was 10.667. The unconventional wing structure weighed just 3 pounds per square foot and included planks (eight per wing) milled from large aluminum billets, rather than being built up using riveted sheet metal, I-beams, and U-channels. The larger wing also gave the U-2R increased internal fuel capacity, and the fuel tank arrangement was altered. In the early U-2 models, having the main tank forward and the auxiliary tank aft resulted in considerable changes in center of gravity as fuel was consumed. This problem was eliminated in the U-2R by placing the 1,169-gallon main tanks inboard and the 239-gallon auxiliaries outboard. Fuel from the main tanks was exhausted first so that the weight of the remaining fuel in the auxiliary tanks helped dampen

---

51. Miller, *Lockheed Skunk Works: The First Fifty Years*, p. 92.

wing bending and torsional loads. An additional 99 gallons in the sump tank gave the U-2R a total capacity of 2,915 gallons, enough to remain airborne for 15 hours, though it was impractical to expect a pilot to endure flying solo in a pressure suit for such an extended length of time.[52]

Herb Nystrom led the team that designed the empennage and tail assembly. Following a series of engineering studies, he opted to include an all-moving tailplane similar to the one Kelly Johnson developed for the Lockheed JetStar. This configuration most effectively distributed pitch forces across the entire horizontal stabilizer assembly, widened the airplane's center-of-gravity limits, and eliminated the need for both ballast and trim tabs.[53]

Ed Baldwin's team was responsible for designing the fuselage assembly. With wide, flaring inlets, it had a Coke bottle shape and was wider and 25 percent longer than that of earlier models. A surplus of internal volume accommodated navigation and communications equipment, defensive avionics, and other items. Mission equipment occupied both the enlarged Q-bay and the nose compartment. Total payload capacity was 1,050 pounds. The cockpit was 45 percent larger than that of the U-2C, allowing the partial-pressure suit to be abandoned in favor of bulkier but more comfortable full-pressure suits. It also accommodated a new ejection seat that could be safely used at even extremely low altitude. Seven experienced U-2 pilots contributed to the design of the cockpit arrangement. Fitted with pressure suits, they took turns sitting in the mockup and evaluating visibility instrument placement and operability of controls and switches.[54]

Although the remaining U-2C airframes had been equipped with the new J75-P-13B engine, the U-2R was powered by an upgraded model that had improved dependability and increased thrust, allowing it to achieve speeds up to 410 knots (Mach 0.72), or about 12 knots faster than the U-2C. Although the U-2R could exceed 74,000 feet, it had a shorter range at maximum altitude than the U-2C. One significant improvement was that in the event that the P-13B engine quit during flight, it could be restarted at 54,000 feet, roughly 10,000 feet higher than the earlier P-13A.[55]

Assembly of the first U-2R began in early 1967. Johnson was very satisfied with his team's workmanship, but by mid-March 1967, he was concerned that construction of the prototype was progressing slowly. "This is basically because I have insisted on much better tooling than on prior models," he wrote in his

52. Pocock, *50 Years of the U-2*, p. 238.
53. Ibid., p. 239.
54. Ibid.
55. Pedlow & Welzenbach, *The CIA and the U-2 Program*, pp. 251–252.

Bill Park piloted the maiden flight of the U-2R on August 28, 1967. (Lockheed Martin)

diary, "and, while it will take us longer to get started, we will get much better airplanes." By April 19, the wings were taking shape and the forward fuselage and cockpit structure were nearly complete. Johnson marveled at the size of the U-2R and lamented that the airframe was about 800 pounds heavier than originally specified, about half of which was due to added customer equipment.[56]

In accordance with Kelly Johnson's schedule, the completed prototype, known as Article 051, was delivered to Edwards in August. Following static ground testing and taxi trials, the unpainted U-2R was prepared for its maiden flight. On August 28, with Bob Schumacher and Johnson flying chase in a Beech Twin Bonanza, Bill Park took off from Rogers Dry Lake and soared into the sky. He found the airplane generally similar to its predecessors. As testing continued over the ensuing months, Park and other test pilots gained an appreciation for the various design improvements. Larger control surfaces and an increased critical Mach number significantly improved the overall flying qualities. Improved margins between stall and Mach buffet at cruising altitudes

---

56. Miller, *Lockheed Skunk Works: The First Fifty Years*, p. 92.

By mid-1968, five U-2R airframes were being flown at Edwards for testing and training. (Lockheed Martin)

allowed more reliable autopilot control, and the U-2R had better longitudinal pitch trim than earlier models.[57]

A second U-2R was delivered in December. Results of flight testing indicated that range and altitude performance was as desired. Maximum altitude was a function of gross takeoff weight and outside air temperature, but a U-2R with a gross takeoff weight of 34,750 pounds (including 12,250 pounds of fuel and a 3,000-pound payload) could fly a 7.5-hour, 3,000-nautical-mile mission, with most of the flight above 70,000 feet. The test team discovered a number of small problems with the air conditioning system, engine oil cooling, fuel-feed system, and tail vibration, but these were easily fixed. A more serious problem was the airplane's tendency to veer to the left during takeoff roll due to nonaxisymmetric thrust. Testing had to be delayed 2 months while Lockheed engineers devised a solution. Their first attempt involved adding a 5-inch extension to the tailpipe, but this caused serious vibration. Ultimately, the original U-2R tailpipe was extended 12 inches and bypass doors were added adjacent to the engine compressor face. These doors provided cooling air to the engine compartment and secondary airflow to the exhaust ejector. During

---

57. Pocock, *50 Years of the U-2*, pp. 240–241.

ground operations, when nacelle pressure was higher than at the compressor face, they remained closed to prevent the compressor from drawing air away from the ejector. During flight, the doors opened when pressure at the engine face was higher.[58]

Production airframes rolled off the assembly line at the rate of approximately one per month. By the end of May 1968, five airplanes were flying and two of those were being used for operational pilot training. The U-2R proved to be a very stable platform for reconnaissance sensors and featured better camera-window glass than had been previously used. Kelly Johnson presented test results and touted the airplane's enhanced capabilities in the hope of attracting customers and keeping the U-2R production line open beyond the 12-unit initial run. He emphasized the reliability and flexibility that built upon prior experience with a family of aircraft that had logged more than 135,000 flight hours since its introduction in 1955. The J75 engine, already in use throughout the fleet, was well proven and capable of enduring 1,200 hours of operation before requiring overhaul. With a multitude of built-in access panels, the U-2R had been designed for ease of maintenance and servicing. It also had a comprehensive suite of communication and navigation equipment, as well as multiple backups for the electrical power system.[59]

Johnson succeeded in impressing senior Air Force leadership, though not as he had intended. Instead of placing a new order that would keep the production line running, they instead tried to acquire all 12 of the existing airframes for use by SAC. For a while, this pitted Director of Central Intelligence Richard Helms against Secretary of Defense Robert McNamara. Eventually, they came to an agreement to split the disposition of the U-2R production between the CIA and Air Force. In November 1968, 1 month prior to the delivery of the last U-2R, the NRO Executive Committee ordered most of the remaining U-2C and U-2G airframes placed in flyable storage to be used later for replacement of any U-2R models lost to attrition.

After the new model was declared operational in January 1969, pilots who had previously flown the U-2C underwent a 20-hour conversion course while transitioning to the U-2R. For reconnaissance sorties, the airplane could be equipped with a variety of different cameras, but with a 24-inch-focal-length stereo design and 12-inch resolution, the Itek IRIS II became the sensor of choice. This panoramic camera had a 140-degree scan angle and carried 10,500 feet of film to cover a 60-mile swath from 70,000 feet. An optical bar system in which the entire mirror-lens assembly rotated continuously

---

58. Ibid., p. 241.
59. Ibid.

eliminated vibration problems that reduced resolution in cameras with recip-
rocating shutters and lenses.[60]

Developmental and experimental testing at Edwards continued as the U-2R
was placed into service elsewhere. Some of these experiments were quite innovative if not terribly successful. One of these, dubbed Chameleon, involved the
application of paint that changed color as temperature varied with altitude. It
was hoped that paint that appeared light blue at low altitudes would change to
dark blue in the cold upper atmosphere, and then back again during descent,
to better camouflage the airplane throughout the course of a mission. Wailing
Wall was an experiment to determine whether specially designed intake duct
linings and various exhaust nozzle shapes would reduce the airplane's acoustic
signature, preventing detection during missions at low altitudes. Lockheed
engineers hoped to make the U-2 inaudible as low as 500 feet above the ground,
but the effort failed. For additional mission flexibility, one proposal involved
development of a probe-and-drogue buddy refueling capability that would
allow one U-2 to refuel another in flight. There was also a study to develop a
night-vision driftsight to allow the pilot to navigate from high altitudes using
terrain features after dark. By far the most practical effort involved an attempt
to provide the U-2R with a high-altitude engine restart capability. This worked
consistently at 50,000 feet, 10,000 feet above the normal J75-P-13B relight
altitude, but worked only occasionally at 56,000 to 58,000 feet. Some test
projects were almost surreal. One involved a method for dropping propaganda
leaflets from 70,000 feet. Another, called Fortune Cookie, called for launching modified AQM-37 supersonic drones from wing pylons. Under the initial
concept, the rocket-powered drone would be equipped with a camera and
recovered at the end of its flight. Later, it was proposed that an expendable
drone would collect electronic intelligence data, which could then be relayed
to the U-2 or another airborne platform within range. Although test results
were promising, no operational missions were undertaken.[61] Kelly Johnson also
pursued the concept of arming the U-2 with bombs and missiles. This would
have required the addition of hard-points on the wings for attaching weapon
pylons and replacing the original landing gear with a tricycle arrangement
consisting of two main gear in mid-wing pods and a nose wheel. This concept
never went beyond testing of a wind tunnel model.[62]

In the summer of 1969, despite continuing Navy opposition, the U-2R
was scheduled for carrier trials under project Blue Gull. Things went a little

60. Ibid., p. 245.
61. Ibid., pp. 255–257.
62. Jenkins, *Lockheed U-2 Dragon Lady*, p. 19.

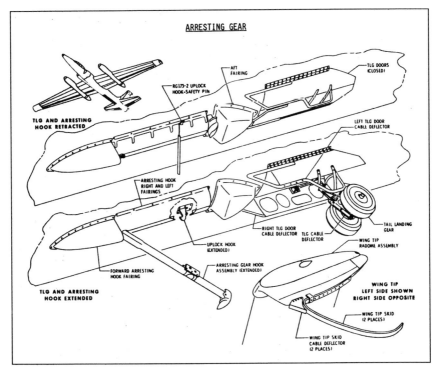

ARRESTING GEAR

For carrier operations, the U-2R was equipped with arresting gear and wingtip skid extensions. (U.S. Air Force)

smoother this time because the U-2R had been designed to accommodate removable arresting gear and the outermost 6 feet of each wing folded upward, allowing the airplane to fit more easily onto the carrier's elevator and inside the hangar deck. The first phase of testing involved 2 days of practice using a mock carrier runway at Naval Air Station Lakehurst, NJ. Thanks to the improved flap configuration and a more responsive throttle, pilots found the carrier landing characteristics of the U-2R much more benign than those of the U-2G. Next, Lockheed test pilot Bill Park, along with two American and two British pilots assigned to the U-2 project, underwent carrier qualification in the T-2B at Pensacola. This time, Lt. Cdr. Lonnie McClung served as the project's resident LSO.[63]

In November 1969, following additional landing practice in the U-2R at Edwards, the team headed east for Blue Gull V carrier trials aboard the USS *America*. Two U-2R aircraft were ferried to NASA's Wallops Island facility on

---

63. Pocock, *50 Years of the U-2*, p. 257.

Deck crewmen prepare the U-2 for takeoff from the USS *America*. (Lockheed Martin)

Virginia's Eastern Shore, and on November 21, Park flew out to the carrier. He made his first approach at a speed of 72 knots with a 20-knot wind over the deck but had to abort when the tailhook failed to deploy. He returned to shore where it was found that someone had forgotten to remove the locking pin prior to takeoff. His second and third attempts resulted in successful full-stop landings on the carrier deck. Park also demonstrated lightweight and heavyweight takeoffs. Overall, he was very satisfied with the airplane's handling characteristics, and he remarked that he scarcely needed to use the arresting gear at all.[64]

Each of the four remaining pilots earned their carrier qualifications in the U-2R, but debate still raged as to whether the Navy would permit operational missions to be carried out. The Blue Gull V exercise had demonstrated that the airplane fit onto the elevator and could be easily moved from hangar deck to flight deck and that flight operations could be easily accomplished with repeated success. Besides the obvious reconnaissance applications, there had been some interest in using the U-2R as a high-altitude communications relay for the carrier air group. Some high-ranking Navy officials, however, still felt that these were not sufficient reasons to take up valuable deck and hangar space and that it was simply too expensive to commit a carrier deployment to what would likely be a single U-2 sortie.[65]

---

64. Ibid., p. 258.
65. Ibid.

There was little clearance between the airplane's wingtip and the carrier's superstructure. (Lockheed Martin)

This didn't stop Kelly Johnson from pursuing other potential naval applications for the U-2R, particularly in the field of maritime surveillance. Up to this point, any airborne platform that relied on photographic means for obtaining imagery was constrained by inclement weather and limited daylight. By the early 1970s, significant advancements in high-speed integrated solid-state circuits made it possible to digitally process radar imaging signals in real time. The resulting increase in coverage and resolution this afforded spurred a revolution in the development of such sensors as synthetic-aperture radar (SAR), in which the airplane's flightpath was used to make a relatively small antenna perform like an extremely large antenna electronically. Collected data could then be processed to generate high-resolution imagery. In 1971, the NRO sponsored Project Senior Lance—flight tests of a prototype imaging radar built by Goodyear Aerospace in Phoenix. When installed in the nose of the U-2R, the sensor provided a commanding view from high altitude. Targets as far as 100 miles away could be identified in all weather conditions, day or night, even when concealed beneath foliage or camouflage netting. Flights made over the ocean provided imagery in which the wakes of individual ships were distinguishable even at great distances.[66]

In the initial phase of testing, Article 061 was equipped with a radar sensor that simply collected and stored all data for later processing. In March 1972, a

66. Ibid., p. 281.

A U-2R was fitted with radar systems to detect oceangoing vessels for the Navy EP-X test program. (Lockheed Martin)

data link was installed in the airplane so that radar returns could be transmitted to the ground for immediate processing and then sent as quickly as possible to military commanders to provide vital, current intelligence. A 3-month test of this capability, dubbed Senior Dagger, took place at McCoy Air Force Base, FL, that summer, with U-2 radar imagery being downlinked to a ground station at Rome Air Force Base, NY. Following completion of these tests, Article 061 was bailed to the Navy for a 6-month, $5.5 million program to evaluate a configuration called Electronics Patrol Experimental (EP-X). Under Project Highboy, the U-2R was equipped with forward-looking radar in the nose compartment and wing pods to contain additional sensors. The nose-mounted system was a variant of the AN/APS-116 X-band weather radar, modified to detect surface vessels or submarine periscopes protruding above the waves.[67] The left pod contained a return-beam vidicon camera, a high-performance electronic imaging sensor capable of making continuous or discrete exposures with performance matching or exceeding that of film, particularly with low-contrast imagery. An AN/ALQ-110 radar signal

---

67. Ibid., p. 282.

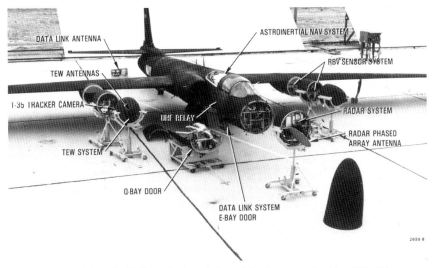

Under Project Highboy, the EP-X test bed carried a variety of sensors. (Lockheed Martin)

receiver was installed in the right pod along with a tracker camera that would normally have been mounted in the nose.[68]

During EP-X tests in early 1973, the U-2R was flown off the coast of California to provide near-real-time information on shipping. The sensors were controlled from the ground and all data were downlinked to analysts at Lockheed's facility in Sunnyvale, CA. In another test, dubbed Outlaw Hawk, sensors aboard the U-2R were downlinked to surface ships including the USS *Kitty Hawk*. In this exercise, the U-2R was flown from Palmdale while the carrier group sailed from San Diego to Pearl Harbor, HI. Despite promising results, the EP-X concept was ultimately abandoned in favor of a combination of more conventional aircraft, such as the EP-3E, and ocean surveillance satellites.[69]

Kelly Johnson's hopes for restarting the U-2R production line under Navy contract were dashed when NRO leadership recommended terminating the CIA portion of the U-2 program. Under this plan, the U-2R fleet would be consolidated within SAC and two airframes could be loaned to the Navy for further EP-X testing. Johnson continued to propose new ideas for his beloved U-2, including a capability to carry two laser-guided bombs

68. Michael J. Cantella, "Application of the High Resolution Return Beam Vidicon," *Optical Engineering* 16, no. 3 (June 1, 1977): 163257, *http://dx.doi.org/10.1117/12.7972141*, accessed July 7, 2013.

69. Norman Polmar, "When the U-2 Went to Sea," *Air Force Magazine* 84, no. 2 (February 2001): 62.

or anti-ship missiles and a U-2RL with a lengthened Q-bay and a refueling probe mounted at the tip of the vertical tail fin. Unfortunately, by this time a series of bribery scandals, as well as developmental and financial problems involving the L-1011 Tristar, threatened to bankrupt the company. The Navy showed no further interest in EP-X, and in 1974, the CIA put an end to the agency's U-2 operation. Johnson retired the following year to be replaced by his deputy, Ben Rich.[70]

Over the next several years, the Air Force sought expanded capabilities for the U-2R, including improved cameras and the Advanced Synthetic Aperture Radar System (ASARS), which had resolution comparable to that of film cameras. Use of interchangeable nose assemblies, the Q-bay, and wing pods made it possible to conduct multisensor missions for simultaneous collection of both imagery and signals intelligence (SIGINT). Lockheed eventually contracted with Texas-based E-Systems to combine multiple SIGINT sensors within two 24-foot-long superpods mounted at midspan on each wing. Each superpod was capable of containing 800 pounds of equipment and was three times larger than the instrument pods used during the EP-X trials. As in the early days of the U-2, the airplane could also be fitted with particulate samplers for collecting debris from foreign nuclear tests; although such tests took place underground, radionuclides were sometimes vented into the atmosphere.[71] This capability was also put to use after a nuclear-powered Soviet ocean surveillance satellite reentered Earth's atmosphere and disintegrated over Canada's Northwestern Territories in January 1978. Five U-2 high-altitude aerial sampling sorties were flown during a joint U.S.-Canadian search-and-recovery effort known as Operation Morning Light.[72] The SAC U-2 fleet was also occasionally called upon to assist with flood control and tornado-damage assessment, hurricane surveillance, and geothermal-energy monitoring. Many such missions were accommodated during routine training sorties.[73]

By the mid-1970s, the Air Force had recognized the value of remotely piloted vehicles (RPVs) for airborne reconnaissance and was seriously considering investing in an extremely long-duration, high-altitude RPV. Drones used during the war in Vietnam produced imagery and other intelligence comparable in quality to that collected by crewed platforms but at considerably lower risk. In a fighter-sized RPV, space normally used for crews and

---

70. Pocock, *50 Years of the U-2*, p. 283.

71. Ibid., pp. 283–290.

72. Mahlon E. Gates et al., "Operation Morning Light: Northwest Territories, Canada, 1978: A Non-technical Summary of United States Participation," U.S. Dept. of Energy NV-198 (1978), p. 30.

73. Miller, *Lockheed Skunk Works: The First Fifty Years*, p. 95.

Advanced synthetic aperture imaging radar and wing-mounted SIGINT equipment expanded the U-2's capabilities. (U.S. Air Force)

life-support systems could be allocated to additional fuel and sensor equipment. Alternatively, such an airframe might be built with a strong, lightweight structure for improved altitude and range. Funding of engineering studies and testing of prototypes bled funding from other programs, including the U-2R. In one such effort, called Compass Cope, both Boeing and Teledyne-Ryan submitted competing designs for a high-altitude, long-range RPV designed for long-endurance photographic reconnaissance and electronic surveillance missions. Sensing an opportunity, Ben Rich proposed that Lockheed develop a remotely piloted version of the U-2R. He argued that since it was based on proven technology, the RPV would be less expensive to produce and be available sooner that either the Boeing or Teledyne-Ryan entries. Moreover, it would have equal or better performance and payload capabilities. It became a moot point when the Compass Cope program was canceled in July 1977 because of difficulties in developing sensor payloads for the aircraft and because Air Force officials apparently had no interest in a U-2 RPV.[74]

---

74. Ibid.

New Production

To the surprise of many, Kelly Johnson's dream of restarting the U-2 production line eventually came true with congressional approval of the fiscal year 1979 defense budget. In 1977, Lockheed proposed upgrading the U-2R to carry side-looking radar and the latest ASARS, sensor packages considered ideal for the type of standoff tactical reconnaissance mission that military planners considered vital for future conflicts. Upon accepting this proposal, the Air Force signed an initial $10.2 million contract with Lockheed to refurbish the original U-2R tooling that had been in storage since 1969 and to create whatever new tooling might be required for constructing the new airframe. This was followed with a $42.4 million production contract to build the first three airframes, two trainers for the Air Force and a single-seat model for NASA to be used as an Earth resources science platform. By the time full-scale production ended, a total of 37 new airframes had been built, including another for NASA and an additional trainer. In keeping with the airplane's new tactical reconnaissance role, the Air Force changed the designation from U-2R to TR-1A for the single-seat model and TR-1B for the trainer.[75] The NASA plane was initially called the ER-1 but was later redesignated ER-2, perhaps to further distinguish the research plane from its military counterpart.

After 12 years of dormancy, restarting the assembly line proved more difficult than anticipated. Lack of experienced labor necessitated enticing some earlier U-2 production veterans out of retirement to augment the less-experienced workforce. The learning curve was steeper than it should have been but shot up dramatically over the first 2 years. Delays resulted from the need for Lockheed to reestablish relationships with vendors and subcontractors. Documentation became a nightmare. Whereas before the Skunk Works team had been able to streamline and minimize paperwork, the Air Force now demanded strict adherence to military specifications (better known as Mil-Spec) that governed procedures and processes. Throughout earlier production runs, Lockheed frequently disregarded Mil-Spec in order to meet the unique design requirements of the U-2, such as the need to minimize structural weight. With the new production, Air Force officials insisted on conformation to regulations. Eventually, the company and the Government reached a compromise that allowed Lockheed to work to the intention, rather than to the letter, of Mil-Spec regulations. There were also a few turf battles. A bureaucratic tug-of-war erupted between the Air Force's Aeronautical Systems Division (ASD) and Air Force Logistics Command (AFLC) over which organization should have overall responsibility

---

75. Ibid., p. 96.

Lockheed workers build a new version of the U-2, now redesignated TR-1. (Lockheed Martin)

for program management; it was settled only after AFLC successfully pressed the argument that the TR-1 was essentially a continuation of the earlier U-2R program. Then, the general in charge of Tactical Air Command sought to wrest ownership of the TR-1 from SAC, since it was at least nominally to be used for tactical reconnaissance rather than strategic reconnaissance. SAC commander Gen. Richard H. Ellis prevailed, contending, "There is absolutely

The TR-1 was publicly unveiled in July 1981. (Lockheed Martin)

no reason why SAC cannot continue to support the tasking requested by theater commanders."[76]

It took 3 long years before TR-1 production began coming in under budget and ahead of schedule. This eventual success was largely due to the program's greatest asset: strong teamwork among Lockheed, ASD, AFLC, and the TR-1 System Program Office. According to ASD commander Lt. Gen. J. Michael Loh during an acceptance ceremony for the final airframe, "Each successive year we got smarter about writing incentives for the TR-1 contracts, Lockheed got better at building it, and AFLC got better at integrating subsystems." This teamwork ultimately resulted in a $26 million savings on budget over the final 6 years of production.[77]

First to roll off the assembly line was the NASA ER-2. Lockheed test pilot Art Peterson made the first flight on May 11, 1981, and NASA pilot Marty Knutson delivered it to Ames Research Center at Moffett Field, CA, on June 10.[78] This occurred with surprisingly little fanfare compared to the subsequent debut of the TR-1. Unlike its predecessors, which had been born in secrecy, the first TR-1A was unveiled publicly during a media event at Lockheed's Palmdale

76. Pocock, *50 Years of the U-2*, pp. 294–295.

77. Ibid., p. 295.

78. Ibid., p. 374.

A trainer variant designated TR-1B was similar in configuration to the U-2CT. (U.S. Air Force)

facility in July 1981. Company test pilot Ken Weir made the first flight on August 1, and by April 1982, six aircraft were flying. Low-rate production continued until the final delivery in early October 1989.[79]

Several airframes were delivered under the designation U-2R and the second trainer as a U-2RT. In October 1991, the TR-1 designation was dropped altogether and the airplanes were once again all referred to as U-2s. By the time the final airframe rolled off the assembly line, the U-2R had evolved into a flexible, multipurpose platform for electro-optical, SIGINT, and radar reconnaissance. It was also considerably less expensive to maintain and operate than its putative successor, the SR-71. Sensor payloads included the ASARS-2 improved imaging radar and the Senior Year Electro-optical Reconnaissance System (SYERS). Both payloads could be installed in the interchangeable nose sections. In addition, the U-2R was capable of serving as a data relay and, when called for, could still carry high-resolution film cameras that were considerably more flexible and reliable than those used in the early days of the program. To further enhance its capabilities, the airplane was equipped with a data link to provide reconnaissance products in near real time. Early versions required the transmitter to be within 200 to 250 miles of a ground station for the line-of-sight downlink to work, otherwise data had to be recorded onboard until the U-2 was within range of the receiver. To escape this limitation, a satellite communications system was developed for the U-2R. Known as Senior Span, it consisted of a steerable

79. Miller, *Lockheed Skunk Works: The First Fifty Years*, pp. 96–97.

A NASA ER-2 equipped with the Senior Span pod. (NASA)

30-inch parabolic antenna housed in an unpressurized dorsal radome. Skunk Works engineers faced the challenge of designing the 17-foot-long antenna dome so that it would not add excessive weight to the airframe or affect the center of gravity. The result was one of the most unusual looking U-2 configurations yet.[80]

Into the 21st Century

In the 1990s, the U-2 fleet received the first of several significant upgrades that modernized the airplane for a new era. Preproduction testing began in 1991 in preparation for retrofitting the fleet with General Electric F118-GE-101 non-afterburning turbofan engines; the antiquated J75-P-13B turbojet engines were becoming increasingly costly to maintain. Evaluation of the new powerplant included engine-airframe integration, basic operation, and demonstration of the airstart system. The new engine was rated at 18,300 pounds of thrust, and flight-test results indicated it would provide the U-2 with a weight savings of 1,300 pounds and use an average of 16 percent less fuel than the J75. The engine's size (39 inches shorter than the J75) and weight improved the airplane's center of gravity. Digital engine controls ensured linear thrust throughout the flight envelope and virtually eliminated the chance of compressor stalls and flameouts.[81] In addition to being 30 percent lighter than the old engine, the F118 was more fuel efficient, more reliable, and easier to maintain, only requiring overhaul every 2,500 hours instead of every 800. The new engine increased the airplane's range by 1,220 nautical miles and increased altitude

---

80. Pocock, *50 Years of the U-2*, pp. 303–305.

81. Ibid., pp. 314–315.

performance by about 3,000 feet.[82] Production modifications began in 1994, and the entire fleet was retrofitted over the course of scheduled major overhauls that were due every 3,400 hours of operation. As each U-2R was modified, it was redesignated a U-2S, and the final engine installation took place in 1998.[83] The F118 was not immune to problems. One U-2 was lost after a bearing failed, causing the engine to seize and rendering the restart system useless; subsequent dual battery failure and loss of altitude through inclement weather doomed the airplane. Another U-2 suffered repeated malfunctions, causing momentary power loss and severe engine vibrations, forcing the pilot to make an emergency landing.[84]

In 2000, Lockheed embarked on a 6-year, $140-million effort called the Power-EMI upgrade that called for equipping the U-2S with an updated electrical system that produced less electromagnetic interference. At the same time, the airplane was equipped with improved GPS navigational capability, a single-piece windscreen for better visibility and de-icing capability, and provisions for integrating an improved SIGINT package. As with engine installation, these improvements were added during scheduled depot maintenance.[85]

There was some consideration given to redesigning the SYERS package to fit inside the Q-bay, thus allowing the U-2S to carry both it and the ASARS-2 sensors simultaneously. This proved impractical, so instead, efforts were focused on upgrading the SYERS multispectral capabilities. The SYERS-2 had seven collection wavebands compared to two with SYERS-1. The sensor now detected three visible, two shortwave infrared, and four medium-wave infrared wavebands, making it easier to detect and identify targets in daylight or at night, even through layers of haze. Improved data links enabled transmission of the increased data streaming from the sensor.[86]

Up to this point, the U-2S was still equipped with a control panel characterized by round dials and a multitude of switches and knobs, just as it had been since 1967. A new so-called "glass cockpit" was introduced in December 2000, replacing conventional analog instruments with electronic displays. Difficulty maintaining and replacing older components and the need to establish a better interface with modern equipment and sensors drove the $93 million U-2 Reconnaissance Avionics Maintainability Program (RAMP). Antiquated cockpit panels crowded with approximately two-dozen gauges were replaced by

82. William E. Burrows, "The U-Deuce," *Air&Space/Smithsonian* (March 2005): 24.
83. Pocock, *50 Years of the U-2*, p. 315.
84. Ibid., p. 329.
85. Ibid., p. 324.
86. Ibid., p. 325.

In 2000, the U-2 fleet was equipped with modern cockpit instruments, right, to replace anti-quated control panels that had been in use since 1967. (Lockheed Martin)

three 8- by 6-inch flat-panel, multifunction color screens. An avionics processor converted analog signals to digital. Vital switches were conveniently grouped together on an upfront display panel within easy reach of the pilot. Many of the old-style switches were replaced with touch controls that were spaced so that they could be easily operated while wearing bulky pressure suit gloves. Such attention to the human-machine interface was a major break-through over the old cockpit configuration in which some radio and navigation controls were located in awkward, out-of-the-way places, and critical information such as fuel quantity was not accurately portrayed. The new cockpit layout, along with such features as an angle-of-attack indicator that provided aural as well as visual warnings, provided the U-2 pilot with substantially improved situational awareness.[87]

As the U-2 entered the 21st century, defense planners began preparations to retire the fleet and replace it with the RQ-4 Global Hawk in an effort to expand the use of remotely piloted and autonomous platforms. The Global Hawk had no need for onboard crew accommodations or life-support systems and could remain aloft for more than 30 hours. Unfortunately, it also had a smaller payload than that of the U-2, less electrical power to operate the sensors, and a lower operational ceiling. Nevertheless, by August 2011, the Air Force was ready to announce that the U-2 would cease flying within 4 years. In a statement at the National Press Club, Global Hawk program manager Lt. Col. Rick Thomas expressed confidence that the RQ-4 would soon be able to match the capabilities of the U-2. In order to do this, engineers had to find a way to successfully integrate the U-2's massive Optical Bar Camera (OBC) with the Global Hawk's composite airframe. This was easier said than done, as it became clear that it would require substantial modifications to both the airplane and sensor package. Another stumbling block to the fleet replacement schedule was proposed congressional legislation that would require the Department of Defense to certify that sustainment costs for the Global Hawk were less than those of maintaining the U-2. At the time, it cost just $31,000 per U-2 flight hour compared to $35,000 for the RQ-4, though Thomas promised that operating costs for the Global Hawk were dropping. Critics acknowledged the Global Hawk's endurance capabilities but lamented that sensors carried by the autonomous aircraft provided less range, less resolution, and less collection capability than those of the U-2.[88]

Once it became clear that the Global Hawk would not be a viable replacement for the U-2 in the near term, the Air Force embarked on another series of upgrades for the venerable platform. Most of the proposed improvements involved sensors carried by the U-2, starting with the OBC, which

---

87. Ibid., p. 326.

88. Dave Majumdar, "Global Hawk to Replace U-2 in 2015," *Defense News*, Digital Edition, August 10, 2011, *http://www.defensenews.com/article/20110810/DEFSECT01/108100302/Global-Hawk-Replace-U-2-2015*, accessed July 23, 2013.

Although the RQ-4 Global Hawk can remain aloft for 30 hours at a time, it has not yet demonstrated sensor capabilities comparable to those of the U-2. (U.S. Air Force)

was upgraded to provide better resolution at lower altitudes. Additionally, the U-2 was to be equipped with a hyperspectral sensor package called the Spectral Infrared Remote Imaging Transition Testbed (SPIRITT), which had been previously tested on NASA's WB-57F. The SPIRITT package was designed to fit into the U-2's Q-bay in place of the OBC, and it could be carried simultaneously with the nose-mounted SYERS-2 high-resolution digital camera. As with other sensor packages, the SPIRITT would be controlled remotely via a data link from a Distributed Common Ground System intelligence analysis station. Other U-2 upgrades included the Cabin Altitude Reduction Effort (CARE), designed to increase air pressure inside the U-2 cockpit to mimic pressures at lower altitudes. Aerospace medical specialists hoped that CARE would reduce instances of decompression sickness and shorten a pilot's recuperation time between sorties. Increased operational tempo due to operations in southwest Asia had resulted in greater numbers of reports of altitude sickness. Even under the best of circumstances, a U-2 pilot was required to spend 3 to 4 days recuperating between flights. With the increased cabin pressure provided by CARE, the same pilots could fly every other day, increasing squadron capabilities. Finally, defense planners began looking into the possibility of replacing the U-2's special fuel with less expensive JP-8, which had become standard for all other Air Force aircraft. To do so would require modifying the kerosene-based JP-8 with an additive to prevent the fuel from freezing at temperatures below −80 °F;

standard JP-8 freezes at around −50 °F. Fortunately, such an additive had already been developed.[89]

According to Maj. Bill Evans, U-2 program element monitor at Air Combat Command Headquarters, Hampton Roads, VA, the only foreseeable problem is parts obsolescence that eventually plagues all aircraft. Although the current fleet was built in the 1980s, from a structural standpoint, the U-2 is in excellent shape. "Right now, the airframe itself is viable though 2040," Evans said. "Structurally, the aircraft is sound for the next 30 years, at least."[90]

89. Dave Majumdar, "Notebook: Plans for Reinvigorated U-2 Include Hyperspectral Sensor," *Defense News*, Digital Edition, March 22, 2012, *http://www.defensenews.com/article/20120322/ C4ISR02/303220012/Notebook-Plans-Reinvigorated-U-2-Include-Hyperspectral-Sensor*, accessed July 23, 2013.

90. Ibid.

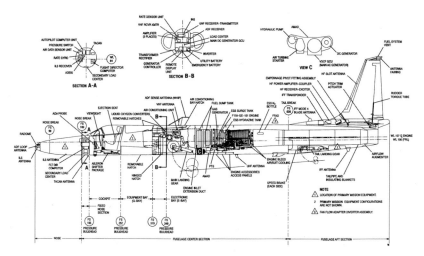

The U-2 is divided into several major assemblies. (U.S. Air Force)

CHAPTER 4

The Stuff Dreams Are Made Of

Although the overall design configuration of the U-2 was extremely inno-vative, the materials and construction methods used to build it were fairly conventional. In its outward appearance, the airplane looked like a typical jet, with the exception of its long, thin wings and bicycle landing gear. Most of the airframe was made from ordinary aluminum alloys, with titanium used sparingly in areas that required additional strength or which were subject to higher temperatures. What set it apart from other craft was Kelly Johnson's elegantly simple design that maximized fuel and payload capacity while mini-mizing gross weight. The airplane's major assemblies included the forward fuselage, wings and mid-fuselage, tail group, landing gear, and powerplant.

Most of the airframe was constructed from aluminum alloys. With the exception of welded assemblies, extrusions, and machined fittings, all alumi-num sheet metal parts were manufactured from clad material. These included 2024 or 7075 sheet varying in thickness from 0.005 to 0.190 inches. Machine parts were typically made from 2024 or 7075 aluminum plate or bar stock. Extruded parts were made using both 2024 and 7075 aluminum. Other components were constructed from 6061-T4 or T6 using a fusion welding process. Wherever necessary, components requiring additional strength were fashioned from stainless steel or carbon steel of varying hardness. For protec-tion against corrosion, aluminum parts were coated with zinc chromate primer or a similar equivalent. Carbon steel components were cadmium plated, but stainless steel parts needed no additional paints or coatings.[1] The airplane included small amounts of titanium alloys in selected areas. Forward flap edges, exhaust ejector skin panels, and miscellaneous fittings and details were made from A110 AT. Parts of the empennage support ring, longeron, other fittings, the main gear piston, and the cylinder consisted of B120 VCA, and the wing-to-fuselage attach bolts were machined from C120 AV.[2]

1. NASA, "U-2 Investigators Handbook," NASA Ames Research Center, pp. VI-6–VI-10.
2. Michael A. Alexander, "TR-1A/TR-1B/U-2R/ER-2 Handbook," U.S. Air Force, 1986, p. 13–15.

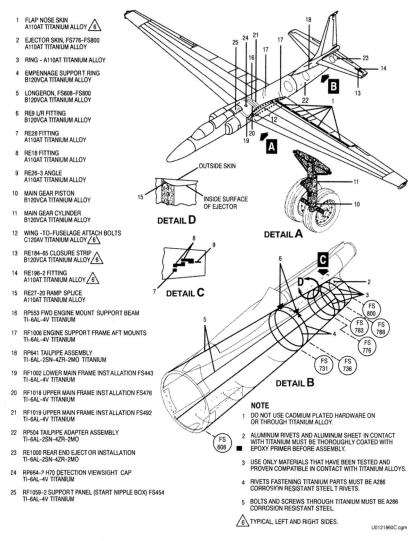

1 FLAP NOSE SKIN
   A110AT TITANIUM ALLOY

2 EJECTOR SKIN, FS776–FS800
   A110AT TITANIUM ALLOY

3 RING – A110AT TITANIUM ALLOY

4 EMPENNAGE SUPPORT RING
   B120VCA TITANIUM ALLOY

5 LONGERON, FS608–FS800
   B120VCA TITANIUM ALLOY

6 RE9 L/R FITTING
   B120VCA TITANIUM ALLOY

7 RE28 FITTING
   A110AT TITANIUM ALLOY

8 RE18 FITTING
   A110AT TITANIUM ALLOY

9 RE26-3 ANGLE
   A110AT TITANIUM ALLOY

10 MAIN GEAR PISTON
   B120VCA TITANIUM ALLOY

11 MAIN GEAR CYLINDER
   B120VCA TITANIUM ALLOY

12 WING-TO-FUSELAGE ATTACH BOLTS
   C120AV TITANIUM ALLOY

13 RE184-65 CLOSURE STRIP
   B120VCA TITANIUM ALLOY

14 RE196-2 FITTING
   A110AT TITANIUM ALLOY

15 RE27-20 RAMP SPLICE
   A110AT TITANIUM ALLOY

16 RP553 FWD ENGINE MOUNT SUPPORT BEAM
   TI-6AL-4V TITANIUM

17 RF1006 ENGINE SUPPORT FRAME AFT MOUNTS
   TI-6AL-4V TITANIUM

18 RP641 TAILPIPE ASSEMBLY
   TI-6AL-2SN-4ZR-2MO TITANIUM

19 RF1002 LOWER MAIN FRAME INSTALLATION FS443
   TI-6AL-4V TITANIUM

20 RF1018 UPPER MAIN FRAME INSTALLATION FS476
   TI-6AL-4V TITANIUM

21 RF1019 UPPER MAIN FRAME INSTALLATION FS492
   TI-6AL-4V TITANIUM

22 RP504 TAILPIPE ADAPTER ASSEMBLY
   TI-6AL-2SN-4ZR-2MO

23 RE1000 REAR END EJECTOR INSTALLATION
   TI-6AL-2SN-4ZR-2MO

24 RP664-? H70 DETECTION VIEWSIGHT CAP
   TI-6AL-4V TITANIUM

25 RF1059-2 SUPPORT PANEL (START NIPPLE BOX) FS454
   TI-6AL-4V TITANIUM

OUTSIDE SKIN

INSIDE SURFACE
OF EJECTOR

DETAIL D

DETAIL A

DETAIL C

DETAIL B

NOTE

1 DO NOT USE CADMIUM PLATED HARDWARE ON
   OR THROUGH TITANIUM ALLOY.

2 ALUMINUM RIVETS AND ALUMINUM SHEET IN CONTACT
   WITH TITANIUM MUST BE THOROUGHLY COATED WITH
   EPOXY PRIMER BEFORE ASSEMBLY.

3 USE ONLY MATERIALS THAT HAVE BEEN TESTED AND
   PROVEN COMPATIBLE IN CONTACT WITH TITANIUM ALLOYS.

4 RIVETS FASTENING TITANIUM PARTS MUST BE A286
   CORROSION RESISTANT STEEL T RIVETS.

5 BOLTS AND SCREWS THROUGH TITANIUM MUST BE A286
   CORROSION RESISTANT STEEL.

6 TYPICAL, LEFT AND RIGHT SIDES.

U0121860C.cgm

Titanium was used in select areas that required additional strength or protection from heating.
(U.S. Air Force)

Forward Fuselage

The forward fuselage included the nose, cockpit, and a space for camera and sensor payloads known as the Q-bay. Many features were common to all U-2 variants while some were specific to certain models. To reduce weight while retaining structural strength, components were machined to the thinnest gauges allowable. Builders used the minimum possible number of ribs and stringers, and flush-riveted skin panels were a mere 0.020- to 0.063-inches thick.[3] Engine air inlet scoops were located on the sides of the fuselage just aft of the cockpit. These scoops featured built-in boundary-layer bleed ducts. Air from the left-hand duct cooled the D.C. generator, and air from the right-hand duct was routed through the air conditioning refrigerator to cool cabin air bled from the engine compressor.[4] Article 341 was originally built using 75-ST aluminum sheet for inlet duct interiors. This material was hand formed, a process that included hammering the thin sheets into the proper shape. Maintenance crews found that the aluminum skin started to crack after about 90 hours of operation. As a result, later airplanes used 24-ST stretch-formed aluminum skin that was less susceptible to cracking. Even so, it was recommended that high-power static ground runs be limited to about 2 minutes to avoid putting too much stress on the inlet skin.[5]

The nose assembly on the early U-2 models had a slender ogival cross section. Internal space was extremely limited and typically served to accommodate various antennas and electronic gear. A special nose assembly was installed during the High-Altitude Sampling Program (HASP). It featured a circular aperture at the tip, with filters to collect airborne particulates. Later U-2R/S and ER-2 models were equipped with a variety of interchangeable nose assemblies capable of carrying a variety of cameras and sensors. Attached to the fuselage with four quick-release latches, the standard nose cone provided a payload volume of 47.8 cubic feet. The 101-inch-long nose compartment was built to accept payloads of up to 650 pounds on custom-built racks. Other nose cones of varying size were available for specialized payloads. Due to forebody weight limits, payloads in the nose section reduced payload weight in the Q-bay on a pound-for-pound basis. At cruise altitudes, the environment inside the nose area was maintained at 27,000 to 30,000 feet pressure altitude. A pilot-operated valve controlled pressurized air in the nose compartment, but the rate of air exchange was solely regulated by the leakage rate of the nose structure, as there were no overboard dump valves. Temperatures inside the nose compartment during flight varied between 68 and –40 °F.[6]

The cockpit compartment was separated from the nose section by a bulkhead and was pressurized to approximately 25,000 feet pressure altitude. The pilot's control panel had a conventional layout with many standard

---

3. Pocock, *50 Years of the U-2*, p. 19.

4. Klinger, "Flight Test Development of the Lockheed U-2 Airplane," p. 8.

5. Ibid., p. 161.

6. NASA, "ER-2 Airborne Laboratory Experimenter Handbook," August 2002, p. III-4.

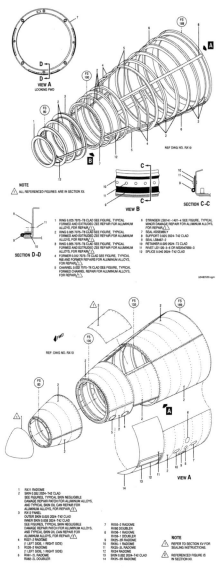

The nose was designed to be lightweight yet capable of supporting mission payloads. (U.S. Air Force)

instruments to provide fundamental information of aircraft systems, speed, altitude, and navigation. Engine power was controlled by a single throttle lever of the same type used in contemporary single-engine jet fighters such as the F-100.[7] Unlike in a fighter, the U-2 pilot used a yoke rather than a stick to make flight control inputs. Otherwise, the controls were conventional. All surfaces (ailerons, rudder, etc.) were directly connected to the yoke and pedals by cables with no hydraulic boost power. An electrically driven system provided trim in pitch and roll. Although there was no provision for directional trim from the cockpit, the autopilot effectively provided yaw trim when operating.[8] Conventional pedals controlled the rudder, permitting 30 degrees of travel in either direction. These pedals were adjustable fore and aft to accommodate pilots with differing leg lengths; but more importantly, the upper portion of each pedal could be rotated to a horizontal position. This feature allowed the pilot to extend and stretch his legs, thus reducing fatigue during long flights.[9] The most unique flight control system feature was the gust alleviation system. This

---

7. CIA, "U-2 Utility Flight Handbook," March 1, 1959, p. I-10.

8. Ibid., p. I-21.

9. U.S. Air Force, "Flight Manual, Models U-2C and U-2F Aircraft," p. I-27.

U-2 pilots found the driftsight, a downward-looking periscope, extremely useful for navigation. (NASA)

device made it possible to raise both ailerons up 10 degrees while simultaneously raising both wing flaps by 4 degrees, thus reducing structural loads on the wings and tail assembly. Use of the gust controls was necessary when flying in turbulent air or when flying at higher speeds in smooth air.[10] Because cloud cover below the airplane's flightpath often prevented the pilot from locating navigational points on the ground through the driftsight periscope, the U-2 was also equipped with a small sextant for making celestial navigation. When clouds were not a factor, however, the driftsight proved highly accurate, and pilots found that they could navigate by dead reckoning with an error of less than 1 nautical mile over a 1,000-nautical-mile course.[11] Much later U-2 models were equipped with an angle-of-attack indicator, which provided the pilot with a visual and aural warning of approach-to-stall. Because the U-2 was designed to operate very close to stall during most phases of flight, this instrument greatly increased pilot safety. Lack of stall warning on earlier variants was indicated as a possible contributing factor in several mishaps.[12]

10. Ibid., p. I-26.

11. Pedlow and Welzenbach, *The CIA and the U-2 Program*, p. 76.

12. Tim Williams, NASA ER-2 pilot, interview with author, April 30, 2014.

A painted sunshade limited visibility through the lightweight canopy. (NASA)

The cockpit was enclosed beneath a lightweight canopy, hinged on the left side. The uppermost portion of the canopy was coated with either white or black paint to provide a sun shield. Although this feature enhanced crew comfort, it also somewhat reduced visibility. In an emergency, the pilot pulled a handle to jettison the canopy and fire a rocket-propelled ejection seat that was qualified for use in zero-speed/zero-altitude ejections. A spur-and-cable arrangement restrained the pilot's legs during ejection to prevent flailing. Life-support equipment included dual normal oxygen systems, an emergency oxygen system, and a pressure garment. Primary breathing air came from a pair of 2.6-gallon liquid-oxygen converters, each providing gaseous oxygen to the pilot's helmet through independent supply lines and pressure regulators. The emergency oxygen system consisted of two gaseous oxygen cylinders located in the survival kit and was used only in the event of ejection or malfunction of the two primary oxygen sources. Activated automatically, the emergency system provided suit pressurization and 15 minutes of breathing oxygen.[13]

The environmental control system (ECS) delivered pressurized and environmentally controlled air to the cockpit, nose, Q-bay, and (on NASA aircraft only) the forward two-thirds of the wing pods. Air in the payload areas and cockpit remained unprocessed below 7,900 feet pressure altitude. As the

---

13. Lockheed, "U-2 Reconnaissance/Surveillance/Earth Resources System Description," pp. II-5 and IV-7.

aircraft climbed higher, the ECS switched to an isobaric control mode, maintaining a pressure altitude of 7,500 feet. Once the U-2 climbed above 18,300 feet, the ECS established a pressure differential of 3.88 pounds per square inch between the ambient atmospheric pressure and that of the cockpit and payload areas. This resulted in a cockpit pressure altitude of approximately 28,500 feet at an aircraft altitude of 70,000 feet. Engine bleed air for pressurization was passed through a heat exchanger, mixing muff, and a turbine, though at altitudes above 25,000 feet, the turbine was bypassed. Fans with or without additional heat were used in the cockpit and payload areas to circulate air for the dual purpose of reducing condensation from windows or optics, and to distribute heat. Although relative humidity was low at stratospheric cruise altitudes, relative humidity could reach 100 percent during descent and landing, allowing condensation to form on surfaces that had been cold-soaked at altitude.[14]

The pressurized equipment bay, or Q-bay, just behind the cockpit, was designed to be the principal location for special equipment packages. Top and bottom access hatches, removable by means of external latches, made it possible to install and remove delicate cameras and sensors quickly and easily. Typically, instrumentation and other equipment was installed on rack assemblies, hoisted upward, and secured to several mounting points. In early model U-2 aircraft, the Q-bay was 67 inches long and 55 inches high, varying in width from top to bottom. This space accommodated payloads weighing between 500 and 750 pounds. Additional equipment could be carried in wing-mounted pods (up to 300 pounds each) and inside a dorsal fairing with a 100-pound capacity.[15] Later model airframes were capable of carrying up to 2,550 pounds of equipment distributed between the Q-bay, nose, and wing pods. Weight distribution between payload areas affected the center of gravity of the aircraft, resulting in reduced allowable payload in some areas. Aside from these primary areas, provisions for instruments were available in several smaller areas, including the aft fuselage, tailcone, wingtips, and spaces on the left and right sides of the forward fuselage. Instrument integration required evaluation of all payloads for weight and balance concerns, aerodynamic effects that might alter the airplane's stability characteristics, and total electrical power consumption.[16] In the U-2R/S and ER-2, the Q-bay provided 64.6 cubic feet of volume and, like earlier models, featured removable upper and lower hatches. Hatches for all models could be configured

---

14. NASA, "ER-2 Airborne Laboratory Experimenter Handbook," p. I-4.

15. NASA, "U-2 Investigators' Handbook," vol. 1, NASA Ames Research Center, pp. I-1-I-7.

16. NASA, "ER-2 Airborne Laboratory Experimenter Handbook," p. I-2.

Technicians install a camera package in the Q-bay of a U-2A. (Lockheed Martin)

to accommodate a wide variety of specialized sensors. The combined weight carried in the forward fuselage area (Q-bay and nose assembly) was normally limited to 1,300 pounds including payload mounting racks, electrical interface panels, and the payload itself.[17]

Payloads carried by the U-2 were subjected to a range of environmental conditions resulting from the airplane's extremely high cruising altitudes. Two regulator valves, located at the bottom of the cockpit aft pressure bulkhead, allowed pressurized air to enter the Q-bay. Available airflow was dependent upon the amount of air bled from the engine's compressor stages, but it typically varied from 0.5 pounds per minute at idle to 3.0 pounds per minute at cruise power settings. Though the compartment's pressure altitude was normally maintained at around 30,000 feet, safety considerations required that payloads be designed to withstand pressure altitudes of up to 70,000 feet in the event of a pressurization system failure. Bleed air from the engine was cooled by a heat exchanger to a nominal temperature of 60 °F. Actual temperatures within the Q-bay depended upon the incoming air temperature, ambient temperature, amount of insulation used on the equipment package, air circulation inside the Q-bay, cockpit controlled heaters and blowers, and the instrument's heat output. At cruise altitude, air temperatures inside the compartment could vary from 10 °F to

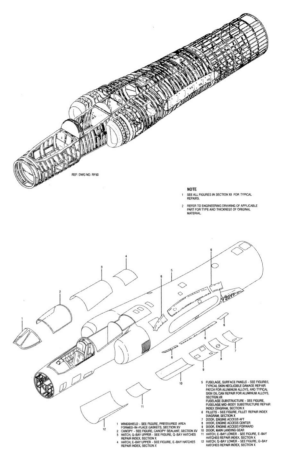

Simple, lightweight construction was the hallmark of the forward fuselage assembly. (U.S. Air Force)

50 °F, though in the summer temperatures could rise above 120 °F during ground operation prior to takeoff.[18]

Wings and Wing Pods

Due to requirements for high aspect ratio and low drag ratio, the wings proved to be among the most challenging design features of the entire airplane. For optimum lift, they needed to be long and narrow with a thin airfoil. They had to be extremely lightweight to reduce overall aircraft gross weight, but for mission endurance, they needed to be capable of carrying most of the airplane's fuel supply. The wings were attached to the rearmost portion of the forward fuselage, at the airplane's center of gravity. In order to meet weight restrictions, the U-2 designers chose an unusual arrangement for attaching the wings to the fuselage. Unlike on conventional airplanes, the U-2's main wing spar did not pass through the fuselage to give the wings continuity and strength. Instead, each wing assembly was entirely separate, attached to the sides of the fuselage with tension bolts as on a sailplane. Absence of a carry-through wing spar left room inside the fuselage for the Q-bay between the cockpit and the engine compartment, improving the aircraft's center of gravity and contributing to overall weight reduction.[19]

As originally designed, the wings were configured with integral fuel tanks extending from the leading edge to the beam at the 48-percent chord line. Spanwise, each main tank extended from the wing root to wing station 440. Auxiliary wing tanks were located from 48 to 65 percent of the chord and extended from the root to wing station 300. The trailing edges consisted of flaps and ailerons that were only unconventional in that they also served to alleviate structural loads on the wings and tail in turbulent air and at high speeds. The gust alleviation system worked by raising the flaps upward 4 degrees while simultaneously shifting the neutral point of the ailerons 10 degrees up. This moved the spanwise center of pressure inboard, reducing the wing's bending moment. This also effectively reduced the wing camber, which reduced the required balancing tail load.[20]

The wing had a mean aerodynamic chord of 100.8 inches. Designers selected an NACA 63A409 airfoil with 9 percent thickness-to-chord ratio for the wing root and an NACA 63A406 airfoil with a 6 percent thickness-to-chord ratio

---

18. Ibid., p. III-3
19. Pedlow & Welzenbach, *The CIA and the U-2 Program*, p. 47.
20. Klinger, "Flight Test Development of the Lockheed U-2 Airplane," p. 8.

for the tip. Incidence varied from 4 degrees at the root to 2 degrees at the tip. The dihedral was 0 degrees, and sweepback at 25 percent chord was 6 degrees. The ailerons had a total area of 35.2 square feet, and the flaps had a combined area of 97.5 square feet.[21]

The wings on the original U-2 spanned 80 feet with 600 square feet of wing area. By contrast, the larger U-2R had a 103-foot span with 1,000 square feet of lifting surface. Bob Wiele, leader of the U-2R wing design team, ensured that the wing structure did not exceed 3 pounds per square foot. For maximum performance, he retained the original NACA airfoils while reducing wing loading for the heavier airframe to the same values attained with the U-2A. The resulting lift-to-drag ratio was 27:1, with a lift coefficient of 0.6 to 0.7 and aspect ratio of 10.667. Larger wings allowed for a greater internal fuel capacity, and the fuel tank arrangement had to be altered. Pilots of the early U-2 models discovered that having the main tank forward and the auxiliary tank aft resulted in considerable center-of-gravity changes as fuel was consumed during flight. Wiele and his team eliminated this problem in the U-2R by placing the 1,169-gallon main tanks inboard and the 239-gallon auxiliaries outboard. This allowed fuel from the main tanks to be exhausted first so that the weight of the remaining fuel in the auxiliary tanks helped dampen wing bending and torsional loads.[22]

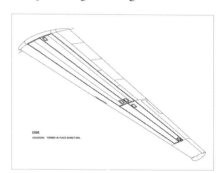 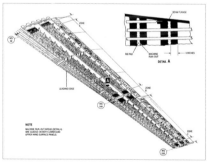

For maximum lift and high-altitude performance, Lockheed engineers designed the U-2 wing using the NACA 64A airfoil. The internal structure was built to be as light as possible while providing sufficient strength. (U.S. Air Force)

Wing pods for the TR-1/U-2R and ER-2 provided approximately 86 cubic feet of payload capacity. Each pod accommodated payloads up to a maximum weight of 600 pounds. The pod structure consisted of five individual segments:

---

21. Ibid., p. 16.
22. Pocock, *50 Years of the U-2*, p. 238.

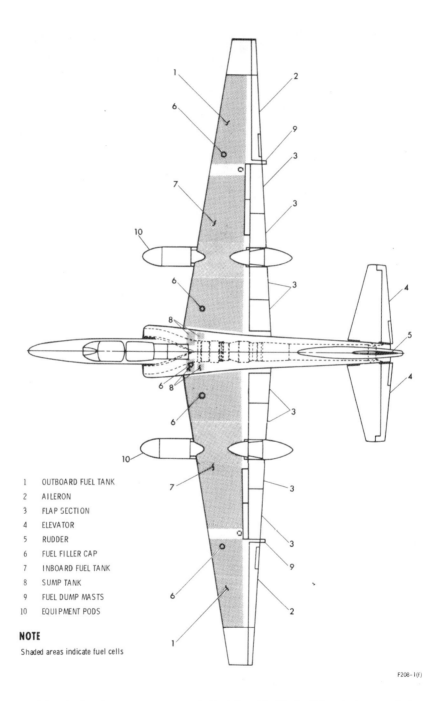

1   OUTBOARD FUEL TANK
2   AILERON
3   FLAP SECTION
4   ELEVATOR
5   RUDDER
6   FUEL FILLER CAP
7   INBOARD FUEL TANK
8   SUMP TANK
9   FUEL DUMP MASTS
10   EQUIPMENT PODS

NOTE

Shaded areas indicate fuel cells

F208-1(f)

Most of the wing interior spaces were occupied by integral fuel tanks. External wing-mounted tanks, or pods, provided additional space for mission equipment. (Lockheed Martin)

nose cone, forward pod, mid-body, aft pod, and tail cone. Latches at the forward and aft ends of the pod mid-body provided easy access for equipment servicing and installation. For the ER-2, the forward two-thirds of each pod was pressurized, but as in the aircraft nose area, there were no overboard dump valves in the pods; the rate of air exchange was a function of the leak rate of the structure and associated pressure sealing. Interior temperatures inside the empty wing pods varied from –40 °F to 20 °F at cruise altitudes. Internal heat sources were normally installed in the pods to produce warmer local temperatures for sensitive equipment. Aeroelastic effects caused the wings to deflect upward during flight. Deflection of the pods was measured to as much as 0.86 degrees from horizontal, though deflection angles tended to vary slightly with altitude, payload weight, fuel load, and atmospheric conditions.[23]

Smaller pods, or tanks, could be pylon-mounted on the wings or along the fuselage centerline, aft of the main landing gear. Unpressurized and lacking temperature control, each tank offered a payload volume of 14 cubic feet and a maximum weight of 350 pounds. Instruments in these tanks were subjected to greater vibrations and more extreme temperatures than elsewhere on the airframe. Centerline installation provided an unobstructed nadir view, but viewports required protection from debris, water, or ice thrown up by the main gear during takeoff and landing. When attached to wing pylons in symmetrical pairs, the tanks were not susceptible to debris from the landing gear. Additional instruments could be accommodated in a fairing called the System 20 pod on the right wing, as well as within the left wingtip, but instrument weight had to be carefully evaluated for its effect on the aircraft's trim condition.[24]

Tail Group

Herb Nystrom and Rod Kreimendahl designed the original U-2A tail assembly. This included the aft fuselage, vertical stabilizer and rudder, and horizontal stabilizer airfoils. These components were constructed almost entirely of aluminum alloys and assembled using the minimum number of parts required for structural strength. The most unusual feature of the tail group was the fact that the aft fuselage was joined to the forward fuselage using just three tension bolts, thus reducing weight and easing assembly.[25]

---

23. NASA, "ER-2 Airborne Laboratory Experimenter Handbook," pp. III-6–III-7.

24. Ibid., p. III-7.

25. Pedlow & Welzenbach, *The CIA and the U-2 Program*, p. 47.

The tail-fuselage interface was designed for ease of assembly and maintenance. (Laughlin Heritage Foundation)

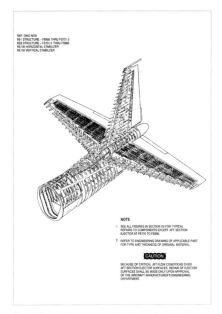
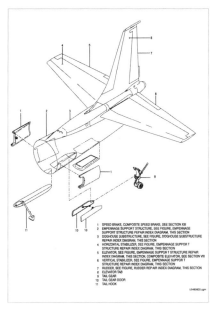

As with the fuselage and wings, the U-2 empennage was constructed from lightweight aluminum alloys. (U.S. Air Force)

The fixed horizontal tail had a total area of 90 square feet, the elevators totaled 20 square feet, and the vertical tail had an area of 49 square feet plus a 9.5-square-foot rudder. As originally configured, the horizontal stabilizer had zero incidence, but this was later increased to 1.5 degrees.[26]

On later models such as the U-2R, the tail group retained the basic configuration, but it was enlarged as necessary to match the new airframe. The tail assembly, or empennage, primarily accommodated the stabilizer airfoils and housed the engine exhaust duct. There was also room for ballast to trim the airplane's center of gravity, and additional space within the fuselage aft cavity and the tail cone to carry small instrument packages.[27] Two speed brakes, each about 7 square feet in area, were installed just aft of the fuselage break. These hydraulically actuated drag devices were used to slow the aircraft. They were hinged at the forward end and capable of opening to approximately 50 degrees. For additional landing deceleration, a 16-foot-diameter ribbon chute was housed in a compartment at the top aft end of the fuselage, at the base of the vertical tail fin.[28]

Landing Gear

The airplane's hydraulically actuated, bicycle-type landing gear consisted of a single oleo strut with two lightweight wheels toward the front of the airplane and two small solid-mount wheels under the tail. Both sets of wheels retracted forward and upward into the gear wells. The entire assembly weighed just 208 pounds yet was capable of withstanding touchdown forces imparted by the 7-ton airframe during landing. The gear was hydraulically operated, but an alternate cable-operated free-fall system was provided in case the normal gear-extension mechanism malfunctioned. For braking, the pilot applied hydraulic pressure equally to both main wheels through toe pressure to the rudder pedals. There was no differential braking. In the event of normal hydraulic system malfunction, an emergency-brake accumulator supplied sufficient pressure for up to five applications of the brakes.[29]

Several landing gear deficiencies were corrected during early testing. Originally, Article 341 was equipped with two brake pads, one on the inboard side of each main wheel; but pilots found this configuration provided

26. Klinger, "Flight Test Development of the Lockheed U-2 Airplane," pp. 16–17.

27. NASA, "ER-2 Airborne Laboratory Experimenter Handbook," p. III-7.

28. Klinger, "Flight Test Development of the Lockheed U-2 Airplane," p. 13.

29. Lockheed, "U-2 Reconnaissance/Surveillance/Earth Resources System Description," p. III-10.

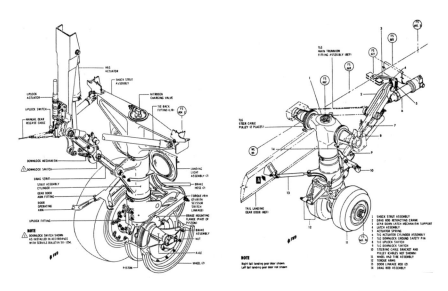

The bicycle landing gear included a set of main wheels and a smaller set of tail wheels. (U.S. Air Force)

unsatisfactory braking and caused the brake mechanism to overheat. To resolve the problem, an additional brake pad was installed on the outboard side of each wheel. Another problem was the tendency of the airplane to porpoise when the pilot touched down on the main gear first. To prevent the U-2 from bouncing, technicians installed a valve in the main gear strut with two orifices of different sizes for metering the hydraulic fluid. The larger orifice helped absorb shock loads while the smaller one prevented rapid springback. This solution proved very effective. Finally, the tail-wheel steering was found to be deficient in early tests. In the original configuration, the steering cables were attached to the rudder horn and then routed to the tail wheel. The design called for 6 degrees of travel in either direction, but due to cable stretch, the most steering that could be obtained was between 3 and 4 degrees. To correct this, the system was revised so that the steering cables were attached directly to the rudder cables and then routed to a bell crank at the tail wheel.[30]

The two wingtip pogo outriggers used for lateral balance during takeoff were made from flat steel bars, curved like the leaf spring on an automobile to absorb shocks during takeoff roll. The lower end of each pogo was equipped with two small wheels with solid rubber tires.[31] These auxiliary gears were

---

30. Klinger, "Flight Test Development of the Lockheed U-2 Airplane," p. 259.

31. Pedlow & Welzenbach, *The CIA and the U-2 Program*, p. 47.

Senior Airman Jordan Mihm installs an outrigger pogo on a U-2R. (U.S. Air Force)

originally designed to be released electrically during the takeoff roll. If released early enough, this method proved fairly reliable, but if the pilot waited until airspeed had increased to 60 or 70 knots, the pogos hung on due to air loads. This created a hazardous situation; in fact, one airplane was lost in a fatal accident while the pilot tried to shake loose a hung pogo. Lockheed designers tried several methods to allow the auxiliary gear to drop at higher airspeeds, including springs, external kickers, and olive-shaped rollers instead of round rollers in the release mechanism. None proved satisfactory. Eventually, they adopted a free-fall system that allowed the pogos to drop out as the wings lifted during the takeoff roll. For training flights where it was desired to retain the pogos to be used for lateral balance during landing, safety pins could be installed to lock the gear in place. The modified system proved highly successful. Occasional subsequent instances of hung pogos were traced to rough or battered pogo heads that hung up in the sockets.[32]

Powerplant

The U-2A was powered by a single J57-type non-afterburning engine featuring an axial flow, twin-spool compressor, and a three-stage turbine. The

---

32. Klinger, "Flight Test Development of the Lockheed U-2 Airplane," p. 260.

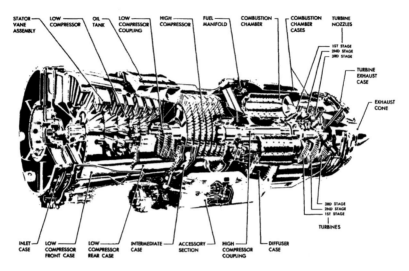

Cutaway of J57 engine. (CIA)

forward compressor was a nine-stage, low-pressure unit connected to the second and third stage turbine wheels by a through-shaft. The seven-stage aft (high-pressure) compressor was mechanically independent of the forward compressor and was connected by a hollow shaft to the first-stage turbine wheel. This arrangement permitted the low-pressure rotor to turn at its most efficient speed and allowed high compression ratios. Engine performance varied depending on which model of the engine was installed. The J57-P-31 developed 11,200 pounds of static thrust at sea level and weighed 3,820 pounds, providing a power-to-weight ratio of 2.9:1. Until the J57-P-31 engines were available, the first U-2 aircraft used J57-P-37 engines, which were 415 pounds heavier and delivered only 10,500 pounds of thrust at sea level, resulting in a power-to-weight ratio of 2.5:1, almost 15 percent less efficient than the P-31. Because the P-31 engine had been designed specifically for high-altitude operation, it offered better thrust and fuel consumption than the P-37, as well as wider operating margins.[33]

The engine received air through a bifurcated inlet system; two external ducts opened on either side of the fuselage just behind the cockpit and merged into a single internal duct at the compressor face. For weight and balance purposes, the engine was installed at mid–wing chord. Fuel consumption varied from 9,000 pounds per hour at sea level to 700 pounds per hour at cruising

---

33. "U-2 Utility Flight Handbook," p. I-3.

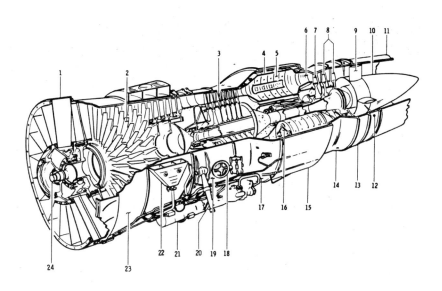

1 COMPRESSOR INLET GUIDE VANES AND SHROUD
2 LOW-PRESSURE COMPRESSOR (EIGHT-STAGE)
3 HIGH-PRESSURE COMPRESSOR (SEVEN-STAGE)
4 COMBUSTION CHAMBER (8)
5 FUEL NOZZLE (6 IN EACH COMUBSTION CHAMBER)
6 TURBINE NOZZLE
7 TURBINE WHEEL, FRONT (ONE, DRIVES HIGH PRESSURE COMPRESSOR)
8 TURBINE WHEEL, REAR (TWO, DRIVE LOW PRESSURE COMPRESSOR)
9 SWIRL STRAIGHTENER VANE (6)
10 EXHAUST CONE
11 EXHAUST TAILPIPE (NOT PART OF ENGINE)
12 EXHAUST GAS TEMPERATURE PROBE(6)
13 TURBINE EXHAUST CASE
14 TURBINE NOZZLE CASE
15 COMBUSTION CHAMBER CASE
16 FUEL MANIFOLD AND NOZZLES
17 DIFFUSER CASE
18 BLEED VALVE
19 COMPRESSOR INTERMEDIATE CASE
20 ENGINE MOUNT (BALL BAT)
21 ACCESSORY CASE (N$_2$)
22 OIL TANK
23 FRONT COMPRESSOR CASE
24 ACCESSORY CASE (N$_1$)

Cutaway of a J75 engine. (U.S. Air Force)

altitudes.[34] As Lockheed engineers refined airframe-powerplant integration during the first year of flight testing, it was only necessary to make a few small changes to the aircraft design. As Ernie Joiner recalled, "The engine tailpipe operated inside an ejector in order to induce cooling air low through the aft fuselage. We were robbing the engine thrust because the jet stream was striking

---

34. Downie and Jarboe, *The Inquisitive Angel*.

the ejector lip. Cutting one inch off the ejector lip solved this." Another change involved engine oil coolers. "We started with one fuel-oil cooler and two air-oil coolers," Joiner noted, "but we found it possible to eliminate one of the air-oil coolers and its outside scoop."[35]

Removing the oil-cooler scoop decreased cooling airflow on the left side of the airplane. This necessitated installation of heat shields inside the fuselage to prevent electrical wiring and hydraulic system components from overheating. Additionally, with the J57-P-31 engine installed, there was overheating of bulkheads at fuselage stations 495 and 504 on the left side and high temperatures at the rear engine mount. The highest temperatures were in the vicinity of the engine turbine nozzle where the exhaust gas temperature was hottest. On the J57-P-31 engine, this area was covered with a single layer of skin that permitted greater thermal radiation than on the J57-P-37, which had a double skin layer in the same area. Lockheed technicians installed an engine-mounted heat shield that lowered temperatures within the aft fuselage to acceptable levels.[36]

To improve performance, the U-2C was equipped with the J75-P-13 powerplant, a 15-stage axial-flow, non-afterburning turbojet that provided 15,800 pounds of thrust at sea level. Larger, fluted air inlets improved airflow to the compressor face.[37] Eventually, the U-2C fleet was equipped with more powerful J75-P-13B engines rated to 17,000 pound of thrust. The U-2R was powered by an upgraded model of the P-13B that improved dependability and increased thrust under climb and cruise conditions. Engine performance was enhanced through changes to turbine vanes, improved turbine disks and compressor blades, and enlargement of the compressor inlet case to increase airflow.[38] An engine-driven fuel pump supplied pressure for both normal and emergency fuel systems. This pump supplied sufficient fuel to maintain flight even if the normal and auxiliary boost pumps failed.[39]

In 1984, the U-2R/TR-1 fleet was grounded following a series of accidents involving the engine exhaust system. In the first mishap, on May 22, Capt. David Bonsi had just taken off in a U-2R when he heard and felt an explosion behind him, and the entire tail section separated from the airframe. Bonsi ejected safely, and although accident investigators were uncertain of the exact cause, they suggested that the explosion might have resulted from a small

35. Joiner, "Testing the U-2," pp. 23–24.
36. Klinger, "Flight Test Development of the Lockheed U-2 Airplane," pp. 161–162.
37. Pocock, *50 Years of the U-2*, p. 399.
38. Koziol, "The U-2 Aircraft Engine," pp. 9–10.
39. U.S. Air Force, "Flight Manual, Models U-2C and U-2F Aircraft," p. I-4.

fuel leak inside the engine compartment. Less than 2 months later, a similar accident occurred in which the tail section of a TR-1 crumpled immediately after takeoff. Capt. Todd Hubbard escaped unharmed after being forced to eject at low altitude. This time, investigators suspected a hydraulic leak, but on October 8 another U-2R was lost. Capt. Tom Dettmer ejected as his airplane broke apart just 1,500 feet above the ground. By now, an inescapable pattern was emerging, and investigators turned their attention to the long cylindrical duct connecting the engine to the exhaust ejector. The duct comprised a forward adaptor section (approximately 4 feet long) that connected the J75 engine to the 12-foot-long tailpipe. The adaptor/tailpipe link, consisting of a U-shaped clamp and two ¼-inch bolts, had apparently come loose and allowed the tailpipe to slip out of alignment. When subjected to increased pressure from takeoff thrust, the tailpipe crumpled, and trapped exhaust gases blew the tail assembly off at its mounts. To fix the problem, Lockheed engineers devised a new clamp and added more bolts to secure it in place. Speculation remained as to why this problem had only manifested after many years of trouble-free operation. Some thought that engine modifications to improve fuel consumption had resulted in more compressor surges, putting added strain on the tailpipe connection. Others suspected inadequate maintenance or assembly procedures.[40]

By the late 1980s, Lockheed was considering potential replacements for the antiquated J75 engines. The leading candidate was General Electric's F101-GE-F29 bypass ratio (0.8:1) mixed-flow turbofan featuring aerodynamically coupled low- and high-pressure rotors. The low-pressure compressor section consisted of a three-stage fan, driven by a two-stage low-pressure turbine. The high-pressure section was composed of a nine-stage compressor; annular combustion chamber; and a single-stage, air-cooled high-pressure turbine. The engine control system combined electronic and hydromechanical elements to achieve stall-free operation throughout the flight envelope regardless of the pilot's throttle input. It was designed for completely automatic operation from start to shutdown.[41]

This engine was redesignated F118-GE-101 prior to the start of preproduction testing in late 1991. The F118 was rated at 18,300 pounds static sea level thrust, which represented a significant improvement over the J75. It was easier to install and remove than older powerplants, hydraulic components were easier to access, and the new gearbox was mounted on the airframe. Known as an airframe-mounted accessory drive (AMAD), this gearbox drove

40. Pocock, *50 Years of the U-2*, pp. 299–300.

41. Lockheed, "U-2 Reconnaissance/Surveillance/Earth Resources System Description," p. III-1.

Technicians install a GE F118 engine in a U-2. (Lockheed Martin)

the airplane's secondary power accessories such as alternating current (ac) and direct current (dc) generators, hydraulic pump, and air turbine starter. The engine powered the AMAD mechanically through a flexible power transmission shaft. A dedicated oil system independent of the engine oil system provided lubrication and cooling for the AMAD and associated accessories, gears, and bearings.[42]

To ease engine maintenance, General Electric developed improved troubleshooting capabilities and provided sophisticated new test equipment. One of the greatest advantages was that the airplane's hydraulic and electrical systems could still be operated with the engine removed. The F118 suffered one notable disadvantage, however. Up to this time, U-2 pilots had responded to a flameout by using a procedure called a windmill restart, a maneuver that takes advantage of the airplane's kinetic energy to force enough air into the engine inlets to spin the rotors and create sufficient pneumatic pressure for ignition. Unlike the J75 turbojet, the new turbofan could not be restarted in flight by windmilling. To remedy this deficiency, Lockheed engineers devised

---

42. Ibid.

an emergency airstart system that ignited a mixture of compressed air and jet fuel in a two-stage compressor. Because this system imposed a significant weight penalty, it was replaced with a lighter, hydrazine-fueled system capable of spooling the engine up to 45 percent core rpm. Use of hydrazine, which is colorless, odorless, and highly toxic, necessitated introduction of special handling procedures.[43]

Life-Support and Environmental Control Systems

The pilot's life-support systems included dual normal oxygen systems, an emergency oxygen system, and a pressure suit. Two independent systems, each supplied by a 10-liter liquid-oxygen converter, provided breathing air to the pilot in the form of 100-percent oxygen. Gaseous oxygen was delivered to the pilot's helmet through independent supply lines and pressure regulators. An emergency oxygen system provided oxygen to the pilot in case of ejection or malfunction of the dual normal system. The emergency system (supplied by dual-redundant, gaseous-oxygen cylinders located in the survival kit) was designed to maintain pressure in the pilot's suit after ejection and provide breathing oxygen for approximately 15 minutes during descent to the ground. Each U-2 pilot wore a pressure suit capable of providing a safe environment regardless of cockpit pressure conditions. A dual pressure/breathing regulator provided breathing oxygen upon demand in the helmet and automatically pressurized the suit in the event of cabin-pressure loss. A fire-retardant outer coverall and harness was worn over the pressure suit and contained a life preserver and fasteners for the parachute release latches.[44]

The environmental control system provided pressurization to the cockpit, equipment bays, and nose section. Engine bleed air passed through a heat exchanger, a mixing muff, and—below 25,000 feet—a turbine. Above 25,000 feet, the turbine was bypassed. At altitude, cabin pressure was maintained at 3.88 psi above atmospheric pressure. This produced a cabin-pressure altitude of approximately 28,500 feet at an aircraft altitude of 70,000 feet. The pilot used a refrigerator bypass valve to regulate cockpit air temperature. An adjustment lever could be used to mix cold outside air and cockpit pressurization air to regulate suit temperature. The cockpit was also equipped with a duct to

---

43. Pocock, *50 Years of the U-2*, p. 314 and 389.

44. Lockheed, "U-2 Reconnaissance/Surveillance/Earth Resources System Description," p. IV-7

provide warm air for defogging the canopy and windshield. On later models, windshield defrosting was augmented with an electrically heated element.[45]

The heated-air defroster originally consisted of a single manifold built into the forward end of the canopy. The manifold was perforated with forward-facing holes to defrost the windshield and aft-facing holes to defrost the canopy. This arrangement proved unsatisfactory, particularly for windshield defrosting. In an effort to improve system performance, a second manifold was added along the base of the windshield, and another was later installed at the top of the windshield where it joined the canopy. This system provided much more efficient distribution of heated air for defrosting both the windshield and canopy. An auxiliary defrosting system consisted of a small, rubber-bladed fan on the left-hand cockpit sill to circulate warm air. This was especially useful during engine-out descents, when the normal source of hot air for defrosting was unavailable.[46]

Cockpit temperature distribution in early model U-2 airplanes was quite inefficient. The pilot's feet became very cold while the head and upper parts of the body were too warm. Eventually, floor-level heat outlets were added—directing warm air at the rudder pedals—as foot warmers. The pilot could reduce heating at head level only by restricting use of the defroster or using the auxiliary fan to improve air circulation in the cockpit.[47]

Temperature control within the equipment bay was also critical. During early high-altitude testing, the Q-bay became too cold, with interior air temperature dropping to –4 °F. The glass in the camera windows sometimes dropped to as low as –29 °F and quickly frosted over if there was any moisture in the air. Lockheed engineers experimented with blowers, various types of insulation, and baffle curtains to control airflow within the Q-bay. A combination of curtains and insulation eventually yielded aft lower equipment bay temperatures of around 32 °F, which was deemed satisfactory. Window defrosting presented a more difficult problem. Liquid solutions caused blurring and deterioration of the optical qualities of the glass. Electrofilm heaters installed along the edges of the windows warmed the glass inefficiently and had a tendency to short out, resulting in a potential fire hazard. Eventually, a hot-air defrosting system was installed, but it was only used during the climb phase and turned off before operating

---

45. Ibid., p. IV-6.

46. Klinger, "Flight Test Development of the Lockheed U-2 Airplane," p. 233.

47. Ibid., p. 235.

the cameras. The camera window heater provided a secondary benefit by improving equipment-bay temperature distribution.[48]

Fuel System

Fuel flowed from the four integrally sealed tanks, one inboard and one outboard in each wing, and through a sump tank within the fuselage before reaching the engine. Bleed air from the engine provided pressurization for the wing tanks and, along with gravity, assured fuel flow from the wings into the sump. The engine consumed fuel from the inboard tanks first, leaving the weight of remaining fuel in the outboard tanks to alleviate wing bending. Two boost pumps fed fuel from the sump tank into the engine. To minimize structural weight, the U-2 designers did not include a single-point refueling system for ground servicing. Instead, each individual tank was equipped with its own filler cap. During flight, a cross-transfer system provided the pilot with a means to correct a lateral imbalance of wing-tank fuel. The transfer pumps allowed fuel to be moved between inboard and outboard tanks or to increase the rate of flow to the sump tank. In an emergency, the pilot could dump fuel from the inboard tanks at a rate of 90 gallons per minute or from the outboard tanks at a rate of 60 gallons per minute. Standpipes in the outboard tanks retained 150 gallons each. Later-model U-2 and ER-2 aircraft were designed to carry up to 19,175 pounds of fuel in the wing and sump tanks.[49]

One interesting characteristic of long-range endurance flights was the apparent ability of the U-2 to manufacture fuel. Robert Schumacher discovered this illusion in Article 344 during a February 1956 flight that lasted more than 9½ hours. In preparation for the test, the airplane was fueled to full capacity (1,362 gallons) and the totalizer instrument was set to 1,335 gallons in order to provide a safety margin. Schumacher's U-2 departed the runway with a gross weight of 19,900 pounds, but this dropped to 11,155 pounds by the end of the 9.58-hour sortie. Based on calculations from the totalizer, the airplane had consumed 1,386 gallons of fuel, 24 more gallons than had been loaded aboard prior to takeoff. More surprising, the mechanics drained an additional 15 gallons from the fuel tanks after landing. The mystery was solved when Lockheed engineers determined that the fuel, which had been cold-soaked for hours, expanded due to heating as it passed through

---

48. Ibid., pp. 249–257.
49. Lockheed, "U-2 Reconnaissance/Surveillance/Earth Resources System Description,"
    pp. III-4–III-6.

the fuel-oil heat exchanger, causing the gauge to indicate a larger volume. A subsequent series of tests consistently revealed an average increase in volume of approximately 3 percent during similar long-range flights.[50]

Although the special low-vapor-pressure LF-1A was selected as the standard fuel for the U-2, two alternate fuels were also evaluated. At the time, most U.S. military aircraft were fueled with JP-4, a 50-50 kerosene-gasoline blend. U-2 operations with JP-4 were restricted to 50,000 feet maximum altitude and 2,000 feet per minute maximum climb rate. Exceeding these limits risked damaging the airplane with excessive wing-tank pressures or possibly losing fuel through the vent system. Consequently, use of JP-4 was restricted to ferry missions or emergency operation when LF-1A was not available. Tests were also conducted using JP-1, a pure kerosene fuel with a high flash point and a low freezing point. Tank pressures were comparable between LF-1A and JP-1, range and fuel consumption were about the same, and both fuels were considered satisfactory for operational use.[51]

Miscellaneous Systems

For electrical power, the U-2 was equipped with a three-phase, 115/200-volt, 400-Hertz ac system and a 28-volt dc system. These provided automatic, in-depth redundancy for flight and mission-critical power requirements. Two 50-ampere-hour silver-zinc batteries were installed to provide backup power to flight instruments and communications equipment and for engine restart capability, in case the main dc generator and transformer rectifier were offline. These batteries could supply power to the essential and emergency dc buses for approximately 1 hour and 20 minutes, along with power to the emergency ac invertor.[52]

A single engine-driven pump supplied pressure to the hydraulic system. A normal pressure of 3,000 psi was used to actuate the wing flaps, speed brakes, roll and lift spoilers, wheel brakes, stabilizer trim system, and standby ac generator, as well as for extension and retraction of the landing gear.[53]

The U-2 was equipped with a variety of communication and navigation systems. Two-way voice communication during flight was accomplished via several installed UHF and VHF radio systems. An interphone system was

50. Klinger, "Flight Test Development of the Lockheed U-2 Airplane," pp. 61–62.
51. Ibid., pp. 108–111.
52. Lockheed, "U-2 Reconnaissance/Surveillance/Earth Resources System Description," p. III-6.
53. Ibid., p. III-7.

available for communicating with ground-crew personnel during preflight or postflight activities. For navigation, the aircraft was equipped with a standard military Tactical Air Navigation (TACAN) ultrahigh-frequency system to provide continuous indication of bearing and distance from a transmitting station, as well as an automatic direction finder (ADF) radio navigation system. Depending on mission requirements, greater accuracy could be achieved using inertial navigation systems (INS), astroinertial navigation systems (ANS), or global positioning systems (GPS). The INS steered the aircraft toward each destination point through the autopilot. The ANS employed a highly accurate star tracker to limit position error, and it could be used in daylight and at night. GPS navigation was designed for near-pinpoint accuracy using transmissions from small groups of orbiting satellites. On approach to airfields equipped with ground-based instrument landing systems (ILS), the U-2 pilot simply homed in on a localizer near the runway; ILS receivers in the aircraft guided the U-2 along the proper glideslope to touchdown.[54]

---

54. Ibid., pp. IV-3–IV-6.

Lockheed test pilot Frank Powers models the MC-3 partial-pressure suit. (Lockheed Martin)

CHAPTER 5
Life Above 50,000 Feet

Among the greatest challenges of flying the U-2 was simply surviving the hostile environment of the stratosphere, the highest layer of Earth's atmosphere in which aircraft can still fly using conventional aerodynamic surfaces. The unprotected human body cannot withstand the combination of extremely low ambient air pressures, diminishing with increasing altitude, and temperatures that drop as low as –112 °F. The human respiratory system is optimized for operation at elevations ranging from sea level to 10,000 feet. Supplemental oxygen or cabin pressurization systems are necessary for flight at higher altitudes, where humans are subject to hypoxia. Above 15,000 feet without such measures, one may experience such physiological symptoms as fatigue, headache, euphoria, decreased visual acuity, impaired memory, and faulty judgment. More extensive protection is required in the space-equivalent zone that extends from 50,000 feet to the outer fringes of the atmosphere. Here, unprotected exposure quickly results in death. Crossing the Armstrong Limit at around 63,000 feet exposes humans to barometric pressure so low that water boils at normal body temperature. As dramatic as this sounds, only superficial bodily fluids are immediately affected, resulting in swelling of exposed tissues as water within the body changes into a gaseous vapor. Therefore, hypoxia and decompression sickness are greater concerns.[1] In order to survive this hostile realm, U-2 pilots were equipped with pressurized garments that protected them during normal operations, as well as in such instances when it became necessary to eject at high altitudes.

Partial-Pressure Suits

When CIA officials needed advice on equipment for high-altitude survival, they turned to Air Force medical experts Col. Donald D. Flickenger, ARDC director of human factors, and Col. W. Randolph Lovelace II. A graduate of Harvard Medical School, Lovelace had been studying high-altitude flight since 1938 and

---

1. András Sóbester, *Stratospheric Flight: Aeronautics at the Limit* (New York: Springer-Praxis, 2011), pp. 7–12.

he helped develop an oxygen mask that had become standard throughout the Air Force. He and Flickenger also conducted a number of high-altitude parachute jumps from B-47 bombers to test pilot-survival gear under extreme conditions. When it came to developing environmental protection equipment for Project Aquatone, Lovelace and Flickenger suggested the David Clark Company of Worcester, MA, which had previously produced the MC-1 partial-pressure suit for use in the RB-36. Having developed the U-2 cockpit pressurization system, the Firewel Company of Buffalo, NY, provided oxygen regulators, valves, and other equipment, and made the company's altitude chamber facilities available for testing the suit.[2]

David Clark's Joe Ruseckas drew the first patterns for the new partial-pressure suit that came to be known as the MC-3. Assisted by John Flagg and about a half-dozen designers, pattern makers, and technicians, he strove to create a suit that would not only protect the U-2 pilot from the stratospheric environment but be sufficiently comfortable to be worn for prolonged periods and allow the pilot enough freedom of movement to control his airplane. When completed, the MC-3 represented a substantial improvement over earlier suits. As in the MC-1 and other early models, capstans provided mechanical counter-pressure on the limbs in the MC-3, but it was also fitted with a full-torso inflatable bladder extending from the shoulders to mid-thigh, completely surrounding the chest, abdomen, hips, and upper thighs. Instead of using separate hoses, as in all earlier suits, pressure leads to the torso bladder and capstans were simply an extension of the bladder system. Lacing, extending up the inner thigh and across the chest and small of the back, provided control of the torso bladder and allowed for more variation in circumferential fit than on previous suits. There were numerous zippers at the ankles, wrists, back, and across the chest from waist to neck. A zipper at the shoulder made the MC-3 easier to don and doff. Cords were sewn into heavy seams to break the continuity of waist and groin bladders, when inflated, to make it easier for the pilot to bend and sit. The suit included nylon pressure gloves with leather palms that had the pressure lead on the thumb side, using positive-lock bayonet connections. Laces on the back of the hand could be used to adjust the fit. The pilot wore standard flight boots because the feet were not included in the pressurization scheme. Breathing oxygen was fed into a Type MA-2 helmet, manufactured by ILC Dover, of Frederica, DE.[3]

2. Pedlow & Welzenbach, *The CIA and the U-2 Program*, p. 63.
3. Dennis, R. Jenkins, *Dressing for Altitude: U.S. Aviation Pressure Suits—Wiley Post to Space Shuttle* (Washington, DC: NASA SP-2011-595, 2012), pp. 153–155.

Since the suits were individually customized, each pilot made two trips to Worcester for fitting. During the first visit, each pilot was carefully measured so that Ruseckas could tailor the initial pattern for a comfortable fit. After the suit was completed, the pilot returned to try it on and determine whether alterations were necessary. Once it was confirmed that the suit was properly tailored, the pilot then journeyed to Buffalo to try it on in Firewel's altitude chamber. After pilots complained that the restraint fabric connecting the helmet to the suit made it difficult to turn their heads, the David Clark Company developed a new Link-Net fabric for the neck section that allowed greater range of motion. Ultimately, the MC-3 became available in 12 standard sizes, as well as in custom-fitted models. The suit was often worn with a protective outer layer to shield the capstans and laces against becoming entangled with switches or other objects in the cramped U-2 cockpit.[4] The MC-3 served as the predecessor to a family of partial-pressure suits that included the MC-3A, MC-4, and S-100.

Lockheed officials contacted David Clark in early 1970 to ask for an improved partial-pressure suit for use with first-generation U-2 airplanes that were still in service. By this time, U-2R crews were wearing full-pressure suits, and although flight testing had proven that a pilot wearing such a garment would fit in the cockpit of a U-2C after certain modifications had been made, the Air Force was hesitant to make those changes. Joe Ruseckas agreed to develop a better partial-pressure suit based on the MC-3A suit and hardware but with a helmet from the A/P22S-6 full-pressure suit. The neck ring required for attaching the new helmet made the shoulder-zipper entry used on most partial-pressure suits impractical, so a rear-entry system was developed for the new suit, by now designated S-100. Integration of the A/P22S-6 helmet with the S-100 suit considerably improved pilot comfort and mobility, which also helped reduce stress and fatigue during long missions.[5]

David Clark eventually fabricated 142 of the new suits for the Air Force and NASA. The S-100 consisted of a coverall much like that of the MC-3, with a restraint assembly, breathing bladder, and capstans extending down the back and along the arms and legs to provide counter pressure. Slide fasteners on the wrists and ankles and at the center of the back facilitated donning, and laces along the arms, legs, chest, and back permitted individual size adjustments. Pressure bladders at the waist and groin were designed to crease in order to facilitate sitting and standing. Wrapped completely around the torso, the breathing bladder was integrated with the neck seal and neck

---

4. Ibid., pp. 155–158.
5. Ibid., pp. 316–318.

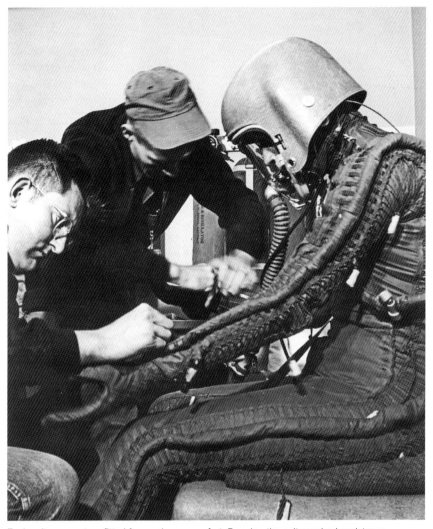

Each suit was custom fitted for maximum comfort. Donning the suit required assistance. (Laughlin Heritage Foundation)

ring and included a perforated inner liner that vented airflow around the wearer. For added protection and utility, a fire-resistant Nomex exterior cover could be worn over the suit, providing pockets and Velcro pads for checklists and other items. The partial-pressure gloves had suede leather palms, elastic cuffs, and lacings on the back of the hand to allow for personal adjustments. The helmet consisted of a Fiberglas shell with a movable visor and separate sunshade, oxygen regulator system, anti-suffocation valve, cushion assembly, and communication equipment. Channels distributed vent air around

The S-100, worn here by NASA pilot Jim Barnes, was a hybrid of a partial-pressure suit and a full-pressure-type helmet. (NASA)

the pilot's head, and a spray bar around the inner edge of the visor opening delivered breathing oxygen and prevented visor fogging. A rubber face seal divided the breathing space from the rest of the helmet, and a spring-loaded valve allowed exhaled air to be exhausted from the breathing space to the pressure-suit breathing-bladder assembly. The system was designed to maintain pressure in the face area slightly higher than the suit pressure in order to provide the pilot with 100-percent oxygen at all times. The helmet was also equipped with a self-sealing drinking and feeding port through which a tube

Lt. Col. Dee Porter demonstrates a prototype S1034 full-pressure suit at Palmdale in 1991. (Lockheed Martin)

could be inserted to enable the pilot to consume liquids and semi-solid foods. Air Force and NASA pilots began using the S-100 in 1972 and continued to do so until the last U-2C was retired in 1989.[6]

6. Ibid., pp. 319–322.

Full-Pressure Suits

With significantly more available cockpit space in the U-2R and subsequent models, it was finally possible to equip pilots with full-pressure suits. Officials from the Air Force, CIA, David Clark, Firewel, and Lockheed met in Burbank in May 1967 to discuss the final configuration of the U-2R cockpit, pressurization system, escape system, and pressure suit. The David Clark Company was contracted to produce the S1010 full-pressure suit, but the first unit would not be ready until September. In the interim, several S901J suits of the type used in the A-12 were modified for use in the U-2R. When the S1010 finally became available, it was very similar to the S901J but with oxygen and electrical connections tailored for the U-2 cockpit. In the event of emergency egress, it included a fully integrated parachute harness, automatic water-activated flotation system, and an optional inflatable thermal-protective garment. For crew comfort during long-duration missions, it had a urine-collection system. In order to minimize pilot stress and fatigue during long sorties, the company designed an entirely new helmet, making every attempt to reduce the amount of weight supported by the pilot's head. The designers achieved this by removing the breathing regulator and oxygen-supply system from the helmet and relocating them within the coverall garment, and by integrating the helmet-disconnect bearing assembly with the helmet via a soft neck section at the base of the Fiberglas shell. They also enlarged and reshaped the S1010 helmet shell to increase headroom over that of the S901J helmet assembly.[7]

At just 31 pounds, the S1010 was surprisingly lightweight; the suit and gloves weighed just 14 pounds, the exterior cover and harness 10 pounds, and the helmet 7 pounds. Without the helmet, the entire suit could be folded into a 2.7-cubic-foot package. Although the coverall and gloves were custom tailored for each pilot, the helmet came in only one size. Interior cushions were used to accommodate individual head sizes. As with earlier David Clark suits, U-2 pilots traveled to Worcester to be measured and fitted. The company produced the suit in two variants. On the S1010A, the oxygen regulator, communication gear, parachute harness, and flotation device were integrally mounted. For the S1010B, designers moved the regulator and communication equipment into the helmet and put the parachute and flotation gear into a separate harness worn over the suit.[8]

In 1978, the David Clark Company began development of a new helmet to replace the S1010 units when they reached the anticipated end of their service

---

7. Ibid., pp. 334–337.
8. Ibid., pp. 337–338.

lives 3 years later. In a continuing effort to minimize helmet-induced stress and fatigue, designers introduced a nonconformal dome helmet that completely eliminated head-borne weight and provided greater freedom of head movement within the helmet. The S1010D helmet provided excellent visibility and greatly reduced the rotational torque associated with neck stress. Instead of the usual conformal padding, the pilot now wore a skullcap that contained a microphone and earphones for the communication system. Testing yielded mixed results; although the helmet was more comfortable, pilots complained that foam cushions—inside the coverall, underneath the helmet neck ring—interfered with the parachute risers and shoulder harness and provided inadequate front-to-back stability for the helmet.[9]

This problem was solved within 3 years. The S1031 was nearly identical to the S1030 developed for the SR-71 except for the placement of oxygen and electrical interfaces, as dictated by each aircraft. In addition, special care was taken to limit bulk on the front of the chest to minimize interference with the U-2 pilot's control yoke; this had not been a problem in the SR-71, which features a standard control stick. The S1031 came in 12 standard sizes and weighed about 35 pounds. It began replacing the S1010 in late 1982 and remained in use until 1996. Starting in 1991, some S1030 and S1031 suits were replaced with the S1031C, a common pressure suit that could be used interchangeably in either the U-2 or SR-71, thus reducing ground support and maintenance requirements. Such improvements and a desire to further improve wearer comfort eventually led to development of the S1034, an entirely new design based on lessons learned from years of crewmember and maintainer experience with earlier suits. For the S1034, designers studied myriad factors that affected crew performance, including comfort, mobility, visibility, tactility and dexterity, oxygen systems, altitude and thermal protection, drinking and feeding necessities, durability, maintainability, and survival characteristics in the event of emergency. The result was a suit with a bladder manufactured from Gore-Tex, a lightweight fabric that allowed perspiration to pass through in the form of water vapor while retaining air pressure. The S1034 was more comfortable and less bulky than earlier full-pressure suits and more durable and easier to maintain. It was easier to don and doff and had better mobility than the S1031. New gloves offered improved comfort, mobility, and dexterity, as well as improved gripping power and wear protection. The helmet was functionally identical to that of the S1031 but made of lighter materials. In 2002, the David Clark Company began development of an improved helmet called the S1034E that was slightly

9. Ibid., pp. 338–339.

larger and more comfortable to wear. This model was put into production in 2006 to replace earlier helmets as they reached the end of their service lives.[10]

Physiological Support

Flying the U-2 would have been impossible without the assistance of a team of specialized physiological support technicians to help the pilot don and doff his pressure suit and ensure the proper attachment and operation of life-support equipment. With the exception of the specific types of personal equipment worn by flightcrews, the process of preparing for a U-2 flight has remained essentially unchanged since 1955.

To avoid decompression sickness during flight, U-2 pilots had to don their pressure suits and begin breathing pure oxygen at least an hour prior to takeoff so that their bodies would have sufficient time to dissipate nitrogen in the bloodstream. This procedure was known as pre-breathing. During high-altitude cruise, the cabin-pressure altitude was maintained between 28,000 and 30,000 feet. The pilot's suit automatically pressurized to 3 psi because breathing pure oxygen at 3 psi at 29,000 feet is equivalent to breathing ambient air at sea level. Without pressurized oxygen, the time of useful consciousness at 70,000 feet is only a few seconds. Typically, the pilot arrived at the ready room about an hour and a half before the flight for a quick examination by a flight surgeon. The preflight physical consisted of checking blood pressure, respiration, pulse, and recent diet. Only low-residue foods were consumed prior to a mission because gas expansion during ascent could cause gastrointestinal distress. Once the examination was complete, two suit technicians and a supervisor provided technical assistance as the pilot donned his suit coverall over long underwear and pulled on boots and gloves. The pilot then lay down for an hour prior to takeoff to pre-breathe pure oxygen for denitrogenation of his blood. This downtime also provided an opportunity for the technicians to integrate and inflate the suit, check out all systems and hardware, and check for leaks. Before leaving the ready room for the crew transport van, the pilot was connected to a portable oxygen system so as not to break the breathing cycle. At the aircraft, the pilot's pressure suit was hooked up to the onboard oxygen system.[11]

Once cocooned within the pressure suit, simple tasks such as eating, drinking, and urination became major problems. To prevent pilots from becoming

---

10. Ibid., pp. 348–361.
11. Ryan Ragsdale, interview with author, NASA Dryden Flight Research Center (now, Armstrong Flight Research Center), August 27, 2013.

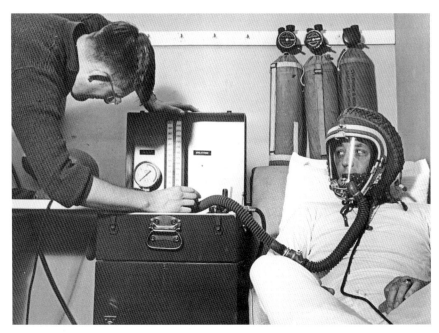

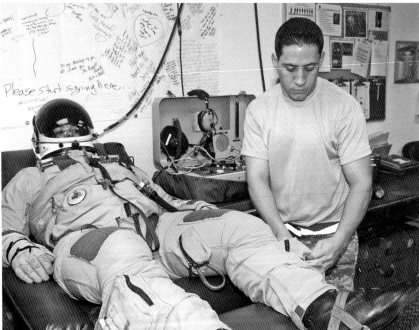

The pre-breathing ritual was the same regardless of whether the partial-pressure or full-pressure garment was worn. In upper photo, a life-support technician checks oxygen levels for Lockheed test pilot Robert Schumacher in 1957. In lower photo, TSgt. Shawn Hansen performs a similar task for Lt. Col. Brian Dickinson in 2008. (U.S. Air Force)

desiccated during long missions—a condition aggravated by having to breathe pure oxygen—provisions were made to allow the pilot to drink sweetened water by way of a tube inserted through a small self-sealing hole in the facemask. Ready-to-eat foods in squeezable containers were also provided. Despite all precautions, U-2 pilots often lost as much as 3 to 6 pounds of body weight through dehydration during an 8-hour mission. To reduce waste elimination, pilots ate a low-bulk, high-protein diet on the day before and the morning of each mission. Early pressure suits made no provision for urination, but a subsequent model required the pilot to be catheterized before donning his flying suit. This method to permit urination during flight proved very uncomfortable and was eventually replaced with an external bladder arrangement that made the catheter unnecessary.[12]

Ryan Ragsdale, a physiological support technician with more than 35 years of experience, started working with both partial- and full-pressure suits at Beale Air Force Base in 1979. He immediately noticed that there was a big difference between the cockpits of the U-2C and U-2R (the C cockpit was about 25 percent smaller than that of the R) and the types of pressure suits worn in each model. At that time, the Air Force was employing a variety of suit configurations for use with the U-2C, U-2R, and SR-71, all aircraft that were stationed at Beale. "The U-2C at that time was not flying operational missions; it was only being used for initial training," he recalled. "We had so few U-2R models that when a pilot came into the program we would first configure him with a partial-pressure suit to fly in the U-2CT trainer for initial certification and acceptance flights, and then for his solo flights in the single-seat U-2C. Once he got through that phase, we would transition him into the S1010 full-pressure suit assembly so he could start flying the U-2R."[13]

Ragsdale first worked with the hybrid S-100 before being trained on the S1010 full-pressure suits. The oxygen regulator for the S1010 was mounted underneath the neck ring inside the suit, and oxygen entered through openings in the neck ring and passed into the helmet's face cavity. "This was problematic," said Ragsdale, "because the neck ring is a movable fixture, so now you had a movable fixture with seals that your oxygen system is going through. We spent a lot of time overhauling, continuously working to keep those suits functioning." The later S1010B, with the regulator located inside the helmet instead of the suit, was a big improvement. But there were always new challenges, including the vexing problem of faceplate fogging. "There was a wire grid within the visor glass, a heating element for defogging. We tried battery

---

12. Pedlow & Welzenbach, *The CIA and the U-2 Program*, pp. 63–65.

13. Ragsdale, interview with author.

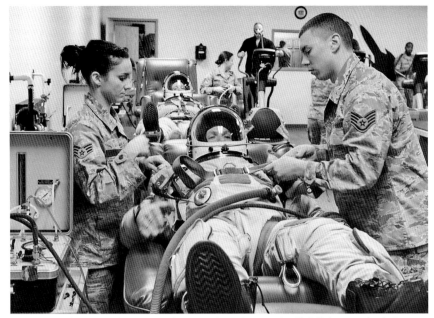

Physiological Support technicians perform a vital role in preparing U-2 flightcrews for their missions. (U.S. Air Force)

power packs, rechargeable power packs; it wasn't very effective." Alternatively, the pilot could insert a food probe into the helmet's feeding port; the pressure change activated the regulator, causing oxygen to flow across the faceplate and evaporate any moisture on the glass. Ragsdale eventually mastered the art of assisting the U-2 pilot through the lengthy process of donning the pressure garment, pre-breathing, and integrating the suit with the airplane's life-support systems. Doffing the suit after a mission was a quicker process as long as all of the systems functioned properly, but the pilot had to be observed for any signs of decompression sickness.[14]

Over the past three decades, suit designers and technicians have learned many lessons. As a result, pressure garments have been made lighter, with increased mobility, and have become easier and more comfortable to wear. Neoprene rubber suit bladders have been replaced with Gore-Tex assemblies that wick moisture away from the pilot's body. "The pilots are coming back much drier than they used to, and the suits are more sustainable because acidic sweat had previously caused the suits to deteriorate faster." There have been surprisingly few improvements in manual dexterity of the gloves, however. "The

---

14. Ibid.

early partial-pressure suit gloves were better," according to Ragsdale, "because they were thin and fit more tightly. Once you have to encase the entire hand in air, you can't have the glove be a snug fit like that. They have tried Velcro on the palms and fingertips, and metal bars across the palms, but there hasn't been a perfect solution." When he first arrived at Beale, Ragsdale was told that he might not be trained to work with the U-2 because it was expected to be phased out of service. "Now here we are more than 30 years later, the SR-71 was retired not once but twice, and the U-2 is still going strong."[15]

High Cuisine

Requirements for long-duration reconnaissance and research flights resulted in the development of special foods and equipment to deliver nourishment and liquid refreshment to the U-2 flightcrews. Pilots wearing bulky, fully pressurized suits have a limited range of motion for feeding themselves and cannot break the integrity of their pressurized environment by opening their helmet visors. In order to overcome this dilemma, the Air Force turned to the expert chefs and nutritionists at the Department of Defense Combat Feeding Directorate (CFD) at the Army's Natick Soldier Research, Development and Engineering Center, Natick, MA. The result was "tube food"—meals in the form of a paste with the consistency of baby food. U-2 pilots are supplied with metallic-foil containers, similar in size to a large tube of toothpaste, each fitted with a plastic straw designed to slip through a sealed port on the pilot's helmet. Breaching this port, which is also used for hydration, does not affect the suit's internal pressure. The CFD has been supplying tube foods to U-2 pilots for more than half a century and has produced approximately 28,000 tubes annually for a community

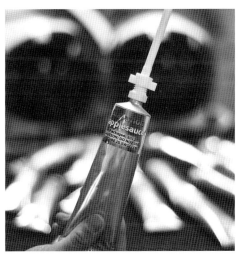

Tube food comes in many flavors, including cinnamon applesauce. (U.S. Air Force)

---

15. Ibid.

of only about 100 pilots. Each has a shelf life of approximately 3 years if stored at a maximum temperature of 80 °F. "We've been making these for years and years," said Dan Nattress, a CFD food technologist, "and constantly adding new flavors."[16]

Pilots usually consume one tube per hour. Although eating peach cobbler, Key lime pie, Chicken à la King, or truffle macaroni and cheese from a tube doesn't compare to a home-cooked meal, U-2 pilots say they enjoy the tube meals while flying long missions. They typically request their favorites while being assisted into their pressure suits. "Depending on the duration of the flight, each pilot is different," said suit technician SSgt. Suzzett Stalesky of the 9th Physiological Support Squadron. "It just depends on the pilot preference. Some pilots take the same thing every flight, and some newer ones are still trying to find what agrees with their body during a flight." While classic flavors such as beef stew or applesauce are popular, there are also more exciting options like chocolate pudding with enough caffeine to satisfy any coffee addict.[17] Since some missions can last as long as 12 hours, caffeine is a popular ingredient among U-2 pilots. "The aircraft itself is very difficult to fly, and it's actually very difficult to land," Nattress said. "[The pilots] want to be very alert when they land. Fairly soon before they're landing, they'll open up a caffeinated product."[18]

In 2010, Air Force officials decided the tube food menu needed a boost and asked the CFD to bring its products into the 21st century. "Things change," said Nattress. "In the 1970s, expectations were different. We had no direct communication with the user prior to 2010." To rectify that, Nattress and Deborah Haley, chef and physical science technician with CFD, visited Beale Air Force Base to gain a firsthand understanding of what the U-2 crews experience. "Things are a lot more difficult," Haley said. "Once you're fully suited and under pressure and connected to oxygen, there's no movement inside the helmet, except when you breathe in and breathe out, so swallowing is a conscious effort. You have to actually think about that, because there's no air movement. It's a lot different sort of feeling to it."[19]

---

16. Shawn Nickel, "Fueling the high flyers—U-2 tube food calms cravings in the cockpit," Air Combat Command News, February 8, 2013, *http://www.acc.af.mil/news/story.asp?id=123335478*, accessed August 30, 2013.

17. Ibid.

18. Bob Reinert, "Natick tube foods keep U-2 pilots flying high," *Army News Archives*, January 18, 2013, *http://www.army.mil/article/94301/Natick_tube_foods_keep_U_2_pilots_flying_high/*, accessed August 30, 2013.

19. Ibid.

SSgt. Suzzett Stalesky, 9th Physiological Support Squadron, demonstrates the proper method for inserting the feeding tube into the helmet. (U.S. Air Force)

After surveying a number of U-2 pilots, Air Force officials asked the CFD to produce four popularly requested flavors including Peach Melba, Beef Stroganoff, Key Lime Pie, and a breakfast item, which became bacon with hash browns. These were added to a revamped 15-item menu, all made with fresh ingredients. "They didn't want us to completely revise all of the products," said Haley, "but we knew that there were things we could do to improve them that wouldn't be major." CFD technicians suggested developing layers of flavors to improve the meal experience. "Now the pilots are getting really excited about the food. It's so much better."[20]

Developing high cuisine for high-altitude flyers is not as easy as it sounds. There have been occasional failures and missteps along the way. In the early stages of developing the Peach Melba, for example, Nattress recalled that it had a "dirty sock kind of taste." Eventually, after some additional tweaking, it became one of the more successful flavors. "It takes a while to find just the right balance," said Haley, "so that when it comes out of the tube, you've hit just the right flavor profile."[21]

20. Ibid.
21. Ibid.

Hazards of High Flight

U-2 pilots have been subjected to a variety of hazards related to high-altitude flying, especially hypoxia (oxygen deficiency) and dysbarism (medical conditions resulting from changes in ambient air pressure). These phenomena were not merely confined to the early days of the program and the use of partial-pressure suits but continued into the 21st century despite advances in aerospace physiology and the development of improved technology for personal survival equipment.

Two fatal U-2 accidents on successive days in July 1958 resulted from hypoxia. The first, on July 8, occurred 6 hours into a high-altitude navigation training flight when Squadron Leader Chris Walker, a British exchange pilot, reported that his aircraft was descending out of control. Although he ejected at a safe altitude, Walker never separated from his seat and perished. The following day, Capt. Al Chapin, Jr., was killed during a similar training sortie. Both were highly qualified pilots. Walker was fully qualified in the U-2 and had hundreds of hours of flight experience in the Canberra (British forerunner to the B-57). Chapin had been awarded the Distinguished Flying Cross for safely landing a disabled U-2 1 year earlier, after a power failure and loss of pressurization at high altitude. The U-2 fleet was grounded following Walker's and Chapin's accidents, while investigators initially focused on suspicions that autopilot failures led to loss of control. This line of thought was abandoned after excessive moisture was discovered in the oxygen systems of other U-2s, leading to the conclusion that ice may have formed in the oxygen systems of the two mishap aircraft. The commander of SAC restricted U-2 operations to a maximum altitude of 20,000 feet until corrective actions were implemented.[22]

That same year, Col. Jack Nole suffered hypoxia while attempting a high-altitude bailout after his U-2 broke apart following inadvertent extension of the wing flaps. As his airplane dove toward the ground, Nole extended the landing gear and speed brakes and reduced engine power to idle, but it was no use. Airframe stresses eventually snapped the bolts holding the tail assembly in place and Nole was battered about inside the cockpit as the plane tumbled end over end. Struggling mightily, he released his harness and was immediately slammed into the canopy, which came loose and sailed away. Nole's survival pack snagged on something, and he found himself pinned halfway out of the cockpit, bent backward against the tumbling fuselage by the powerful slipstream. He eventually wrenched free but soon came to the realization that he had failed to initiate his emergency oxygen feed. As he depleted his remaining air, Nole felt the onset

---

22. Pocock, *50 Years of the U-2*, pp. 339–341.

of hypoxia and determined that he had two choices. "The first," he later recalled, "was to let myself fall until my parachute opened automatically at the preset 14,000 feet. But it would take more than two minutes to free-fall those seven and a half miles; by that time, there was a good chance I'd have suffocated."[23]

His second choice was to immediately open his parachute and hope he could find and activate his emergency oxygen bottle. Tempting though this was, it carried a number of risks. The first stemmed from the fact that a human body could accelerate to as much as 375 miles per hour in the thin atmosphere. Even if his shroud lines did not become tangled, the force of the parachute snapping open at such speed could shred the fabric or cause great bodily harm due to sudden deceleration. Successful chute deployment did not guarantee survival either since it might take up to a half-hour to descend to the ground from 53,000 feet. Nole decided to chance it and pulled his ripcord. He was pleasantly surprised when the parachute opened gently, without the slightest shock, possibly as a result of his being propelled upward during egress and, by chance, opening the chute while at the apex of his arc. Nole managed to activate his emergency oxygen but then had to contend with wild oscillations beneath the parachute canopy, exacerbated by the thin air, which provided little resistance. "Each time I swung, I was afraid that air would spill from the chute's high side, and that it would collapse, dropping me like a stone." At 20,000 feet and still swinging wildly, he opened his faceplate and was violently airsick. Finally, 22 minutes after exiting the cockpit, he touched down safely on a gently rolling Texas prairie. He later learned that his descent should have lasted at least another 10 minutes, but air spillage during his oscillations sped his fall, allowing him to more quickly reach warmer, thicker air before his emergency supply ran out.[24]

In another incident, Capt. Pat Halloran suffered oxygen deprivation due to faulty connection of his life-support equipment by technicians prior to takeoff. After his oxygen hose came loose during cruise at around 64,000 feet, Halloran began to feel warning signs of hypoxia, including flushing and hyperventilation. His helmet bladder collapsed around his head and he had difficulty breathing as the pressurized oxygen feed suddenly ceased. He was now breathing only the ambient cockpit air, which was pressurized to around 30,000 feet pressure altitude. His vision dimming, he checked the airplane's oxygen controls and found nothing amiss, but when he looked in a rearview mirror, he noticed the hose dangling loose from its connector. Working quickly, he re-established the proper connection and felt immediate relief as oxygen began to flow into his

23. Ibid., p. 340.
24. Ibid.

Ground crewmen assist Col. Jack Nole with last-minute preparations for a U-2 flight. (Laughlin Heritage Foundation)

helmet. The ensuing investigation resulted in modifications to prevent acciden-tal disconnection during flight.[25]

Later U-2 pilots equipped with full-pressure suits were likewise vulnerable to the vicissitudes of high-altitude flight. In 2006, a 47-year-old pilot began feel-ing various aches and pains 2½ hours into a long-endurance sortie. He tried to alleviate discomfort in his knees and ankles by adjusting his rudder pedals and then by increasing the pressure in his suit. The situation became increasingly worse over the next 2 hours as he experienced confusion, headache, fatigue, and degraded ability to concentrate. Eating, drinking, and adjusting his oxygen supply gave no relief, and only after another 4 hours had passed did he report his problems to ground control. He was immediately instructed to return to base, but he almost did not make it. He was sick in his helmet several times, and his mental and physical capacities (including hearing and vision) deteriorated until he could no longer communicate via the radio. Upon arrival at his home base, he attempted to land on the wrong runway three times before finally touching down safely. Following a thorough physical examination, the pilot was diagnosed with severe decompression sickness with neurological symptoms

---

25. Ibid., p. 341.

and incipient cardiovascular collapse. Although investigators found no technical problems with the airplane's environmental systems, the pilot's symptoms had apparently been brought on by the pressure changing from that experienced on the airfield before takeoff to that of the minimum ambient pressure in the cabin of the U-2 in cruise. Decompression sickness, known to divers as the bends, results from the formation of tiny bubbles from gases (mainly nitrogen) dissolved in body tissues due to a reduction in the environmental pressure. It can strike aviators exposed to altitudes above 18,000 feet or so, and the symptoms can range from a mild case of the bends to serious neurological problems. In this case, the U-2 pilot seemed to recover within a few months, but he was eventually found to have suffered permanent brain damage severe enough to end his flying career.[26]

In the first decade of the 21st century, according to Lt Col. Edward "Tadd" Sholtis, the Air Force's deputy director of public affairs at Air Combat Command Headquarters, a higher operations tempo for the U-2 coincided with an increased number of pilots suffering from neurologic decompression sickness (NDCS). In fact, between 2006 and 2010, the number of reported NDCS incidents increased from 0.076 percent to 0.23 percent of missions flown. "By late 2010, officials believed there was enough cause for concern to initiate a study," said Sholtis in an interview with *Air Force Times*. "What we knew or suspected about the problem was briefed to decision makers in early 2011, and the study was authorized in March 2011." By October 2012, the Air Force had conducted magnetic resonance imaging (MRI) tests on more than 100 U-2 pilots, ranging in age from 26 to 50, said Dr. Stephen McGuire, a neurologist and retired Air Force colonel who led the study. Of those pilots examined, 75 percent had more brain lesions than they should have for their age and health status. McGuire noted that these were the same type of lesions normally associated with repeated head trauma.[27]

The study, published in *Neurology* in August 2013, compared MRI images from 102 Air Force pilots assigned to U-2 squadrons with 91 brain scans from a control group matched by age, health, and education. Citing previous research from other scientists, McGuire and his colleagues showed that high-altitude pilots' exposure to low-air-pressure environments can lead to NDCS, affecting the central nervous system. Symptoms include slowed thought processes,

---

26. Sóbester, *Stratospheric Flight: Aeronautics at the Limit*, pp. 13–14.

27. Jeff Schogol, "Air Force re-pressurizes U-2 cabin to prevent brain lesions in pilots," *Air Force Times*, August 28, 2013, *http://www.airforcetimes.com/article/20130828/ NEWS04/308280019/Air-Force-re-pressurizes-U-2-cabin-prevent-brain-lesions-pilots*, accessed August 30, 2013.

anomia (impaired ability to name things), confusion, unresponsiveness, and permanent cognitive decline. The researchers who performed the study found a link between clinical NDCS and white-matter hyperintensity brain lesions, possibly related to microbubbles of predominantly nitrogen gas formed during high-altitude flying. In testing whether the entire U-2 pilot population might exhibit significantly more lesions than members of the control group, they discovered a 375 percent increase in the volume of lesions among the pilots and a 295 percent rise in the number of white-matter hyperintensities. Lesion volume and count are important markers of cerebral integrity and have been previously used to measure age-related cognitive decline as indicated by declines in executive functioning, processing speed, and general cognitive ability. Brain scans of the U-2 pilots indicated white-matter damage different from that occurring in normal aging, further bolstering the hypothesis that the pilots' lesions resulted from microemboli (tiny gas bubbles) in the brain tissue.[28]

Interestingly, pilots with the most U-2 flight time did not always have the highest number of brain lesions. Instead, the main contributing factors to lesion formation included the amount of nitrogen the pilots were able to get out of their system while breathing 100 percent oxygen before flying, mission duration, and the amount of recovery time pilots were given before making another high-altitude sortie. In order to alleviate the risks of NDCS, the Air Force took steps to improve cockpit pressurization in the U-2 and minimize hypobaric exposure. The Cabin Altitude Reduction Effort reduced the pressure altitude U-2 pilots were exposed to during operational missions from 29,000 to 15,000 feet. This was a significant improvement as research has shown that the risk of developing decompression sickness becomes virtually nonexistent below 18,000 feet. "What we've done is bring the pilots down below what is commonly thought to be the threshold for DCS and we think that will prevent any further occurrence of lesions," McGuire subsequently reported. Technicians completed CARE upgrades to the fleet in June 2013 along with other cockpit modifications, including reinforcement of frames, bulkheads, and the canopy. McGuire acknowledged that it is unknown whether U-2 pilots would be at greater risk of having health problems later in life as a result of hypobaric expose. "In all other neurological disease, these types of lesions are associated with cognitive impairment," he said. "We have not seen any clinical impairment in any of our U-2 pilots, and they are all still flying. But, being conservative, the commanders rightly made the decision [to implement CARE], 'Let's not push the

---

28. Markus MacGill, "Mental-decline brain lesions found in high-flying military pilots," *Medical News Today*, August 21, 2013, *http://www.medicalnewstoday.com/articles/265036.php*, accessed August 30, 2013.

To reduce the chance of decompression sickness, cockpit upgrades have improved cabin-pressure altitude. (U.S. Air Force)

envelope; let's protect our pilots.'"[29] As an additional precaution, according to Sholtis, "The Air Force is in the process of reviewing flight operations guidance to potentially increase downtime between high flights longer than nine hours, as well as limiting the length of deployments."[30]

Even flight at lower altitudes can carry the risk of hypoxia. In December 2011, veteran U-2 and ER-2 pilot Denis Steele was flying a NASA sortie from Palmdale when his oxygen regulator failed. Since the maximum planned cruise altitude for the mission was only 45,000 feet, Steele was not wearing a pressure suit. His oxygen supply was delivered through a standard mask and regulator of the type used in fighter-type aircraft such as the F-15 and F-18. Typically, regulator failure results from a rupture of one of two diaphragms within the assembly. The regulator is designed to fail in the full open position, providing a continuous flow of oxygen. According to Ryan Ragsdale, "It's going to be uncomfortable breathing because now it's going to be equivalent to pressure breathing, but at least you still have oxygen, which gives you time so you can safely descend to a lower altitude." Steele's incident was unusual in that his regulator ceased to function, leaving him with no oxygen flow whatsoever. He could not even activate his emergency oxygen," Ragsdale said, "because it all went through the

29. Schogol, "Air Force re-pressurizes U-2 cabin to prevent brain lesions in pilots."

30. MacGill, "Mental-decline brain lesions found in high-flying military pilots."

same regulator."[31] At that point in the flight, the ER-2's cockpit had a pressure altitude of 23,000 feet, which gave the pilot approximately 3 minutes of useful consciousness before he was unable to fly the airplane. Steele needed to reduce his altitude quickly before he succumbed to hypoxia, but he had to be careful not to descend too quickly and risk overstressing the airframe. He declared an emergency, engaged the autopilot, and attempted to balance his need to get down quickly enough to remain conscious with a requirement to descend slowly enough to keep his airplane intact. During his long descent, he felt the onset of hypoxia and worried that he might become so cognitively impaired that he would lose control of the airplane. As his symptoms worsened, he even considered the possibility that he might have to eject. Frustration mounted as air-traffic controllers tried to convince Steele to descend more slowly in order to avoid commercial air traffic in the flight corridor above Palmdale. They did not seem to grasp the severity of his predicament. Somehow, he managed to retain control of the airplane and remain conscious long enough to reach a lower altitude, where his hypoxic symptoms subsided and he was able to safely land the airplane. For these actions, Steel was later awarded the NASA Exceptional Bravery Medal. Investigators determined that the faulty regulator had been used well past its service life.[32]

Another hazard of high-altitude flight comes from ionizing radiation. Earth's atmosphere shields humans and other life forms living at ground level from galactic cosmic rays (GCR); the denser the atmosphere, the greater the protection. The intensity of atmospheric background radiation levels varies with altitude, latitude, and phase of the solar cycle, which ranges from minimum to maximum about every 11 years. When solar activity is at a minimum GCR, levels are at their highest, and vice versa. GCR consist of energetic nuclei of all naturally occurring elements, interacting with atmospheric constituents, primarily through atomic and nuclear collisions. At flight altitudes above 10,000 feet, the dominant contributor to the effective dose comes from secondary neutrons. GCR exposure approximately doubles with every 6,000 feet of increased altitude. At sea level, the exposure rate is a miniscule 0.03 microsieverts per hour (μSv/h). At altitudes of 30,000 to 40,000 feet, typical of those used for commercial airline traffic, the exposure rates increase to approximately 5 to 10 μSv/h. At typical operating altitudes for the U-2, and those of proposed future high-speed commercial passenger aircraft (59,000–65,000 feet), the estimated dose equivalent rates range from 10 to 20 μSv/h. As an example, measurements

---

31. Ragsdale, interview with author.
32. Jim Smolka, Director of Flight Operations, remarks during the NASA Honor Awards ceremony, Dryden Flight Research Center, August 6, 2013.

taken aboard the Concorde supersonic transport in October 1996 averaged 14.1 µSv/h. In the future, commercial aircraft may be developed that fly higher, faster, and farther than currently possible. This will result in increased effective doses of atmospheric radiation for aircrews and passengers.[33]

In order to more accurately characterize radiation levels at high altitudes, scientists from the NASA High Speed Research Project Office at Langley Research Center conducted a study in 1997 with assistance from Johnson Space Center, Ames Research Center, the Department of Energy's Environmental Measurements Laboratory, Canadian Defense Research Establishment, U.K. National Radiological Protection Board, Boeing Company, and several researchers from domestic and foreign universities. For the Atmospheric Ionizing Radiation (AIR) project, a NASA ER-2 aircraft conducted five high-altitude sorties from Moffett Field to measure galactic cosmic radiation during a solar minimum. On flights ranging over the Pacific Ocean, southwestern U.S., and western Canada, the ER-2 carried 14 different instruments in the nose, Q-bay, and wing pods. These included a multisphere neutron spectrometer, ionization chamber, scintillation counters, two spherical tissue-equivalent proportional counters, and two particle telescopes. Data from the AIR program are potentially useful in developing not only more accurate radiation models for high-altitude flight but also for planning human exploration of the planet Mars, which has a radiation environment very similar to that of Earth's atmosphere at 70,000 feet.[34]

Flight operations in the stratosphere have proven challenging and hazardous to U-2 flightcrews but have immeasurably increased knowledge of aerospace physiology and aided in the development of improved life-support systems. Many lessons came at a high cost, but despite heavy losses in the early days of the U-2 program, Air Force officials are quick to point out that the airplane has a pretty good overall safety record. According to Sholtis in an August 2013 interview, "[During] U-2 operations since 1963, for every 100,000 hours flown there were eight mishaps that resulted in the death of the pilot." Analysis of these mishaps resulted in a variety of procedural, educational, and technological changes made to improve safety. "We have reduced the fatality rate to 0.1 per 100,000 hours over the past 10 years."[35]

33. Lawrence W. Townsend, "Radiation exposures of aircrew in high altitude flight," *Journal of Radiological Protection* 21, no. 1 (March 2001): pp. 5–8.

34. Susan Bailey, "Air crew radiation exposure—An overview," *Nuclear News*, January 2000, pp. 32–40.

35. MacGill, "Mental-decline brain lesions found in high-flying military pilots."

Pilots learn to fly the U-2ST trainer before going solo. (U.S. Air Force)

CHAPTER 6

Flight Operations and Performance

The U-2 has always been a difficult airplane to fly, challenging even the best pilots. Lightweight construction and long, thin wings give it terrific soaring ability but also make it hard to land. As the airplane approaches the ground, it floats on a cushion of air—known as ground effect—that causes the U-2 to remain airborne even at idle. The pilot almost has to force it down using spoilers to extinguish any remaining lift. A safe touchdown is further complicated by the unusual landing gear configuration. Near or on the ground, the U-2 appears to be a clumsy beast. The mysterious Dragon Lady seems at ease only when soaring to altitude or cruising through the stratosphere. Even there, danger lurks within the thin margin between Mach buffet and stall speed, the dreaded "coffin corner" of the flight envelope. Technological improvements have eased such problems as high-altitude engine flameouts and balky autopilots, but only a select few can hope to admire Earth's curvature from more than 12 miles above the surface in what has been dubbed the Near-Space Plane.

Crew Selection and Training

U-2 pilots come from every type of military flying background—fighters, bombers, tankers, transports, and trainers—and have included inter-service transfer officers from the Navy, Marines, and Coast Guard. Candidates for crew selection must submit an extensive application package. Finalists undergo a formal interview with several commanders at Beale Air Force Base, home of the 9th Reconnaissance Wing.

Those selected for interview generally possess a strong flight-evaluation history and solid officer-performance evaluations and exceed minimum flight experience requirements. Because the U-2 does not meet military specifications for handling qualities, selectees must also pass a demanding three-sortie profile in the two-seat U-2ST to determine their suitability for further training. If all goes well, they are soon inducted into a very select community. Trainee pilots are initially assigned to the 1st Reconnaissance Squadron, a unit that traces its origins to the earliest days of military aviation. Training lasts approximately 10 months, including about 3 months for inprocessing and qualification in the supersonic T-38. This is followed by a 22-sortie U-2 training syllabus that includes Basic Qualification and Mission Qualification prior to operational assignment. Line pilots typically alternate between 2-month deployments flying operational missions and 2 to 3 months at Beale for continuation training.[1]

Pilots fly the T-38 to maintain basic qualifications and proficiency in aerobatic maneuvering and instrument flying. The trainer is less expensive to operate than the U-2 and does not require use of a pressure suit. Operational pilots typically fly the T-38 twice a week and the U-2 two to three times per month. Flying the U-2, even during training flights, is largely a solitary affair. According to Capt. Neal Hinson, a U-2 pilot assigned to the 99th Reconnaissance Squadron, "You train mostly on your own after the initial solo flight and instructors monitor the pilot's objectives using GPS."[2]

Flying the Mission

Flying the U-2 requires a great deal of teamwork and coordination. While pilots are honing their flying skills, life-support technicians prepare pressure suits and survival gear, and maintainers keep the airplanes flyable, and the mission planners develop all the necessary material required to complete each mission. This group consists of about a dozen inactive pilots who use their flying experience to create flight route plans and other information for the current U-2 pilots prior to each sortie. Among the products they create are items such as navigation plans, fuel-consumption tables, and radio frequency communication cards mounted on cardboard so they can be handled more easily by a pressure suited pilot. After a flight is completed, charts and flight plans are collected and stored for possible use in future missions. "Mission planners," said 99th RS Mission Planning Flight Commander Lt. Col. Eddie Efsic, "are hired to transform distributed ground systems products into something pilots can use to efficiently and safely collect [imaging] targets."[3]

---

1. U-2 Pilot Application, June 14, 2012, *http://www.beale.af.mil/library/factsheets/factsheet. asp?id=5077*, accessed July 27, 2013.

2. Chuck Broadway, "A U-2 Dragon Lady Pilot: From interview to altitude," *Air Combat Command News*, April 3, 2009, *http://www.acc.af.mil/news/story.asp?id=123142867*, accessed August 26, 2013.

3. Ibid.

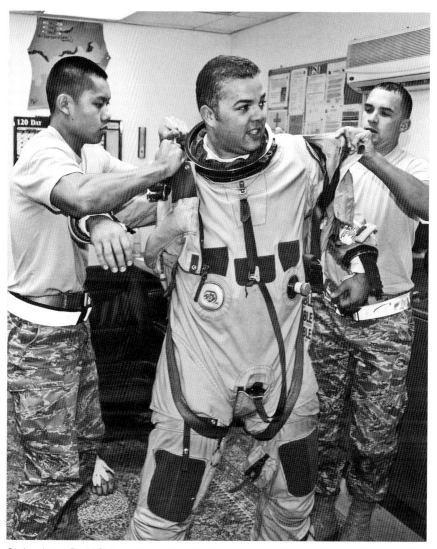

Senior airmen David Sivixay, left, and Allen Smith assist Lt. Col. Brian Dickinson with donning his pressure suit. (U.S. Air Force)

Following a mission briefing and preflight physical examination, the pilot is helped into the pressure suit and spends the next hour pre-breathing pure oxygen. Shortly prior to takeoff, the physiological support crew switches the pilot to a portable oxygen system and boards a van for transport to the flightline. Entering the cockpit is a difficult task while wearing a bulky pressure suit. Additional time is consumed with connecting the oxygen hoses, communications cables, seat harnesses, and boot stirrups. The pilot then taxies to

U-2 pilot glances out the left side of the cockpit while making a turn. (U.S. Air Force)

the runway and pauses while the ground crew removes locking pins from the outrigger pogos.[4]

A normal mission profile begins with a short takeoff roll followed by a steep initial climb angle in the first 25,000 feet and a high rate of climb to altitude. Depending upon total gross takeoff weight, the U-2 will usually attain an intermediate cruise altitude of 60,000 feet within 30 to 45 minutes. At this time, the pilot initiates cruise climb and engages the autopilot to hold a constant Mach number. Altitude increases as fuel is burned off and the weight of the aircraft decreases. Depending on payload weight, the U-2 may climb to cruising altitudes above 70,000 feet. Local air conditions can affect cruise climb performance; colder air allows a more rapid climb whereas warmer air reduces climb performance. In standard cruise climb, the U-2 normally flies at a zero pitch (level) angle, though this varies approximately ±1 degree as the autopilot seeks a constant Mach number. Pitch attitudes during takeoff and climb can reach 20 degrees nose up, 10 degrees nose down during descent. Bank angles are a function of desired turn radius but are normally held to less than 30 degrees. At cruise altitude, the pilot holds the airplane at a constant Mach number of about 0.70, equivalent to a true airspeed of approximately 410 knots. A normal 6.5-hour mission will cover a range of approximately 2,400 nautical miles, spending about 5.5 hours at altitudes above 60,000 feet. An 8-hour mission can cover a distance of 3,000 nautical miles with about 7 hours time at altitude.[5] The automatic flight control system provides

4. Pocock, *50 Years of the U-2*, p. 395.

5. NASA, "ER-2 Airborne Laboratory Experimenter Handbook," p. I-2.

A mobile chase car follows a U-2 down the runway during landing. (U.S. Air Force)

stability augmentation in yaw, pitch, and roll and also incorporates autopilot functions including Mach hold and automatic navigation via the inertial navigation system (INS).[6]

According to the flight plan, the pilot navigates between waypoints using any of several navigation systems. The INS operates by sensing accelerations from a gyro-stabilized, all-attitude platform and using a digital computer to integrate this information to provide an indication of present position (latitude and longitude), attitude data (pitch and roll), and course-line computation referenced to great circle routes. A control display in the cockpit allows the pilot to store navigation waypoints and to change the flight track en route. An update function allows for GPS updating of the INS with accuracy typically better than ±20 meters. A backup or secondary navigation system allows for a safe return to base or to an alternate landing site should the primary INS fail. Additionally, the U-2 is equipped with several systems that enable navigation with respect to ground-based radio beacons, and the optical viewsight offers the pilot visual coverage of the terrain beneath the aircraft for navigation purposes.[7]

Approximately 30 minutes prior to landing, the pilot initiates descent from high altitude by bringing the throttle to idle, opens the speed brakes, and extends the landing gear. This results in a descent rate of approximately 2,000 feet per minute. Sometimes, several 360-degree turns may be required to bleed off altitude. At 1,500 feet, the pilot sets trim for landing. The

---

6. Ibid., pp. I-1–I-6.
7. Ibid., pp. II-1–II-2.

U-2 crosses the runway threshold with a speed of approximately 75 knots.[8] Now comes the most challenging and difficult phase of flight: the landing. Typically, pilots are fatigued after long hours of flying in a pressure suit, so to make landing easier, a chase car follows the U-2 down the runway. Using a radio, a qualified U-2 pilot riding in the car communicates the plane's altitude during the last few feet before touchdown. As airspeed drops, the pilot works to keep the wings straight and level until the U-2 tilts to one side on its bicycle landing gear with one wingtip dragging on the ground. Ground crew then reinsert the pogo wheels so that the U-2 can taxi to a hangar. Chase cars, known as mobiles, have been used since the earliest days of U-2 operations. The Air Force initially used Chevy El Caminos then later switched to Ford Mustangs. More recently, these were replaced with the Chevy Camaro Z28. According to Capt. Spencer Thomas, a pilot who previously served as a U-2 crew chief, "The driver is always a U-2 pilot. That ensures identical mindsets. When I'm not flying a mission, I'm 'mobiling.'"[9]

Performance Characteristics

Flying the U-2 has always been a challenge because its unusual handling qualities require precision and skill. In adapting to the airplane's peculiar flight characteristics at altitude, early U-2 test pilots developed several standard flight profiles. One of these, for reaching maximum altitude, required a stair-step approach. Following takeoff, the pilot began a rapid climb to 55,000 feet at a specified speed schedule. After slowly gaining another 10,000 feet, the pilot set power for a cruise climb for the remainder of the flight, with the airplane rising slowly higher as fuel was depleted. Maximum altitude depended on a number of variables, such as aircraft gross takeoff weight and outside air temperature.[10]

Early U-2 pilots routinely exceeded world altitude records but were unable to take credit for these feats due to secrecy concerns. A number of tests were conducted to obtain true altitude in order to calibrate the altimeter used in the U-2 and to collect data required for camera development. These checks were made by placing targets of known dimensions on a dry lakebed and photographing them from an indicated pressure altitude of 70,000 feet. The surveyed elevation of the lakebed was 4,440 feet above sea level. The airplane's true altitude above the ground was determined by two methods, first by scaling

---

8. Pocock, *50 Years of the U-2*, p. 396.

9. John B. Dendy IV, "Crouching Airmen, Hidden Dragon," *Airman* 46, no. 7 (July 2002): p. 20.

10. Pocock, *50 Years of the U-2*, p. 27.

the target size from the pictures and then checking the altimeter reading by correcting for instrument error, static location error, and deviations from standard pressure and temperature. The agreement between these two independent methods proved quite good, differing only 200 feet between the true altitude as measured from the photographs and that calculated from the indicated pressure altitude.[11]

As altitude increased, the margin between the aircraft's stalling speed and its maximum speed quickly diminished. This created a hazardous situation because poor aerodynamic control-surface response in the thin upper atmosphere made stall recovery difficult. Excess speed could be a serious problem. The sleek U-2 had been designed to slice through the air with very little drag, but this beneficial characteristic could also pose a danger. At low altitudes, the early model U-2 airframes were restricted from exceeding 190 knots in smooth air or 150 knots in rough air. At operational cruising altitudes, where the atmosphere was less dense, later models of the airplane had a maximum cruising speed of 410 knots (Mach 0.72). Speeds in excess of these limits would subject the airplane to structural failure. U-2 pilots had to be extremely careful to keep the airplane in a slightly nose-up attitude when flying at operational altitudes. If the nose dropped as little as a few degrees into a nose-down attitude, the airplane gained speed at an alarming rate, exceeding the maximum permitted speed within a matter of seconds. Since there was no physical sensation of speed at 65,000 feet due to the lack of nearby objects to provide visual reference, the pilot had to pay close attention to the airspeed indicator. In fact, airspeed was such a critical factor that the difference between stall speed and never-to-exceed speed differed by only 6 knots at maximum altitude for the early U-2 models and 20 knots for later models. Pilots called this narrow range of acceptable airspeeds the "coffin corner" because it represented the point at which the U-2 was constantly on the brink of falling out of the sky. Too little speed could result in stalling, and the sudden drop might overstress the airframe to the point of structural failure. The same could happen at speeds high enough to induce Mach limit buffet.[12] If a pilot turned too sharply, the airplane might be subjected to both conditions simultaneously as the inside wing entered stall buffet while the outside wing experienced Mach buffet. The fact that these two sources of buffet feel very much the same made it difficult for the pilot to make a proper corrective response.[13]

---

11. Klinger, "Flight Test Development of the Lockheed U-2 Airplane," pp. 38–39.

12. Pedlow & Welzenbach, *The CIA and the U-2 Program*, pp. 76–79.

13. Joiner, "Testing the U-2," p. 23.

A U-2A makes a steep initial climb during ascent to cruise altitude. (Lockheed Martin)

One example of exceeding the speed envelope occurred on February 25, 1966, while Robert E. "Deke" Hall was flying Article 342 on an aerial-refueling training mission. Hall completed a series of nine dry hookups with a KC-135 tanker as planned, terminating the exercise with a practice emergency break-away from the tanker. Flight conditions were smooth with no noticeable turbu-lence. After the final breakaway, Hall dropped back, then pulled up alongside the KC-135, about 200 to 300 feet off the tanker's right wingtip. He then retracted the U-2's speed brakes and began a steep, climbing turn to the right. As soon as he began the maneuver, Hall felt a slight shudder and heard a loud crunching noise. Crewmembers on board the tanker watched in horror as the U-2's left wing snapped off. Its right wing came off as well, and the airplane disintegrated into several pieces, including the cockpit and nose section, aft fuselage, tail, and engine. Hall managed to eject despite being battered inside the tumbling wreckage. He parachuted to safety while pieces of the U-2 fell around him.[14]

The demanding requirements of flying the U-2 made use of an autopilot almost a necessity, particularly during long flights. Without the benefit of an autopilot during initial flight trials, test pilots found flying the airplane

---

14. CIA, "Aircraft Accident Investigation, U-2F N800X (342), 25 February 1966," CIA-RDP74B00447R000100010064-1 (March 1966), approved for release June 18, 2002,.

A U-2D, foreground, and a U-2A make a graceful turn over Edwards Air Force Base. (U.S. Air Force)

excessively challenging. Lockheed eventually provided an autopilot that could hold the airspeed to within a few knots, but it was still incumbent on the pilot to ensure that the aircraft remained within the proper speed regime.[15] Ernie Joiner recalled one of the first long-duration test flights, in which Ray Goudey was aloft for 6 hours: "He didn't have an autopilot and was really tired when we helped him out of the cockpit."[16] Flying without the autopilot was not advisable, according to test pilot Robert Schumacher: "It was as difficult as hell, especially around 70,000 feet, where you are near the Mach and stall buffets and must fly precisely." On one occasion he flew the aircraft for 4 hours without using the autopilot and found it very challenging to control the airplane while simultaneously peering through the driftsight, activating the camera controls, and attempting to carry out a variety of other tasks. It was particularly difficult "because your hands must be on the [control] column… you can't let it alone for a second."[17]

For operational purposes, the three most important flight characteristics were altitude, range, and endurance. The original J57-P-37 engine limited the

---

15. Jenkins, *Dressing for Altitude: U.S. Aviation Pressure Suits—Wiley Post to Space Shuttle*, p. 151.

16. Joiner, "Testing the U-2," p. 23.

17. Pocock, *50 Years of the U-2*, p. 27.

U-2A to maximum operational altitudes between 65,000 and 73,000 feet. It had a range of 3,775 nautical miles and an endurance of about 9 hours. Improved performance with the J57-P-31 increased the altitude capability to around 72,500 feet with a 4,000-nautical-mile range and 10-hour endurance. The U-2C, equipped with the J75-P-13B engine and slipper tanks, had a maximum range of 4,600 nautical miles and could stay aloft for more than 11 hours at altitudes up to 76,000 feet. These early models of the U-2 had a maximum gross takeoff weight of between 20,000 and 24,000 pounds. The much heavier U-2R and TR-1 family weighed in somewhere between 35,000 and 40,000 pounds depending on aircraft configuration. The U-2R in a clean configuration (no wing tanks or pods) could climb above 75,000 feet and fly for 15 hours with a range of 6,300 nautical miles. The later TR-1, ER-2, and U-2S were all capable of exceeding 70,000 feet altitude; but with its GE-F118-GE-101 turbofan engine, the U-2S had a range of more than 7,000 nautical miles and a maximum flight duration exceeding 14 hours.[18]

Maximum range was determined by conducting several test flights during which the pilot cruised at normal speeds until the low-fuel warning light came on. Airspeeds selected for maximum endurance flights were chosen for ease of flying and minimum fuel consumption. The J57-P-31 engine demonstrated a 10 percent improvement in fuel economy over the J57-P-37. It was possible to fly the airplane at idle above 40,000 feet with the P-37 and above 50,000 feet with the P-31.[19] At high altitudes, the U-2 was capable of gliding for vast distances in the event of engine failure. During readiness exercises in the spring of 1956, a westward-bound U-2 experienced a flameout over the Mississippi River near the Tennessee border. After restarting the engine, the pilot reported a second flameout and violent engine vibrations that caused him to abort further attempts to start the engine. It was clear that he would be unable to return to the test site, so he began preparations for landing at a contingency airfield. By now, he was over Arkansas and, given the prevailing winds and the airplane's glide ratio, he believed that he could safely reach Albuquerque. Pentagon officials who had been monitoring the flight's progress called the commander of Kirtland Air Force Base, informing him that an airplane would make a dead-stick landing at his airfield within abut 30 minutes and would require special security. After a half-hour passed, the base commander called the Pentagon to inquire as to the status of the crippled aircraft. As he was speaking, the U-2 glided silently to a landing on the Kirtland runway. Security police officers were startled to see what looked like a "man from Mars" emerging from the cockpit

---

18. Ibid., p. 399
19. Klinger, "Flight Test Development of the Lockheed U-2 Airplane," p. 69.

wearing a "space suit." The pilot later reported that from the beginning of the first flameout through landing at Albuquerque, the U-2 had flown more than 900 miles, including more than 300 miles by gliding.[20]

Stability and Control

Early flight tests indicated that the U-2 had no inherent stability, control, or handling problems. The airplane's flight characteristics generally proved to be about as expected, though the U-2 was susceptible to the same tuck and buzz tendencies associated with most subsonic aircraft. Mach tuck results from an aft shift in the center of lift that causes the airplane's nose to pitch down. Usually not dangerous, aileron and rudder buzz is a very rapid oscillation encountered at certain critical airspeeds and often caused by shock-induced boundary layer separation. Tests of the U-2A were conducted in cruise condition with the gust controls both faired and shifted. The airplane's center of gravity was kept between 26 and 28 percent mean aerodynamic chord in accordance with design parameters for the primary mission: aerial photography. Lockheed engineers anticipated that equipment bay loading would range from a minimum of 450 pounds to a maximum of 760 pounds.[21]

The airplane configuration initially had a zero stabilizer incidence, but this was later changed to a positive 1.5-degree incidence to reduce elevator deflection at cruise speeds and altitudes, thus reducing trim drag. The airplane had positive stability with both settings, but with positive incidence, less downward elevator was required throughout the speed range. At high altitudes with gust controls faired, the elevator angle was close to neutral between 110 and 130 knots indicated airspeed. Test pilots also reported that the U-2 felt more stable at higher Mach numbers when the elevator had a positive incidence.[22] Mach number characteristics were evaluated for both the faired and shifted configurations at various altitudes up to 70,000 feet. In order to obtain necessary data, the pilot gradually increased Mach number while maintaining approximately constant altitude. The maximum Mach number was determined by the severity of the tuck, buffet, or buzz phenomena encountered, and each test was terminated at the pilot's discretion before the condition became excessive.[23]

20. Pedlow and Welzenbach, *The CIA and the U-2 Program*, pp. 78–79.
21. Klinger, "Flight Test Development of the Lockheed U-2 Airplane," p. 118.
22. Ibid., p. 125.
23. Ibid., p. 130.

At lower altitudes, between 35,000 and 50,000 feet with gust controls shifted, pilots noted excessive rudder buzz but only slight tuck at Mach numbers varying from 0.78 to 0.83. Fairing the gust controls and increasing speed to between 0.83 and 0.85 Mach number resulted in moderate tuck and buffet. At altitudes between 60,000 and 65,000 feet and Mach numbers between 0.80 and 0.84, the airplane experienced moderate tuck and buffet and some aileron buzz, although fairing the gust controls resulted in milder tuck phenomena. Tests conducted at 70,000 feet at Mach numbers from 0.80 to 0.82 indicated better performance with the gust controls shifted. Some data were also obtained during high-speed descents. It was during such tests that the U-2A attained a maximum speed of Mach 0.87 at 62,000 feet. The pilot noted both excessive aileron buzz and Mach tuck under these conditions. Ultimately, the U-2A was placarded to a nominal Mach number of 0.80, though it was possible with some configurations to extend the maximum speed to Mach 0.85 with only moderately adverse effects. At altitudes below 35,000 feet, no difficulties due to Mach effects were experienced up to the placarded airspeed of 260 knots.[24]

24. Ibid., pp. 130–134.

A U-2A painted in spurious NACA markings at the test site. (Laughlin Heritage Foundation)

CHAPTER 7

The NACA and the U-2

Use of the U-2 as a civilian research platform had its dubious start in February 1956. Anticipating a surge in off-range training sorties and eventual deployment overseas, the CIA devised a cover story to explain the airplane's unique capabilities and disguise its true mission from the world. This necessary fiction did, however, contain elements of truth that served as a foundation for later research efforts.

Initially, there was some debate as to whether the Air Force's Air Weather Service or the NACA—NASA's predecessor—should be named as the airplane's prime sponsor for cover purposes. Ultimately, Bissell felt it best to use the civilian agency and to paint the project aircraft in NACA markings.[1] NACA officials then drafted a press release at the request of CIA Headquarters, and on May 7, 1956, NACA director Hugh L. Dryden announced a program in which U-2 aircraft would conduct high-altitude weather research with Air Force support while operating from Watertown Strip, NV. In order to explain the presence of U-2 operations elsewhere, Dryden added that "USAF facilities overseas will be used as the program gets underway, to enable gathering research information necessary to reflect accurately conditions along the high-altitude air routes of tomorrow in many parts of the world."[2] This statement was timed to coincide with deployment of the U-2 to Europe and emphasized the use of civilian planes with civilian pilots conducting meteorological studies.

In June 1956, the initial operational detachment, masquerading as Weather Reconnaissance Squadron (Provisional) One, or WRSP-1, was deployed to Lakenheath, England, where its stated purpose was met with skepticism. Two sarcastic editorials in the British *Flight* magazine belittled the weather research cover story and questioned the excessive security surrounding the U-2

---

1. Memorandum for Project Security Officer, "Cover Meeting with AWS and NACA," CIA-RDP33-02415A000200390051-1 (March 20, 1956), declassified and released by the CIA April 11, 2000.

2. Hugh L. Dryden, "NACA Announces Start of New Research Program," May 7, 1956, NASA Historical Reference Collection, NASA Headquarters Washington, DC.

operation.[3] A spokesman for the NACA announced on July 9 that preliminary data-gathering flights had been made from Lakenheath. He also reported that the initial high-altitude weather data gathered by the U-2 had been processed and that it had proved the value of the aircraft as a research tool.[4] The most significant element of the cover story was the fact that the airplanes actually carried NACA weather instrumentation during training and proficiency flights. Real data were being collected within a flight regime previously unattainable by conventional aircraft. Transferring these data to scientists would not only bolster the cover story but also yield a treasure trove of information applicable to civil and military aviation.

Turbulent Relationship

Not everyone at the NACA seemed enthusiastic about supporting the U-2 cover story. In August, the Aquatone project cover officer expressed some concern to Richard Bissell over the need for publication of NACA research papers based on data collected at altitudes within the range that had been admitted. Such documents would serve as unimpeachable proof that the U-2 was being used in a research capacity. But Harry Press, chief aeronautical research scientist of NACA Langley Memorial Aeronautical Laboratory's Gust Loads Division, had shown a pronounced lack of enthusiasm with regard to publishing such material. The CIA officer recommended putting pressure on NACA Headquarters to "emphasize to Mr. Press the need for his taking immediate action toward preparing our much needed research study with completion at a very early date." Agency officials subsequently drafted a letter for the NACA assistant director for research, Richard V. Rhode, to emphasize the need "for a counterpropaganda weapon for use in the event of a compromise to one of our aircraft."[5]

The Aquatone Project assistant security officer met with Rhode on November 16 to request that he expedite publication of NACA research studies being prepared with data obtained during U-2 weather research missions and to request additional instrumentation for use in project aircraft. The CIA provided Rhode

---

3. Pocock, *50 Years of the U-2*, p. 51.

4. Peter W. Merlin, "U-2 Cover Story Timeline," NASA Armstrong Flight Research Center historical reference collection, July 2004.

5. Memorandum for Project Director, "Cover Research Releases (NACA)," SAPC-8675, CIA-RDP33-02415A000200390031-2 (August 22, 1956), declassified and released by the CIA April 11, 2000.

with all weather data accumulated thus far by the various U-2 detachments for inclusion in the planned research papers. During the meeting, the project security officer also suggested that U-2 pilots "should carry some NACA documentation else their story would not hold up when they are required to identify their association with NACA to friends, military establishments, etc."[6]

The NACA cover story was put to its first test when a deployed U-2 crashed near Wiesbaden, Germany, on September 17, but the incident caused little sensation in the media. When CIA pilot Robert J. Ericson was forced to bail out over Arizona 3 months later, he was identified to inquiring reporters as "Robert J. Everett, a civilian pilot for NACA." As with the earlier Wiesbaden incident, an Air Force spokesman stated that the plane was owned by the NACA and was "engaged in high altitude research jointly with the Air Force studying air turbulence and the jet stream."[7]

First Research Data

In January 1957, Richard Bissell and his staff coordinated plans to publicly surface the U-2 for the first time. This entailed the release of photos and publication of research data. After discussions with CIA officials, Hugh Dryden arranged for the first official picture to be released by the NACA in early February.[8] In order to further support the cover story, the photo depicted the airplane with the tail number NACA 320 painted below a yellow and black band with the NACA's winged shield insignia. The following month, Langley gust loads researchers Thomas L. Coleman and Jack Funk published NACA Research Memorandum No. L57A11, "Preliminary Measurements of Atmospheric Turbulence at High Altitude as Determined from Acceleration

---

6. Memorandum for the Record, "Cover Discussions with NACA," CIA-RDP33-02415A000200390025-9 (November 19, 1956), declassified and released by the CIA April 11, 2000.

7. "Research Plane Explodes; Altitude Pilot Bails Out," *The Washington Post and Times Herald*, December 20, 1956, p. A2, Clotaire Wood files, NASA Headquarters Historical Reference Collection.

8. Richard M. Bissell, Jr., Memorandum for Deputy Project Director, "Arrangements with NACA and Kelly Johnson re Release of U-2 Photographs," SAPC-12313, CIA-RDP33-02415A000200390023-1 (January 26, 1957), declassified and released by the CIA April 11, 2000.

Measurements on Lockheed U-2 Airplane."[9] Several months later, Coleman wrote a second report with Emilie C. Coe, this time comparing turbulence data taken over the United States with that collected over England and Western Europe.[10]

These reports included an analysis of turbulence data obtained using velocity, gravity, and height (VGH) recorders carried aboard the U-2. Developed at Langley for collecting gust-loads data, these instruments provide time-history records of airspeed (velocity, or v), acceleration (measured in g units), and altitude (indicated as height, or h) for continuous periods up to 100 hours. A strip of photographic paper moved through each VGH recorder at sufficient speed to permit statistical determination of gust distribution and also provide, on a condensed time scale, general operational data. VGH data collected during flights over England and Western Europe indicated a substantial reduction in the number and intensity of atmospheric gusts with increasing altitude. These results were in agreement with atmospheric turbulence models developed using data previously obtained with other airplanes and balloon-borne instrumentation.[11]

Up to this point, the collection of detailed scientific information on atmospheric turbulence and other meteorological conditions had been limited by aircraft performance to altitudes below approximately 45,000 feet. Use of balloons permitted limited measurements up to about 60,000 feet. In addition to altitude limitations, previous methods (particularly balloon-borne instruments) were limited in regard to geographic areas covered and were largely confined to the United States. With the U-2, NACA scientists now had access to information on turbulent conditions around the world and at higher altitudes than previously available. Such data were useful for aircraft design studies and operational analysis, especially in regard to structural loads and stability and control problems.[12] Unfortunately, as long as the U-2 was acknowledged to be capable of reaching only 55,000 feet, researchers were unable to use any data collected at the airplane's maximum cruising altitudes (upward of 70,000 feet).

9. Thomas L. Coleman and Jack Funk, "Preliminary Measurements of Atmospheric Turbulence at High Altitude as Determined from Acceleration Measurements on Lockheed U-2 Airplane," NACA Research Memorandum L57A11 (March 1957).
10. Thomas L. Coleman and Emilie C. Coe, "Airplane Measurements of Atmospheric Turbulence for Altitudes Between 20,000 and 50,000 Feet Over the Western Part of the United States," NACA Research Memorandum L57G02 (August 1957).
11. Ibid., p. 1.
12. Ibid.

The U-2 was ideally suited to collecting data on high-altitude turbulence. (Lockheed Martin)

Initial research missions had taken place over the United States during training flights, and then over England and Western Europe in conjunction with the first operational deployments. Data collected during these operations included measurements covering approximately 22,000 flight miles. VGH measurements were obtained on 17 flights between May and September 1956. A typical flight profile consisted of an initial climb to 45,000 feet followed by a slower ascent to higher altitudes as fuel load decreased, and then descent to landing. Research flight opportunities were dictated entirely by operational priorities, and no attempt was made to schedule flights to sample turbulence associated with specific meteorological conditions. U-2 pilots avoided adverse weather, such as heavy cumulus clouds or thunderstorms, meaning that the VGH data represented only clear-air turbulence. "Although this sample is small," Coleman wrote, "the initial results appear to be of sufficient interest to warrant publication."[13]

The U-2 not only provided a platform for gathering badly needed high-altitude meteorological data, but it also gave NACA and Air Force researchers the opportunity to test new, lightweight instrumentation packages under operational conditions. The NACA-developed VGH recorder took continuous readings of airspeed, altitude, and acceleration. Another

---

13. Ibid., pp. 2–3.

instrument traced peak acceleration values and a turn-meter recorded pitch and yaw rates. Instrumentation provided by the Air Force Wright Air Development Center included a turbulence recorder, a vortex temperature probe, temperature and humidity sensors, and an infrared hygrometer for accurate measurement of dew point.[14]

Throughout the spring of 1957, NACA officials continued to promote the U-2's research capabilities. Dryden released a statement announcing publication of the first research paper and claiming that the Gust-Loads Research Panel of the NACA's Technical Subcommittee on Aircraft Loads had originally recommended using the high-altitude research program for statistical studies of turbulence. He explained that the primary goal was collection of data on turbulence associated with the jet stream, convective clouds, temperature variations at different altitudes, wind shear, and other weather phenomena. Such a program, he said, would not have been possible without substantial cooperation from the Air Weather Service, which had furnished state-of-the-art meteorological instrumentation, and the Geophysical Research Directorate, which would use the data for developing methods of forecasting meteorological phenomena important to high-altitude flight. Dryden also described expected future benefits to commercial air travel. "Research which we are gaining on a global basis," he said, "will make it reasonable for tomorrow's air traveler to expect degrees of speed, safety, and comfort beyond the capabilities of today's air transport."[15]

In July, Dryden and NACA Public Information Officer Walter T. Bonney met with CIA officials to discuss modifications to the U-2 cover story, which now included details of the High-Altitude Sampling Program (HASP). This effort, sponsored by Strategic Air Command and the Armed Forces Special Weapons Project (AFSWP), involved the collection of atmospheric particulate samples from radioactive fallout resulting from testing of nuclear weapons. The modified U-2 cover story stated that operationally ready facilities of NACA would be used for HASP activities. "Rather than for HASP to establish their own facilities and organization in areas where NACA has been conducting its meteorological research, AFSWP has arranged for use of these facilities overseas to collect data as required for HASP. AWS will remain, as before, the executive

---

14. CIA, "Proposed NACA Press Release," CIA-RDP33-02415A000200390018-7 (April 24, 1957), declassified and released by the CIA April 11, 2000, pp. 1–4.

15. Ibid., p. 2.

For the HASP mission, the U-2 was configured with a particulate sample in the nose and other instruments. (U.S. Air Force)

agent. The pilots for the U-2 will continue to be civilians under contract with NACA, but will be reimbursed by AFSWP funds."[16]

Bonney had previously received a memo outlining a cover story for the unusual appearance of U-2 aircraft that bore the Project Rainbow anti-radar treatments, as some of those had been deployed despite the associated aerodynamic penalties. The unclassified nickname, Thermos, was to be used in lieu of the classified code word, Rainbow. If queried, Bonney was to say that the unusual configurations were part of "a data gathering program…designed to measure…certain physical phenomena which could be affected by nuclear explosions." The high-frequency-band radar-absorbent material was described as a special impregnated, plasticized coating applied directly over various parts of the aircraft to reduce the effects of glare, blast, and radiation damage from nuclear explosions. The cover story accounted for the wires associated with the low-frequency-band anti-radar system by describing it as a unique antenna system to record thermal phenomena under varying conditions at high altitude. The project was said to be a joint effort involving participation by the ARDC, AFSWP, and NACA. Associating the project with ARDC

16. Chairman of the Planning Group, Memorandum for Project Director, "Planning Group Report," CIA-RDP33-02415A000400040001-9 (July 15, 1957), p. 3.

organizations at Edwards Air Force Base served to explain the presence of the U-2 at the Edwards North Base facility. To explain the presence of the specially configured U-2 aircraft at overseas detachments, the Rainbow cover story also asserted that the location of overseas units afforded a wide range of climatological and other desirable environmental conditions for study.[17]

Despite these and other misleading statements regarding the U-2's mission and capabilities, the airplane continued to serve as an occasional platform for bona fide meteorological research. On November 14, 1957, a CIA pilot assigned to Detachment C, known for cover purposes as the 3rd Weather Reconnaissance Squadron (Provisional), flew over the eye of Typhoon Kit in the western Pacific Ocean north of the Philippine island of Luzon. He used a Perkin-Elmer Model 501 tracking camera to photograph the storm, producing, for the first time, photos of a tropical cyclone from directly overhead. Lt. Col. Robert C. Bundgaard of the Air Weather Service publicized the results in a magazine article several months later.[18]

Breaking Cover

The U-2 cover story could not last forever and, in fact, began to erode as early as May 1957, when the North American Newspaper Alliance published a syndicated article stating that Lockheed U-2 aircraft routinely operated at ceilings above 65,000 feet and were being used by the U.S. Air Force to map large areas of Earth's surface for use in guided-missile warfare. This was the first reasonably accurate description of the airplane's capabilities published by the news media. The article's unnamed writer also claimed that the "Air Force is reliably reported to be using the Lockheed U-2 in West Germany to monitor the stratosphere for evidence of Soviet nuclear tests, and presumably in the cartography project."[19] By the end of the month, the *London Daily Express* had reported, "Lockheed U-2 high-altitude aircraft of the U.S. Air Force have been flying at 65,000 feet, out of reach of Soviet interceptors, mapping large areas behind the Iron Curtain with revolutionary new aerial cameras. They are making mathematically precise maps essential to bombardment with missile

---

17. Memorandum describing Project Rainbow cover story, Walter Bonney files, NASA Headquarters Historical Reference Collection, June 21, 1957.

18. Robert C. Bundgaard, "The First Flyover of a Tropical Cyclone," *Weatherwise* 11, no. 3 (June 1958): pp. 79–83.

19. North American Newspaper Alliance, "U.S. Mapping World for Missile War," May 19, 1957, NASA Headquarters historical reference collection.

Some U-2s deployed to Atsugi, Japan, bore NACA markings and others Air Force weather squadron insignia. The airplanes carried special weather research instrumentation during training flights. (Lockheed Martin)

weapons." Despite this exposure, U.S. officials stubbornly refused to admit any connection between the U-2 and airborne reconnaissance.[20]

At CIA Headquarters, Aquatone administrative officer James Cunningham reacted strongly to suggestions that more information be made public regarding the airplane's altitude capabilities. "I am inclined to believe," he wrote in one memo, "that while having considerable value in theory, a move of this sort…would ultimately involve us in a series of inquiries which would be difficult to handle without giving away the fact that our capability was in excess of the announced record altitude figure." He noted with some alarm that Kelly Johnson had apparently told NACA officials at the Lewis Propulsion Laboratory in Cleveland that the U-2 was capable of reaching 70,000 feet. Cunningham further noted that releasing an altitude figure greater than previously admitted but less than the actual capability could lead to some embarrassment and might still not have the desired effect. Intelligence sources had suggested that the Soviet air defense radar was capable of tracking the U-2 with sufficient accuracy that the new cover altitude would fail to deceive "the only opposition activity that we are basically attempting to defraud."[21]

---

20. Pocock, *50 Years of the U-2*, p. 51.

21. James A. Cunningham, Memorandum for Project Director, "Proposed Cover Modifications," SAPC-18216, CIA-RDP33-02415A000200390016-9 (August 6, 1957), declassified and released by the CIA April 11, 2000, pp. 1–2.

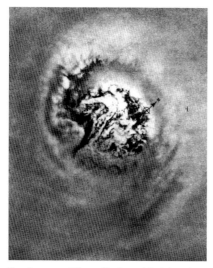 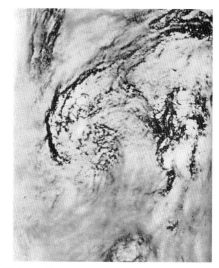

Two images of Super Typhoon Ida taken from a U-2 near Taiwan in July 1958. (National Hurricane Center)

Another matter under consideration was whether to make available to researchers any data collected at altitudes above 55,000 feet. Richard Bissell sent a memorandum to the Aquatone Project Cover Officer stating that he could not agree to the "declassification or general dissemination of data obtained at altitudes from 55,000 to 70,000 feet or to the granting of Aquatone clearances to a wider circle of individuals who might be interested in having access to this data." He suggested instead downgrading the data from Top Secret to Secret and making the information available to a limited number of contractors who might make good use of it, providing that "a suitable explanation can be devised of the way in which the data was collected which will attribute it to some source or sources other than the U-2." As an example, Bissell suggested a story in which a variety of NACA research aircraft were instrumented to collect turbulence data. This new story would make it clear that such data resulted from aircraft flights rather than from balloons or rockets; but stating that a number of different aircraft were involved "would tend to divert attention away from speculation concerning what particular aircraft was used."[22]

Propaganda and stories of the deception surrounding the U-2 operation tend to overshadow the very real scientific and technical accomplishments of

---

22. Richard M. Bissell, Jr., Memorandum for Project Cover Officer, "Release of NACA Top Secret Research Data to Select Contractors," SAPC-25666, CIA-RDP33-02415A000200390014-1 (March 25, 1958), declassified and released by the CIA April 11, 2000, pp. 1–2.

the program. While officials in Washington debated how much information to release, U-2 pilots flying out of Atsugi, Japan, took advantage of opportunities to collect weather data and photos unlike any previously taken. In July 1958, several flights were made over Super Typhoon Winnie off the coast of Taiwan (then known as Formosa). Winnie's powerful winds exceeded 175 mph, causing severe damage to the western end of the island. From a perch high above the raging storm, a U-2 pilot took pictures as Winnie tore across the Taiwan Strait and struck the southeastern coast of mainland China. A few months later, while awaiting clear weather in which to conduct tactical reconnaissance coverage of Chinese troop movements and naval operations, additional missions were flown over Super Typhoons Ida and Helen. Photographs of spectacular cloud structures and the aircraft's capacity to look straight down into the eye of each storm bolstered the weather reconnaissance cover story while providing a credible reason for the presence of the U-2 in the region.[23]

---

23. David Reade, "U-2 Spyplanes: What You Didn't Know About Them!," *http://www.roadrunnersin-ternationale.com/u-2/u-2_science_3.html*, accessed April 4, 2013.

Francis G. "Frank" Powers, right, discusses U-2 performance with Kelly Johnson. (Lockheed Martin)

CHAPTER 8

NASA and the U-2

After the NACA became the National Aeronautics and Space Administration in October 1958, the Agency continued to maintain the U-2 cover story. A NASA press release issued in June 1959 reaffirmed that the airplane was being used for weather research missions. In order to provide an explanation for U-2 operations in Turkey, which happened to be a CIA staging area for over-flights of the Soviet Union, NASA published Memorandum No. 4-17-59L, "Airplane Measurements of Atmospheric Turbulence for Altitudes Between 20,000 and 55,000 Feet for Four Geographic Areas," by Thomas Coleman and May T. Meadows. This report built upon the two previous NACA reports, adding data collected during missions flown from Japan and Turkey.[1] The fact that U-2 missions had produced very real weather data fooled no one as to the airplane's true mission. George Carroll, aviation editor of the *New York Journal-American*, wrote in the November 1959 issue that the U-2 was being used for reconnaissance over Russia, and the following month an article in *Soviet Aviation* discussed U.S. strategic reconnaissance with the U-2 and gave some design details of the aircraft. But the worst was yet to come, as the cover story was soon to be irrevocably blown in one of the most infamous incidents of the Cold War.[2]

Secrets Exposed

In the spring of 1960, the CIA detachment at Incirlik, Turkey, attempted the most ambitious U-2 mission yet. Article 360 was deployed to Peshawar, Pakistan, to begin a nonstop flight over Afghanistan, the Hindu Kush, Aral Sea, Baikonur Cosmodrome (the primary Soviet space launch complex), Chelyabinsk, Sverdlosvk, Kirov, Arkhangelsk, the Kola Peninsula, Murmansk,

---

1. Thomas L. Coleman and May T. Meadows, "Airplane Measurements of Atmospheric Turbulence for Altitudes Between 20,000 and 55,000 Feet for Four Geographic Areas," NASA Memorandum 4-17-59L (June 1959).
2. Merlin, "U-2 Cover Story Timeline."

and eventually land in Bodø, Norway. With a planned duration of approximately 9 hours, the flightpath would cover some 3,800 miles, a true test of the airplane's range. Logistical and technical difficulties aside, there was also significant risk involved because more than three quarters of the route was over the Soviet Union.[3]

Frank Powers flew the mission on Sunday, May 1, 1960. At first, all went as planned, but while making a turn southeast of Sverdlovsk, there was a bright flash and a dull thump, and the airplane lurched forward. Powers instinctively grabbed for the throttle and scanned his instruments. The engine was functioning normally and the ailerons seemed effective, but the nose began to drop precipitously. Aerodynamic loads increased until the wings snapped and the airplane began to tumble wildly, shedding parts. The pilot's suit inflated as the airplane's cabin depressurized, and Powers activated his emergency oxygen supply. The cockpit was now pointed upward and spinning. Centrifugal force made ejection nearly impossible because Powers could not completely retract his legs into escape position. Instead, he jettisoned the canopy manually and bailed out.[4]

When the U-2 failed to arrive at Bodø as expected, the recovery crew began to worry. After waiting 5 hours, they finally called CIA Headquarters to report that Powers was missing. It was assumed that the U-2 had crashed or been shot down over Russia, and by Monday morning, officials were scrambling to modify the cover story. The details were revised to make a convincing claim that a NASA weather reconnaissance mission had strayed off course after the pilot reported having difficulties with his oxygen system somewhere in the vicinity of Lake Van, Turkey. Officials backstopped the story by providing a flight plan for release to the media and by deploying search aircraft to the Lake Van area. Representatives of the CIA and Department of State also discussed preparing a question-and-answer brief, principally for use by NASA in the event of Soviet disclosure, but designed to be circulated to all affected parties. This consisted of answers to hypothetical questions that might be asked by the press regarding the airplane and the NASA upper atmosphere research program, and it also provided details supporting the cover story mission for Powers's flight.[5] By Wednesday, the Soviets had yet to make any announcement acknowledging the incident.

---

3. Powers and Gentry, *Operation Overflight*, pp. 73–74.

4. Ibid., pp. 82–84.

5. Memo from Acting Deputy Director of Plans, "Chronological Account of Handling of U-2 Incident," CIA-RDP33-02415A000300300007-7 (August 10, 1960), declassified and released by the CIA August 21, 2000, pp. 1–5.

The following day, Soviet Premier Nikita Khrushchev announced that an unmarked American aircraft had crossed into Russian airspace and had been shot down. He gave no further details and did not mention the fate of the pilot. Afterward, CIA and State Department officials met and decided that President Eisenhower should not be personally involved and that the State Department would handle all publicity regarding the incident. White House Press Secretary James C. Hagerty had already drafted a release stating that Eisenhower had ordered an investigation of the entire matter, and he suggested to Walter Bonney that NASA hold a press conference as soon as possible. Unfortunately, notification that press relations were to be handled entirely by the State Department did not reach NASA in time to prevent the press conference from taking place. Bonney reiterated the cover story and included a brief description of the flight plan, the pilot's alleged oxygen problems, and the search for the missing plane. He also said that the remaining U-2 aircraft had been grounded for equipment checks, which subsequently resulted in emergency messages being sent to all U-2 detachments to stand down until further notice. In response to reporters' queries, Bonney—apparently unaware that Powers was flying an unmarked plane—described the aircraft's NASA markings in great detail. With the airplane accounted for, the dummy air search was called off.[6]

As a result of arrangements made by the CIA with Lockheed to meet insistent press demands for detailed information on the plane and to further support the innocuous uses of the airplane, a U-2 assigned to the CIA was painted with a fictitious serial number and NASA markings and shown to news media representatives at the NASA Flight Research Center at Edwards on May 6. That same day, the State Department held two radio and press briefings. In one, State Department spokesman Lincoln White stated that there was "absolutely no deliberate attempt to violate Soviet airspace, and there never has been."[7]

This seems to be precisely what Khrushchev had been waiting for. In a speech before the Supreme Soviet on May 7, he announced that the American pilot had been captured and had admitted his mission of spying on the Soviet Union. He also produced identifiable parts of the U-2 and the pilot's equipment, clearly exposing the true nature of Powers's mission. As CIA Director Allen Dulles later testified to the Senate Foreign Relations Committee, the cover

6. Ibid., pp. 2–3.
7. Ibid., p. 4.

One of the CIA U-2s from Detachment G, painted in fictitious NASA markings, was displayed to the press to bolster the cover story. (NASA)

story had been masterfully outflanked.[8] Under the circumstances, President Eisenhower decided to suspend U-2 fights over the Soviet Union indefinitely.

At a meeting of senior CIA, NASA, and State Department officials later that month, NASA Administrator T. Keith Glennan said that NASA "would be well advised to disengage from the U-2 program as rapidly as possible."[9] Dulles, however, in a statement to the Senate Foreign Relations Committee, lauded the scientific value of the weather data collected with the airplane and justified NASA's interest. "NASA was very much concerned with the scientific advances which operations of these U-2s could make towards greater knowledge of the upper atmosphere and for other scientific purposes." He asserted that the aircraft had "undertaken many weather and related missions and their functions in this respect have been publicized by NASA, and this publicity has been distributed freely to the world."[10]

NASA Deputy Administrator Hugh Dryden testified in executive session before the Senate Committee on Foreign Relations regarding the NASA relationship to the U-2 program. "In this program which began in 1956, there have been 200 weather flights of U-2 aircraft with NASA and Air Weather Service

---

8. Allen W. Dulles, Director of Central Intelligence, "Statement to the Senate Foreign Relations Committee," May 31, 1960, *http://www.foia.cia.gov/sites/default/files/document_conversions/89801/DOC_0000009190.pdf*, accessed April 21, 2013, p. 18.

9. Pedlow & Welzenbach, *The CIA and the U-2 Program*, note 39, p. 182.

10. Dulles, "Statement to the Senate Foreign Relations Committee," p. 16.

In this humorous cartoon, NASA graphic artist Jerry Lyons brilliantly captured the awkwardness of the U-2 cover story's exposure. (NASA)

instrumentation covering flights extended over about 264,000 miles," he said. Dryden admitted knowledge of classified intelligence operations involving the U-2, but he said that the NACA (and later NASA) saw an opportunity to take advantage of technical capabilities that were not otherwise available to the agency.[11] As might be expected, NASA subsequently received harsh criticism for its role in the U-2 affair. Robert Hotz, a senior editor of *Aviation Week & Space Technology* magazine, wrote that NASA researchers had "their hard-won reputation for scientific integrity shredded overnight by exposure of their role as unwitting dupes of the Central Intelligence Agency." He further asserted that the "damage to NASA's scientific integrity may count for little in the calloused calculations of CIA supersleuths, but it will do irreparable harm in the international scientific community...."[12]

11. Jeremiah A. O'Leary, "NASA Issued U-2 Cover Story on CIA Advice," *Washington Star*, June 1, 1960, p. 1.

12. Robert Hotz, "Lockheed U-2 Over Sverdlovsk: A Study in Fabrication," reprinted in *Congressional Record, Proceedings and Debates of the 86th Congress, Second Session*, vol. 106, Part 9 (Washington, DC: U.S. Government Printing Office, June 16, 1960), p. 11,976.

Such dire predictions proved unfounded, however, as NASA suffered no long-term consequences from the incident. Administrator Glennan and the Agency as a whole were spared intimate involvement in the U-2 affair by Dryden's assumption of full responsibility for his role in originating the cover story. Nor did the Powers debacle end the Agency's association with the U-2. In 1968 and 1969, U-2 aircraft were tasked with photographing portions of the Western United States for comparison with pictures taken by the Apollo astronauts, and eventually NASA would have its own small fleet of U-2 airplanes to conduct dedicated research missions.[13]

A U-2 for NASA

By the late 1960s, Government officials were looking at ways to transfer U-2 technology to civil applications. Thus far, both CIA and Air Force U-2 airplanes had supported civilian agencies only occasionally, when schedules permitted. The CIA did sometimes provide a limited amount of classified overhead photography to other Government agencies, and in 1968 Arthur C. Lundahl, director of the National Photographic Interpretation Center, recommended creating a new center to provide declassified imagery for emergency management purposes.[14] This idea gained further traction as it became apparent that the U-2R attrition rate was less than had been predicted. A number of older U-2C and U-2G models retained in storage for use as replacements were now considered surplus.[15]

In early 1970, two study groups chaired by Dr. F. Robert Naka, deputy director of the National Reconnaissance Office, reviewed requirements and utilization of the U-2R. These studies concluded that the existing fleet of 12 U-2R airframes was sufficient to meet both NRO and Air Force requirements. There were at that time a total of eight U-2C/G airframes in both flyable and nonflyable storage conditions. The annual cost for storing these aircraft was relatively low, but the analysts recognized that the Government had made a substantial investment with regard to acquisition of the early model U-2 aircraft, along with ground support equipment, spare parts, and miscellaneous hardware. Estimates from the maintenance depot indicated that there were

---

13. Pedlow & Welzenbach, *The CIA and the U-2 Program*, p. 254.

14. Pocock, *50 Years of the U-2*, p. 370.

15. Bernard L. Bailey, draft memo to NASA from John L. McLucas, Director, National Reconnaissance Office, "Subject: U-2C/G Aircraft," May 16, 1970, *http://www.nro.gov/foia/declass/NROStaffRecords/1055.pdf*, accessed April 2, 2013.

ample stocks on hand to support the entire U-2C/G fleet for between 6 and 9 months without any additional purchases. At least one study indicated a potential requirement for two of the aircraft to be used for transitional training and test purposes in support of the U-2R fleet. Otherwise, they determined that there were no known NRO, CIA, or Air Force requirements with sufficiently high priority to warrant reactivating the stored aircraft in the near future. Based on the aircraft's unique capabilities, possibility of future utilization, low annual upkeep support costs, and the substantial investment in depot stocks, the study groups recommended exploring the possibility of transferring the airplanes and associated materiel "to another agency such as NASA."[16]

On March 16, 1970, Col. Bernard Bailey, director of operations for NRO aerial reconnaissance programs, drafted a memo to be sent to NASA Headquarters by NRO Director John L. McLucas. The memo outlined the status of the U-2C/G fleet and suggested that by virtue of the airplane's unique altitude, airspeed, and loiter capabilities, the U-2 might serve as a valuable collection platform for the NASA Earth Resources program.[17] NASA officials were eager to take advantage of the offer, and they drafted a plan to take responsibility for two of the aircraft. Carl Duckett, CIA deputy director for science and technology, reviewed the plan and found that it lacked a proper appreciation for how complicated it could be to conduct U-2 flight operations. He subsequently approached Marty Knutson, a 15-year veteran of the agency's U-2 program who had accumulated 4,000 hours of flight time, to request that he lend his expertise to the NASA project. Knutson had been planning to retire, but he was soon persuaded to sign on as project manager. He helped NASA officials redraft their plan and made arrangements for Lockheed to overhaul two U-2G models. Additionally, Lockheed was contracted to provide pilots and field maintenance, including physiological support. Kelly Johnson immediately hired three of Knutson's former colleagues, Jim Barnes, Bob Ericson, and Ivor "Chunky" Webster. Frank Powers also applied, but he was turned down due to his notoriety from the U-2 incident in 1960. Senior NASA officials wished to downplay the U-2's reputation as a spy plane as much as possible.[18]

The two airplanes, articles 348 and 349, were moved from storage at Edwards to Lockheed's Palmdale facility. There, technicians removed the special carrier landing modifications peculiar to the U-2G along with other

16. Frank W. Hartley, Jr., draft of memo to John L. McLucas, Director, National Reconnaissance Office, "Subject: U-2C/G Storage Costs," February 26, 1970, *http://www.nro.gov/foia/declass/NROStaffRecords/1056.pdf*, accessed April 2, 2013.
17. Bailey, draft memo to NASA from John L. McLucas.
18. Pocock, *50 Years of the U-2*, p. 370.

Marty Knutson spearheaded the effort to acquire two U-2 airplanes for use as NASA research platforms. (NASA)

unnecessary items, reducing the airplane's empty weight to 13,800 pounds. Now reconfigured as U-2C models, the Air Force serial numbers on the tails were replaced with civil registrations. Webster flew functional checkout flights on each airframe and then delivered them to Ames Research Center at Moffett Field, CA, in early June 1971. By midsummer, they were ready for operational missions and, following a number of familiarization sorties, the first data flight occurred on August 31.[19]

By 1978, the two airplanes were flying an average of 100 sorties annually and had logged more than 4,000 flight hours. Although based at Ames, they routinely flew Earth Resources missions from NASA's facility at Wallops Island, VA, as well as being deployed to Hawaii, Alaska, Texas, Maine, South Dakota, and Panama. The versatile U-2 provided a wide range of capabilities including resource studies, disaster assessment, land-use surveys, sensor development, stratospheric sampling, and satellite support. For example, during drought years, the California Department of Water Resources used photos taken from the U-2 to measure water levels in rivers and reservoirs. Similarly, high-altitude

---

19. Ibid.

A U-2C during deployment to Wallops Island, VA. (NASA)

aerial imagery of the San Francisco Bay aided the U.S. Geological Survey in a study of tidal patterns and water movement. Firefighters used infrared imagery for faster containment of wildfires, more efficient use of personnel and equipment, and protecting forest watersheds and wildlife habitat. Survey pictures of areas affected by floods and earthquakes were useful in assessing damage and assigning repair priorities. In another experiment, researchers used U-2 imagery to develop a land-use-management database for both the public and private sectors. Such data have been valuable for evaluating urban growth, traffic patterns, and pollution, as well as in preparing environmental impact statements. Sensors on board the U-2 were used to measure the distribution of gases and aerosol particles at altitudes up to 65,000 feet to develop a better understanding of the effects of natural and humanmade actions on the atmosphere's protective ozone layer. Additionally, comparison of U-2 imagery to that taken with NASA's Landsat satellites supported investigations in forestry, water management, coastal-zone processes, rangeland management, and land use.[20]

Sensor Platform

NASA researchers routinely used the U-2 to carry a variety of sensors, including aerial mapping cameras, electronic scanners, and atmospheric sampling

---

20. NASA Ames Research Center staff, *High Altitude Perspective* (Washington, DC: NASA SP-427), 1978, pp. 2–3.

The U-2C was capable of carrying a variety of research instruments and cameras. (NASA)

devices. Taking advantage of the airplane's original design characteristics, the NASA U-2 aircraft were also used extensively to carry out photographic missions. There were several different camera configurations, affording researchers the opportunity to employ a variety of focal lengths, film types and formats, and multispectral capabilities. Additionally, the U-2 could carry a range of non-photographic sensors. Most equipment was palletized to allow technicians to easily switch payloads in or out of the aircraft or from one aircraft to the other.[21]

During the 1970s, NASA maintained an inventory of cameras at Ames that had been used extensively in Earth observation studies. Much of this equipment had been used in support of satellite missions such as Landsat, which eventually became the longest-running enterprise for the acquisition of space-based Earth imagery. Ground coverage and resolution are functions of lens focal length and film format. Higher-resolution imagery was obtained using large-format (9- by 9-inch or 9- by 18-inch) film and 6-inch, 12-inch, 24-inch, or 36-inch focal-length lenses. A single frame taken from an altitude of 63,000 feet with a Wild-Heerbrugg RC-10 camera using a 12-inch focal length lens covered 80 square miles at resolutions ranging from 59 to 157 inches. The highest resolution was provided by the Research Camera System,

---

21. Ibid., p. 7.

which was equipped with a 24-inch, 3.5 focal ratio lens capable of resolving objects significantly less than 40 inches across. Depending on the intended use of the resulting imagery, the cameras were equipped with standard or infrared color or black-and-white film. Infrared imagery highlights details that are beyond the range of human vision and effectively penetrates atmospheric haze by filtering out blue light. Color infrared film is sensitive to the green, red, and near-infrared portions of the spectrum, which makes it particularly useful for aerial and space photographic surveys for land-use and vegetation studies. Researchers used infrared images to distinguish between healthy vegetation and that which was diseased or stressed.[22]

Nonphotographic sensors were typically supplied and funded by outside researchers and organizations. All such equipment was installed in specific areas of the airplane subject to load factors, safety standards, and technical constraints (size, weight, materials, power requirements, etc.). Most of these sensors fit within several categories. NASA's Goddard Space Flight Center in Greenbelt, MD, and the University of California's Lawrence Berkeley Laboratory (LBL) sponsored astronomy and astrophysics research with the U-2. LBL physicists supplied two microwave radiometers for mapping the temperature of deep space and examining fundamental questions about the origin of the universe. Investigators at Goddard installed an instrument for measuring solar spectral radiance and its variation with the solar cycle. Scientists at Goddard and Ames used the U-2 as a workhorse for Earth observation studies and to evaluate instrumentation that would later be used on spacecraft. The Heat Capacity Mapping Radiometer was used to evaluate thermal pollution, wetlands environments, and soil moisture. An instrument called the Ocean Color Scanner, forerunner of the Nimbus satellite's Coastal Zone Color Scanner, was a multispectral imager for detecting subtle variations in upwelling spectral radiance of seawater.[23]

A multispectral scanner made available through a cooperative agreement between NASA and the Environmental Protection Agency gave scientists an 11-channel digital system with 10 channels in the visible to near-visible spectral region and 1 in the thermal infrared. This device was primarily used in support of Landsat investigations. Ames also supplied a thermal infrared roll-stabilized line-scanner video system and a line-scan camera visible-imaging system that provided real-time imagery to a ground receiving station via telemetry link for use in disaster response. Finally, the U-2 served as a platform for conducting stratospheric and atmospheric studies with a variety of sensors. The Ames

---

22. Ibid., pp. 9–16.
23. Ibid., pp. 17–20.

By 1978, the two NASA U-2s were flying an average of 100 missions annually and had logged more than 4,000 flight hours. (NASA)

Stratospheric Air Sampler used chemiluminescent reactions to measure seasonal variations in atmospheric gases. Another instrument contained four cryogenically cooled samplers plus two whole-air samplers for measuring ozone-depleting compounds such as halocarbons, nitrous oxide, and carbon tetrachloride. Other methods for measuring atmospheric pollutants included use of an infrared scanning spectrometer and a high-speed interferometer. Samples of halogen compounds and aerosols were also collected using a variety of filters exposed to the airstream by pilot command. Scientists from the National Oceanic and Atmospheric Administration (NOAA) analyzed data collected with a radiometer in order to determine the total amount of atmospheric water vapor above the U-2 at cruise altitude. A downward-looking infrared radiometer measured atmospheric non-uniformities in order to better understand convective instabilities and atmospheric mixing processes.[24]

One NASA research effort with the U-2C involved acquiring small-scale, low-resolution, multispectral photography over selected representative ecosystems to simulate the Return Beam Vidicon (RBV) data system then being developed for the Earth Resources Technology Satellite (ERTS, later named Landsat 1). Instrumentation technicians installed four 70-millimeter framing cameras in the airplane's Q-bay to take simultaneous images of the same target area on the ground. Three cameras were equipped with 1.75-inch-focal-length lenses and black-and-white emulsion film, spectrally filtered to image the green, red, and near-infrared portions of the electromagnetic spectrum. The fourth camera carried color infrared film. Researchers selected five target areas: Feather River Basin in Northern California was chosen as representative of western U.S. forests, mountainous, and agricultural areas; the San Francisco Bay region and Los Angeles Basin as representative of urbanized areas; Phoenix and Tucson in southern Arizona as characteristic of arid regions; and the Chesapeake Bay region, representing wetland ecosystems. Survey missions were flown over each target region every 18 days to simulate the ERTS's planned orbit cycle. In early 1972, the research team added a single 24-inch-focal-length, 9- by 18-inch Type A-1 film camera, along with an accompanying trimetragon array of 6-inch-focal-length cameras. A multispectral scanner built at NASA's Goddard Space Flight Center was also integrated into the aircraft, providing complete ERTS sensor simulation capability. Concurrent integration of a Wild-Heerbrugg RC-10 film camera into the satellite simulation package resulted in a five-instrument system that saw extensive use on later research flights.[25]

In the summer of 1972, scientists at NASA and the United States Geological Survey (USGS) initiated a cooperative program with the state of Arizona to produce improved mapping imagery for developing a land-use-management database. The primary goal of the Arizona Land Use Experiment was the acquisition of cloud-free black-and-white panchromatic metric photography in addition to the standard ERTS simulation multispectral photography. The USGS used this imagery to produce 7.5-minute, 1:24,000-scale orthophoto quadrangle sheets. Unlike standard topographic maps that represent terrain elevation with contour lines and depict humanmade features with simple graphics, the orthophoto maps show land features using either black-and-white or color-enhanced photographic images that have been processed to show details

---

24. Ibid., pp. 17–20.
25. NASA Fact Sheet, "ER-2 Program History," *http://www.nasa.gov/centers/dryden/research/AirSci/ER-2/history.html*, accessed July 8, 2013.

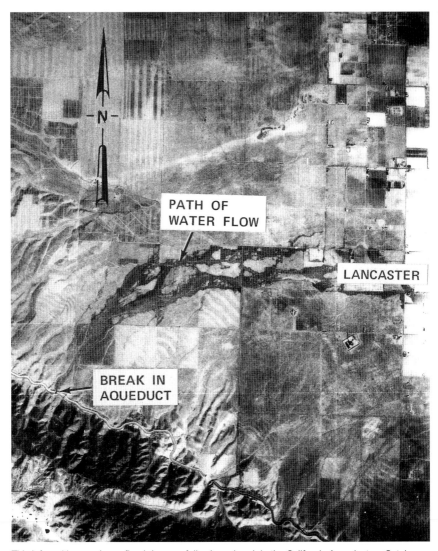

This infrared image shows flood damage following a break in the California Aqueduct on October 12, 1971. The rupture released 100 million gallons of water, damaging roads, farm fields, and widely scattered homes west of the city of Lancaster. (NASA)

in their true positions. Such imagery depicts terrain and cultural features in a more true-to-life manner than conventional line maps. This was the first demonstration of the use of high-altitude aircraft data for quadrangle map production over large areas. With the launch of ERTS-1 on July 23, 1972, investigators began requesting that the U-2 overfly specific target sites, often simultaneously with the satellite overpass. Most of these flights carried a Vinten/RC-10 system

Infrared image of San Diego taken from an altitude of 65,000 feet. (NASA)

that provided small-scale satellite simulation data along with larger-scale, larger-format data. Throughout the remainder of the year, NASA expanded the scope of the U-2 project. Flights over the eastern and western regions of the United States were flown in support of crew training for the Skylab space station. Resulting imagery was used in the Skylab simulator in Houston. Additionally, the U-2 was flown for disaster-assessment missions, with data-collection flights over areas damaged by hurricane and wildfire.[26]

In early 1973, researchers equipped the U-2 with a trimetragon array of 24-inch-focal-length, 9- by 18-inch film format cameras called the A-3 configuration. Mounted vertically, the A-3 provided a multi-emulsion, multispectral photographic capability. This system was employed over Roseville, CA, following a munitions train explosion in a railroad classification yard, as well as over a number of wilderness fires in support of firefighting efforts by the California Department of Forestry. Later that year, researchers embarked on the first systematic development of a global stratospheric model. In the summer of 1974, NASA deployed a U-2 equipped with two specialized instruments, the Stratospheric Air Sampler and the Aerosol Particulate Sampler, to Eielson Air Force Base, near Fairbanks, AK. From there, six flights were made over the northern polar region to collect air samples and to acquire high-altitude

---

26. Ibid.

Exclusive homes in the Hollywood Hills as seen from 12 miles above the ground. Some California citizens saw U-2 imagery as an invasion of privacy. (NASA)

photographic data over a number of Arctic and sub-Arctic ecosystems in support of ERTS investigations. Additional stratospheric sampling missions took place near equatorial latitudes with a deployment to Hickam Air Force Base, HI, in October. These two deployments, along with local sampling flights over California, provided scientists with the first comprehensive sampling of stratospheric constituents in the northern hemisphere and aided in the development of latitudinal distribution models of the upper atmosphere. In late 1974, NASA acquired additional instrumentation for the U-2. This included an Itek Optical Bar Camera, a 120-degree-field-of-view, 24-inch-focal-length panoramic camera similar to the Lunar Mapper instrument carried aboard the Apollo spacecraft; a thermal scanner developed by HRB-Singer; and Goddard Space Flight Center's Heat Capacity Mapper. The following year, further stratospheric air-sampling deployments were conducted from Eielson and Hickam and from Wallops Island, VA. Sampling missions were expanded in 1976 to include deployments to Howard Air Force Base, Panama, and Loring Air Force Base, ME, further widening the database.[27]

Sensor development continued in 1977 with integration of the Aether Drift astrophysics experiment. The instrument package consisted of a pair of

---

27. Ibid.

upward-looking microwave antennae and associated processing and recording systems that were carried to altitudes well above terrestrial sources of radiation. During numerous missions flown over the span of 2 years, scientists observed background radiation differentials from the two antennae in order to validate or reject a catastrophic evolutionary (Big Bang) theory of the formation of the universe. The project entailed multiple deployments over several years, including flights from Lima, Peru, to collect data in the southern hemisphere.[28]

In 1978, the NASA U-2 aircraft took part in the Alaska High-Altitude Photography Program. Faced with responsibility for the administration, mapping, surveying, and conveyance of Federal lands to the state and to native corporations, a consortium of Federal and state agencies requested NASA's assistance in acquiring both black-and-white and color infrared imagery of the entire state of Alaska. This program spanned 8 years and resulted in 95-percent coverage of the state's total area. Most impressive was the fact that the imagery was accomplished with less than 10-percent cloud cover. Technicians at Ames integrated the Daedalus Multispectral Scanner onto one of the aircraft in 1979, providing the U-2 for the first time with a digitally recorded multispectral instrument. Stratospheric sampling continued in 1979 and 1980 from Ames, Alaska, and Panama, along with continued efforts in support of Landsat. Additionally, the NASA U-2 was used to collect photographic data for the National Wetlands Inventory. This covered the Prairie Potholes region within portions of Minnesota, Iowa, North Dakota, South Dakota, and Montana, an important breeding habitat for migratory birds and other wildlife.[29] All imagery collected by the NASA U-2 was available for public inspection at Ames via a computerized data retrieval system, and anyone could purchase high-resolution prints of any frame through the USGS in Sioux Falls, SD. Not everyone was happy about this development. Images commissioned by the Coastal Conservation Commission for a wetlands survey also revealed unlicensed construction in the coastal zone. Citizens of the town of Bolinas, north of San Francisco, saw the U-2 imagery as an invasion of privacy. "I do have this gut reaction to this eye in the sky able to look at all the little things in people's backyards," said one local attorney.[30]

By this point, NASA had been flying the U-2C for nearly a decade and would continue to do so until the late 1980s. But as soon as Lockheed received a contract to restart U-2 production, NASA officials were quick to order one of the new models.

---

28. Ibid.

29. Ibid.

30. Pocock, *50 Years of the U-2*, p. 373.

An ER-2 and U-2C fly over San Francisco Bay and the Golden Gate Bridge. (NASA)

CHAPTER 9

ER-2 Expands NASA Horizons

NASA's high-altitude capabilities expanded after Marty Knutson delivered the first ER-2 to Ames Research Center, on June 10, 1981. While technicians readied the new airplane to join the science fleet, the older models remained engaged in important work. For example, the U-2C was employed in a multiyear cooperative effort among NASA, the U.S. Forest Service, and several eastern seaboard states to detect and monitor Gypsy Moth caterpillar infestations in the northeast region of the country and assess the effectiveness of insecticide-spraying programs. Researchers used high-resolution color infrared photography to evaluate the severity of infestation from New York to North Carolina on an annual basis. Data had to be acquired within a narrow biological window dictated by latitude, elevation, and annual weather conditions in order to successfully discriminate the severity of defoliation attributable to the Gypsy Moth.[1]

NASA U-2 and ER-2 aircraft also took part in a variety of missions in support of Department of Defense projects, most notably Teal Ruby, a satellite designed to detect and track aircraft from space by measuring their infrared signatures. The greatest challenge was separating these signatures from the normal background signal. In order to build a database of background measurements, the ER-2 was equipped with a multiwavelength infrared sensor similar to that to be carried by the spacecraft. Throughout the yearlong Highly Calibrated Airborne Measurements Program (Hi-CAMP), researchers used the special instrument to collect precise measurements of infrared background clutter caused by atmospheric, terrestrial, and oceanic phenomena. During a series of highly coordinated missions over the Western United States and Europe, they also tested the Hi-CAMP sensor's capabilities for tracking aircraft ranging in size from a T-38 trainer to a C-15 cargo transport.[2] The results assisted engineers in developing data-processing algorithms and provided useful information for future programs. Unfortunately, following a string of management problems, cost overruns, and delays, the planned launch of the Teal Ruby

---

1. NASA Fact Sheet, "ER-2 Program History."
2. Ibid., pp. 374–375.

satellite was postponed and eventually canceled altogether. In the absence of Teal Ruby, the Hi-CAMP database became the single most comprehensive source of infrared air-vehicle detection data for designing and testing detection algorithms, selecting spectral passbands, and sizing air or missile defense systems that operate within the relevant spectral regions.[3]

A Hi-CAMP deployment to Alconbury, England, in 1985 was followed in early 1987 with a deployment to Darwin, Australia, for the Stratosphere-Troposphere Exchange Project (STEP), a continuation of earlier atmospheric sampling efforts using the U-2C. NASA and NOAA jointly funded STEP to obtain more data on the mechanisms and rate of transfer of particles, trace gases, and aerosols from the troposphere into the stratosphere. That same year, scientists from NASA's Jet Propulsion Laboratory in Pasadena, CA, oversaw engineering and integration test flights of the Airborne Visible and Infrared Imaging Spectrometer (AVIRIS). The ER-2 served as a convenient and cost-effective platform for testing the instrument, a 224-band multispectral scanner designed primarily for use on satellites.[4]

With its unique capabilities, the ER-2 was ideally suited to play an important role in Earth Science research focused on the study of ozone depletion over Antarctica and the Arctic. In late summer 1987, the aircraft was deployed to South America for subpolar stratospheric sampling over the Antarctic continent while operating from Punta Arenas, Chile. The most significant data collected during these missions confirmed the existence of an "ozone hole" over the southern polar region and provided information suggesting that human-made chemical compounds, specifically chlorofluorocarbons, were primarily responsible for ozone depletion over the Antarctic region. The data also repudiated long-held theoretical polar symmetry models of the upper atmosphere. Researchers moved their efforts to the opposite side of the globe in January 1989, when the ER-2 was deployed to Stavanger, Norway, in support of the Airborne Arctic Stratospheric Expedition. This stratospheric sampling program included multiple flights over northern Europe.[5]

Researchers at Ames also employed the ER-2 in a continuing NASA effort to leverage high-altitude, long-range, and sensor capabilities for fighting wildfires. In 1988, wilderness fires devastated much of Yellowstone National Park as several different blazes merged into a single conflagration that became the

---

3. Richard H. Van Atta, Sidney G. Reed, and Seymour J. Deitchman, "IR Surveillance: Teal Ruby/ Hi-CAMP," *DARPA Technical Accomplishments Vol. II: An Historical Review of Selected DARPA Projects*, chapter 9, Institute for Defense Analyses, April 1991, pp. 1–7.

4. NASA Fact Sheet, "ER-2 Program History."

5. Ibid.

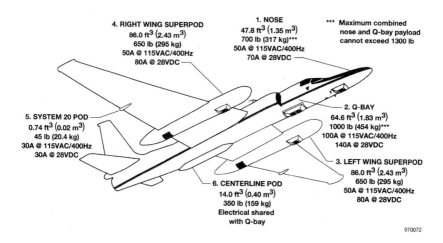

4. RIGHT WING SUPERPOD
86.0 ft^3 (2.43 m^3)
650 lb (295 kg)
50A @ 115VAC/400Hz
80A @ 28VDC

1. NOSE
47.8 ft^3 (1.35 m^3)
700 lb (317 kg)***
50A @ 115VAC/400Hz
70A @ 28VDC

*** Maximum combined
nose and Q-bay payload
cannot exceed 1300 lb

5. SYSTEM 20 POD
0.74 ft^3 (0.02 m^3)
45 lb (20.4 kg)
30A @ 115VAC/400Hz
30A @ 28VDC

2. Q-BAY
64.6 ft^3 (1.83 m^3)
1000 lb (454 kg)***
100A @ 115VAC/400Hz
140A @ 28VDC

3. LEFT WING SUPERPOD
86.0 ft^3 (2.43 m^3)
650 lb (295 kg)
50A @ 115VAC/400Hz
80A @ 28VDC

6. CENTERLINE POD
14.0 ft^3 (0.40 m^3)
350 lb (159 kg)
Electrical shared
with Q-bay

070072

The ER-2 can accommodate payloads in nose and fuselage compartments as well as within wing and centerline pods. (NASA)

largest wildfire in U.S. history. In a groundbreaking moment in fire-management strategy, Chief Naturalist George Robinson requested that NASA provide high-altitude imagery of the region. In response, NASA tasked Landsat-4 to collect images from orbit while additional types of aerial surveillance were accomplished from high and medium altitudes using the ER-2 and C-130B aircraft. Both aircraft were equipped with infrared sensors capable of penetrating smoke and haze to assist in delineating and mapping the multiple fire complexes. Operating from Moffett Field, the aircraft flew multiple missions over the greater Yellowstone area, relaying thermal and near-infrared imagery data in real time to a ground receiving station in West Yellowstone, WY.[6] Resulting data provided firefighters with their first comprehensive view of the multiple fire fronts and their interrelationships. Detailed information about the fire's location, size, rate of spread, and intensity allowed incident commanders to battle the blaze while simultaneously protecting firefighters on the ground from what had proved to be an aggressive and unpredictable fire. This effort served as the blueprint for future programs such as the Western States Fire Missions in 2006 and 2007, which employed NASA's Altair and Ikhana remotely piloted aircraft.

As the ER-2 received an expanded role on such vital missions, the two U-2C models were rapidly approaching the end of their 30-year flying careers. The first NASA U-2C was retired at Moffett Field in mid-1987 after logging 10,000

6. Ibid.

hours of service. It was immediately replaced with a former TR-1A, on loan from the Air Force and temporarily converted to an ER-2. The second NASA U-2C—that last of the original U-2 models still flying—was retired in the spring of 1989, but not until Lockheed secured permission to attempt two last recordbreaking flights. Jerry Hoyt took off from Edwards on April 17, 1989, with only 395 gallons of fuel on board. Reaching 9,842 feet in 52 seconds, and eventually attaining 49,212 feet within 6 minutes 15 seconds, the U-2C easily broke previous world time-to-climb records and sustained altitude records for its weight category. This was three times faster than a previous record set with a Learjet that had ultimately topped out at 54,370 feet. Hoyt passed through 65,617 feet in a little over 12 minutes. A mere 16 minutes after takeoff, the U-2 reached a maximum altitude of 73,700 feet. The following day, Ron Williams broke records in a higher weight category, taking off with the aircraft fueled to a gross weight of 20,900 pounds. Observers from the Federation Aeronautique Internationale (FAI) verified the records, and the airplane was subsequently returned to Lockheed in Palmdale, where it was painted black for its final role as a museum exhibit. Shortly afterward, Doyle Krumrey flew the final sortie in an original U-2 while delivering the aircraft to Robins Air Force Base, GA, for permanent display.[7]

Meanwhile, research missions with the Airborne Science fleet continued at a blistering pace. An ER-2 deployed to Alconbury in June 1991, bringing the AVIRIS, Thematic Mapper Simulator, and RC-10 Camera to Europe. Multiple sorties were flown over Iceland, Wales, England, France, Italy, Spain, Austria, Germany, and the Netherlands. After returning to the United States, the aircraft was used to conduct stratospheric sampling from Alaska to the North Pole.[8] Next, the airplane was equipped with the Moderate-resolution Imaging Spectroradiometer (MODIS) Airborne Simulator (MAS), a modified Daedalus Wildfire scanning spectrometer designed to provide spectral information similar to that which was to be provided by the MODIS, then scheduled for launch aboard the EOS-AM satellite. Researchers conducted initial testing in coordination with other aircraft and satellites over Coffeyville, KS, and along the Texas and Louisiana coast in November 1991. The modified wildfire instrument was converted to MAS configuration in January 1992 and was then flown over portions of the Atlantic Ocean in the region of the Azores. Each mission combined coordinated satellite, airborne, and surface observations

---

7. Pocock, *50 Years of the U-2*, pp. 377–378.
8. NASA Fact Sheet, "ER-2 Program History."

The U-2C resided at Ames Research Center for nearly two decades. (NASA)

with modeling studies to investigate cloud properties and physical processes of cloud systems.[9]

Several ER-2 research projects in 1992 and 1993 contributed to the development of commercial aeronautics. At the time, NASA was investigating whether emissions from future fleets of supersonic transports (SSTs) might deplete the ozone layer. During one project, an ER-2 carried instruments to measure known ozone depletion catalysts along projected air routes for the SST. In another, an ER-2 flew through the wake of an Air France Concorde to collect particulate samples. Researchers concluded that there would be little impact on the ozone layer as a result of additional SST traffic. In an unusual low-altitude mission for the ER-2, the aircraft was used to measure the effect of the world's growing fleet of subsonic airliners on cirrus cloud formation.[10]

Perhaps ironically, the ER-2 was used to gather significant data for weather research. In early 1993, one aircraft was deployed to Townsville, Australia, to

---

9. Michael D. King and Paul Menzel, "First ISCCP Regional Experiment (FIRE) NASA ER-2 Moderate Resolution Imaging Spectroradiometer (MODIS) Airborne Simulator (MAS) Langley DAAC Data Set Document," Atmospheric Data Science Center, October 1996, *https://eosweb. larc.nasa.gov/sites/default/files/project/fire/guide/base_fire_ci2_er2_mas_dataset.pdf*, accessed July 27, 2013.

10. Pocock, *50 Years of the U-2*, p. 378.

carry a suite of nine sensors over a warm region of the Pacific Ocean northeast of Papua New Guinea where tropical storms frequently developed. Research results were intended for application in development of future satellite sensor systems for predicting storm formation and movement. In 1994, researchers at Ames equipped an ER-2 with the Lidar Atmospheric Sensing Experiment (LASE), a 1,000-pound instrument built by NASA Langley at a cost of $20 million. The LASE system fired a 20-megawatt burst of laser energy straight downward to analyze water vapor in the atmosphere. During sorties from Wallops Island, researchers conducted coordinated experiments using lidar instruments on the ER-2, the Space Shuttle, and aircraft at lower altitudes to characterize water vapor levels throughout the atmospheric cross section.[11]

For a time, NASA was operating three ER-2 aircraft simultaneously. One was returned to the Air Force in 1995 and the other two eventually received new F118 engines while undergoing routine maintenance over the next 2 years. Lockheed (now Lockheed Martin, following a March 1995 merger with Martin Marietta) provided four pilots under contract to NASA, along with maintainers and physiological support personnel. In 1998, as part of a cost-saving effort to consolidate NASA aircraft fleets, both remaining ER-2s were transferred to NASA Dryden Flight Research Center (now NASA Armstrong Flight Research Center) at Edwards. Later that same year, the ER-2 was used to set a new world altitude record in the mid-weight class, with a gross takeoff weight totaling between 26,455 and 35,274 pounds. The previous record of 62,500 feet had been set 10 years earlier using the Russian P-42, a stripped-down version of the Su-27 twin-engine jet fighter that had been built specifically to beat time-to-climb records. The new record was set on November 19, during a scheduled airborne science mission to measure water vapor, ozone, and other atmospheric particles. Although the ER-2 routinely operated at 70,000 feet and above, this flight to 68,700 feet was the first time the aircraft's performance was documented by the FAI and made public. While emphasizing that the science mission was the flight's primary goal, pilot Jim Barrilleaux expressed his opinion that "achieving the world altitude record verifies all of the outstanding efforts by the people who have worked on the NASA ER-2s and U-2s throughout the years—designers, builders, operators, maintainers and scientists."[12]

The following winter, the NASA Airborne Science team deployed an ER-2 to Kiruna, Sweden, north of the Arctic Circle, as part of the SAGE III Ozone Loss and Validation Experiment (SOLVE). Besides investigating the processes

11. Ibid.

12. NASA, "NASA Aircraft Sets New World Altitude Record," *ScienceDaily*, November 24, 1998, *http://www.sciencedaily.com/releases/1998/11/981124064046.htm*, accessed July 27, 2013.

During the early 1990s, NASA operated three ER-2 aircraft simultaneously. One was returned to the Air Force in 1995. (NASA)

that control polar and mid-latitude winter and spring ozone levels, scientists hoped to validate measurements from the satellite-based Stratospheric Aerosol and Gas Experiment (SAGE) instrument. Although SAGE III was not launched on schedule, researchers were able to take advantage of other satellite assets. Managed by the Upper Atmosphere Research Program of NASA's Office of Earth Science, the intensive effort also involved a DC-8 flying science platform and was the largest international field experiment ever conducted to measure ozone in the Arctic stratosphere. Scientists hoped that stratospheric measurements collected during the SOLVE campaign would provide a better understanding of the complicated chemistry involved with ozone loss. Unusually low levels of ozone over the Arctic during previous winters raised concerns that an ozone hole was developing just as in the Antarctic region. Research teams included more than 350 scientists from the United States, Europe, Russia, Japan, and Canada.[13]

---

13. NASA, "NASA ER-2 Flies Over Russia on Ozone Research Mission," News Release 00-14, January 27, 2000, *http://www.nasa.gov/centers/dryden/news/NewsReleases/2000/00-14. html*, accessed August 1, 2013.

The first SOLVE mission was a flight from Kiruna to the North Pole and back, a dangerous feat in a single-engine plane over an extremely hostile environment. In order to reduce potential risks, the ER-2 was equipped with backup communications systems, and the JP-TS fuel was specially refined for extreme cold weather use. Arctic survival instructors assured pilot Dee Porter that if he had to eject at altitude, where the air temperature was expected to be approximately −117 °F, survival would not be an issue because he would be frozen long before reaching the ground. Porter made the entire flight in total darkness, successfully accomplishing all science goals without experiencing any technical problems with the aircraft.[14]

The most unusual aspect of the SOLVE campaign was that it required multiple ER-2 sorties over Russia. Since this was to be the first flight of a U-2-type aircraft through Russian airspace since the downing of Frank Powers in 1960, the missions were closely coordinated with Russian observers. While preparing for his first such flight Dee Porter asked a Russian Air Force general for assurance that all air traffic control centers and air defense sites along the planned route would be notified in advance. The general told him not to worry, insisting, "There will not be a second incident."[15]

Porter piloted the first 6-hour sortie across Russia on January 27, 2000, flying a straight line from the Finnish border southeast past Moscow to the Ukrainian border and back. Per prior agreement, he had to enter and exit Russian airspace at strictly defined navigational waypoints. The airplane was loaded with more than a ton of scientific instruments that would be used to perform 17 different environmental experiments. A second flight on February 5 lasted 8 hours and required a more complicated route across the Barents Sea and over northern Russia. Jan Nystrom piloted additional flights over Russia in March during the third and final phase of the campaign.[16]

The ER-2 team was deployed to warmer climes in the summer of 2000 for the Southern African Regional Science Initiative (SAFARI), based in Pietersburg, Republic of South Africa. This time, researchers used the MAS multispectral scanner in an effort to increase understanding of southern African ecological and climate systems. After returning to the U.S., the airplane prepared for deployment the following summer to Jacksonville, FL, for the Convection And Moisture EXperiment (CAMEX). This series of field research investigations focused on the study of tropical cyclone development, tracking, intensification, and landfall impacts. Measurements of cloud microphysics were aimed at

---

14. Pocock, *50 Years of the U-2*, pp. 379–380.
15. Ibid., p. 380.
16. Ibid., pp. 380–381.

improving hurricane predictions. A similar campaign in July 2005 was based in Costa Rica, with the ER-2 carrying instruments to measure the buildup and behavior of tropical storm systems over Mexico and Central America, and in the eastern Pacific Ocean, Caribbean, and the Gulf of Mexico. During the course of CAMEX-4, researchers had the opportunity to fly the aircraft over several hurricanes, including Emily and Dennis, both violent Category 4–5 storms, and collect information on their entire vertical structures. Additional data were collected regarding the temperature, humidity, precipitation, and wind related to tropical cyclones and other phenomena that lead to the development of powerful storms at sea.[17]

The ER-2 also served as a test bed for direct detection Doppler lidar systems. In September 2009, researchers at Dryden integrated the Tropospheric Wind Lidar Technology Experiment (TWiLiTE) into the ER-2 to measure vertical wind profiles. The primary objectives of the TWiLiTE program were to develop technologies and subsystems for a future space-based Global Wind Mission, conduct engineering flight tests of a fully autonomous airborne Doppler lidar, and demonstrate tropospheric wind profile measurements from a high-altitude, downward-looking, moving platform to simulate spaceborne measurements using similar instruments.[18] The following December, the ER-2 carried the Multiple Altimeter Beam Experimental Lidar (MABEL) to simulate instruments to be carried by the second Ice, Cloud and land Elevation Satellite (ICESat-2). In a second series of tests, in March 2011, the MABEL instrument, developed at NASA's Goddard Space Flight Center, was again mounted in the airplane's nose for flights over a variety of different terrains. In April 2012, the ER-2 carried MABEL to study Greenland's ice sheet, glaciers, and sea ice. The deployment, based at Keflavik, Iceland, included more than 100 hours of flying during 16 sorties, including 14 data collection flights over Greenland and surrounding sea ice areas. Several missions were conducted concurrently and on the same flight tracks as flights of other NASA environmental science aircraft involved in the Arctic IceBridge campaign in order to compare data being recorded by the MABEL with instruments on the other aircraft. This challenging effort ended on April 27 with a lengthy transit flight from Keflavik to the Dryden Aircraft Operations Facility in Palmdale. Pilot Stu Broce landed

---

17. NASA, "ER-2 High Altitude Airborne Science Aircraft," NASA Fact Sheet FS-2007-4-046-DFRC, 2007, *http://www.nasa.gov/centers/dryden/pdf/171831main_FS-2007-04-046-ER-2.pdf*, accessed July 27, 2013.

18. Bruce Gentry et al., "Flight Testing of the TWiLiTE Airborne Molecular Doppler Lidar," *http://ntrs.nasa.gov/archive/nasa/casi.ntrs.nasa.gov/20100026400_2010028473.pdf*, accessed July 27, 2013.

The icy expanse of Greenland seen from 62,000 feet during a MABEL research mission on April 2, 2012. (NASA)

the ER-2 in California after being airborne for nearly 10.5 hours, during which time he collected MABEL data over the broadleaf deciduous forests of Wisconsin.[19]

In a continuing effort to develop instruments for space-based platforms, the ER-2 was configured for the Polarimeter Definition Experiment (PODEX) in January 2013. The primary goal was the development of instruments for use with the Aerosol-Cloud-Ecosystem (ACE) satellite mission. During the course of seven flights over 3 weeks, research teams collected data using a new class of polarimeters, instruments that provide detailed information about clouds and their interaction with tiny airborne particles from a variety of sources, including automotive emissions, dust, and sea spray lofted by the wind. These aerosols can remain suspended in the atmosphere for up to a week, affecting human health, cloud formation, precipitation, and Earth's radiation budget.[20]

Similar particles and their behavior were investigated in the summer of 2013. During the Studies of Emissions, Atmospheric Composition, Clouds and Climate Coupling by Regional Surveys (SEAC4RS) campaign, more than

19. Alan Brown and Beth Hagenauer, "NASA's ER-2 Completes MABEL Validation Deployment," May 1, 2012, *http://www.nasa.gov/topics/earth/features/ER-2_completes_MABEL_deployment. html*, accessed July 24, 2013.

20. Kathryn Hansen, "PODEX Experiment to Reshape Future of Atmospheric Science" January 16, 2013, *http://www.nasa.gov/topics/earth/features/qa-starr.html*, accessed July 29, 2013.

250 scientists, engineers, and flight personnel examined the ways in which air pollution and natural emissions affect atmospheric composition and climate. ER-2 and DC-8 aircraft involved in SEAC4RS carried sensors to probe the atmosphere from top to bottom at a critical time of year when weather systems were sufficiently strong and regional air pollution and natural emissions were prolific enough to pump gases and particles high into the atmosphere. The results may provide new insights into the effects of gases and aerosol particles on Earth's atmosphere and climate. The mission targeted two major regional sources of summertime emissions: intense smoke from wildland fires in the Western United States and natural emissions of isoprene, a carbon compound, from forests in the Southeast.[21]

Over the years, NASA U-2 and ER-2 aircraft have supported airborne research in the United States and around the globe. Worldwide deployments have made it possible to acquire extensive digital multispectral imagery and aerial photography from altitudes achievable by no other aircraft. U-2 and ER-2 missions tested prototype satellite-imaging sensors and acquired Earth resources data for application to projects sponsored by NASA and Federal agencies such as the Forest Service, the Environmental Protection Agency, Fish and Wildlife Service, and the Army Corps of Engineers. By using airplanes like the U-2 and ER-2 for high-altitude research, NASA scientists gained knowledge of advanced aircraft capabilities and technologies and aerospace physiology, and they expanded their understanding of how humans interact with the environment. Research results may yield improved weather forecasts, tools for managing agriculture and forests, information for fisheries and local planners, and the ability to predict how climate will change in the future. Additionally, engineers will use lessons learned in future designs for aircraft and aerospace vehicles.[22]

21. NASA, "NASA SEAC4RS Mission Targets How Pollution, Storms And Climate Mix," June 6, 2013, *http://www.nasa.gov/topics/earth/features/seac4rs_2013.html*, accessed August 1, 2013.

22. NASA, "ER-2 High Altitude Airborne Science Aircraft," NASA Fact Sheet FS-2007-4-046-DFRC, 2007, *http://www.nasa.gov/centers/dryden/pdf/171831main_FS-2007-04-046-ER-2.pdf*, accessed July 27, 2013.

Contrary to popular belief, the U-2 is not yet ready to fly off into the sunset. (U.S. Air Force)

Conclusions

Over the span of more than six decades, the U-2 evolved from a relatively basic, high-altitude camera platform for performing clandestine reconnaissance missions into a complex, multisensor platform that has been adapted for a multitude of civil and military roles. Variants in more than a dozen configurations have been used for intelligence gathering, strategic and tactical reconnaissance, communications relay, battle-damage assessment, treaty monitoring and verification, disaster relief, environmental and Earth resources studies, and a wide variety of scientific research. Born of a Cold War necessity to maintain the balance of power between East and West, the U-2 now serves equally well as a high-altitude tool for tracking terrorists in the mountains of Afghanistan or for tracking the migration of destructive spruce bark beetles through the forests of Alaska.

Perhaps most surprising is the seemingly unending span of the U-2's service life. Those who conceived of and designed the airplane anticipated that it would remain viable for only a few years at most, but it has surpassed expectations with relatively modest changes to the basic configuration. Since its earliest days, the U-2 was consistently characterized as a delicate aircraft, designed for minimal aerodynamic stress. The airframe had been manufactured for optimum altitude performance at the expense of strict adherence to military specifications. Surprisingly, up until the late 1990s, no systematic study had been made to determine the consequences of this engineering approach. So, to ascertain the fatigue life of the U-2S, strain gauges and accelerometers were installed in several aircraft. The astonishing results of these measurements indicated that the U-2S could likely withstand 750,000 hours of operation. At the time of the study, those airframes with the most flight time had less than 30,000 hours. This meant that if the flight rate remained unchanged, the airplanes would be flyable for another 150 years. This low airframe wear can be attributed in part to the relatively benign high-altitude environment, where stresses from gusts and turbulence are minimal. But the most important factor ensuring the U-2's longevity may be its innovative design. Fred Carmody, a Lockheed field service

U-2 imagery of an SA-2 missile site at La Coloma, left, provided valuable intelligence during the Cuban Missile Crisis in October 1962; pictures of a collapsed freeway interchange helped California officials plan disaster-relief efforts following the Sylmar Earthquake in February 1971. (CIA)

manager who spent 25 years helping to maintain the U-2, said in 1994, "The key is good initial design, maturity of the design, and proper maintenance."[1]

At one time, the Air Force slated the U-2 for retirement in 2015, but Department of Defense cutbacks and rising costs of its proposed replacement, the RQ-4, gave Kelly Johnson's angel a new lease on life. The Global Hawk's price tag had gradually risen to $176 million per airframe, according to Deputy Secretary of Defense Ashton Carter at a January 2012 news conference, and Pentagon analysts determined that continuing to operate the U-2 would be less expensive for the foreseeable future. Through the various upgrade programs (engine, electrical, cockpit, etc.), the Air Force has already invested a substantial sum—at least $1.7 billion since 1994—to modernize the U-2, so it makes sense to leverage this investment rather than spend money on a new platform.[2]

Not surprisingly, officials from Northrop Grumman, builder of the Global Hawk, contested this decision, arguing that by flying into hostile airspace, the U-2 exposes pilots to danger, and that the airplane has limited mission

1. Pocock, *50 Years of the U-2*, pp. 334–335.
2. William J. Hennigan, "U-2 spy plane to linger overhead a bit longer," *Los Angeles Times*, January 28, 2012.

endurance and limited sensor capacity. Nevertheless, U-2 pilots have flown more than 95,000 hours since 2003, providing vital intelligence, surveillance, and reconnaissance data to military planners and soldiers in the field. Each year, the Air Force trains approximately 18 new U-2 pilots and 60 new RQ-4 operators. "They might want to start training more U-2 pilots," said Lexington Institute defense policy analyst Dr. Loren B. Thompson in a 2012 interview with the *Los Angeles Times*. Thompson estimated that the U-2 would probably not be retired before 2023. "There's still a lot of fight in that aircraft."[3]

Indeed there is. Pentagon officials have expressed a desire to continue flying the U-2 beyond 2040, and, presumably, NASA will fly the ER-2 as long as possible. Six decades after its conception, the U-2 remains a viable reconnaissance and research platform, but it will inevitably succumb to obsolescence. Perhaps somewhere in a windowless building at Palmdale, Skunk Works engineers are brewing up the next high-altitude craft to probe the sky's unlimited horizons.

---

3. Ibid.

Aircraft Specifications

U-2A/C/G

Length: 50 feet
Span: 80 feet
Wing Area: 600 square feet
Height: 15 feet
Zero-Fuel Weight: 13,071–14,250 pounds
Max. Gross Takeoff Weight: 22,542–24,150 pounds
Max. Unrefueled Range: 2,500 nautical miles
Cruise Duration: 8.0 hours
Operational Ceiling: above 70,000 feet
Cruising Speed: 400 knots (460 mph) at 65,000 feet

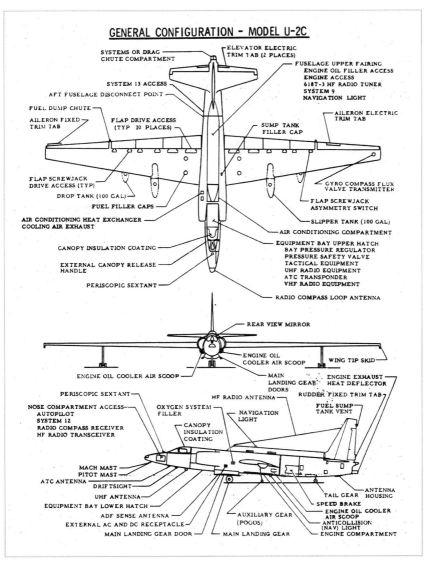

Early model U-2 general configuration. (U.S. Air Force)

U-2R/TR-1/U-2S/ER-2

Length: 62 feet
Span: 103 feet
Wing Area: 1,000 square feet
Height: 15 feet
Zero-Fuel Weight: 14,900–17,800 pounds
Max. Gross Takeoff Weight: 30,700–41,000 pounds
Max. Unrefueled Range: 4,270 nautical miles
Cruise Duration: 10.4 hours
Operational Ceiling: above 70,000 feet
Cruising Speed: 413 knots (475 mph) at 65,000 feet

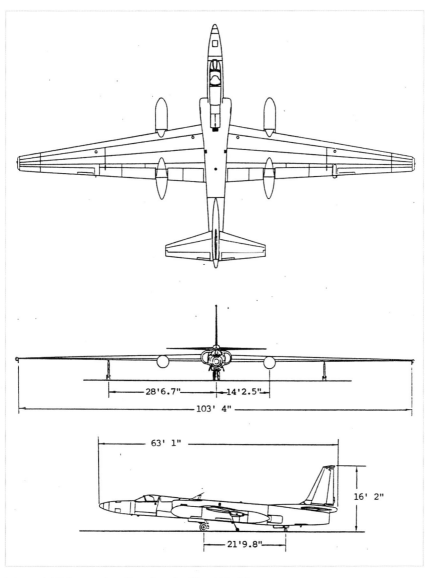

Late model U-2 general configuration. (Lockheed Martin)

Production Summary

The U-2 fleet was produced in several batches. The first production run was built for the CIA with 20 airframes constructed at Burbank, CA, under contract SP-1913. A second batch of 29 airframes was constructed at Oildale, CA, under contract SP-1914. An additional airframe was built as part of this batch, possibly using parts from crash-damaged airframes. Each U-2 airframe was identified by a three-digit Lockheed construction number, called an article number. Air Force serial numbers were assigned in 1956. The original prototype (Article 341) never received a U.S. Air Force serial number. Article 390 was allocated a serial number that had been previously assigned to Article 357, which was lost in a nonfatal accident. The Air Force ordered a supplementary batch of five airframes in 1958. In 1967 and 1968, the CIA and Air Force received 12 U-2R airframes, four of which survived to be converted to U-2S configuration. Between 1981 and 1989, a total of 37 new airframes were built under the designations TR-1A, TR-1B, U-2R, and ER-2. The TR-1 series aircraft were redesignated U-2R in October 1991 and later converted to U-2S.

Original Production Batch

Article No.	Serial No.	Model	User	History
341	N/A	U-2A	Lockheed CIA	Prototype was delivered to the test site on July 25, 1955, for test and development flights. First flight on August 1, 1955. Crashed April 4, 1957, killing Lockheed test pilot Robert Sieker.

Article No.	Serial No.	Model	User	History
342	56-6675 N800X	U-2A U-2C U-2F	Lockheed CIA	Delivered to test site on September 11, 1955. Used for developmental testing. Converted to U-2C prototype and first flown in new configuration on May 13, 1959. Converted to U-2F prototype in May 1961. Deployed to CIA operating locations overseas and at Edwards Air Force Base. Crashed February 25, 1966, following refueling practice. CIA pilot Robert "Deke" Hall ejected safely.
343	56-6676	U-2A U-2F	CIA USAF	Delivered to test site on October 16, 1955. Used for training in 1956–57, and then for test and development. Converted to U-2F in 1961. Loaned to USAF during Cuban Missile Crisis and shot down over Cuba on October 27, 1962, killing Maj. Rudolph Anderson.
344	56-6677 N315X	U-2A U-2F	CIA USAF	Delivered to the test site on November 20, 1955. Used in test and development work though most of 1956. Converted to U-2F by October 1961. Crashed near Edwards AFB during refueling trials on March 1, 1962, killing Capt. John Campbell.
345	56-6678	U-2A	CIA	Delivered to the test site on December 16, 1955. Crashed during training flight on May 15, 1956, killing Wilburn "Billy" Rose.

Article No.	Serial No.	Model	User	History
346	56-6679	U-2A	CIA	Delivered to the test site on January 13, 1956. Deployed to Europe with Detachment A. Crashed near Wiesbaden, Germany, killing Howard Carey.
347	56-6680	U-2A U-2E U-2F U-2C	CIA USAF	Delivered to the test site on February 8, 1956. Transferred to SAC in late 1957. Converted to U-2E in mid-1962. First SAC U-2 to be painted all black in 1964. Converted to U-2F in 1966. Placed in flyable storage in 1969. Converted to U-2C for Advanced Location Strike System project in 1972. Stored in 1980 and transferred to the National Air and Space Museum, Washington, DC, in 1985.
348	N801X 56-6681 N708NA	U-2A U-2G U-2C	CIA USAF Lockheed NASA	Delivered to the test site on March 5, 1956. Deployed with Detachment A in April 1956. Returned to U.S. in November 1957. Transferred to SAC but retained by Lockheed for testing through January 1959. Returned to CIA in 1963 for conversion to U-2G. Placed in flyable storage in 1969. Transferred to NASA in 1971 and returned to U-2C configuration. Retired in August 1987. Initially displayed at Ames Research Center, Moffett Field, CA. Later transferred to Moffett Field Historical Society Museum.

Article No.	Serial No.	Model	User	History
349	56-6682 N709NA	U-2A U-2H U 2G U-2C	CIA USAF NASA	Delivered to the test site on March 29, 1956. Damaged in April 1960 forced landing in Thailand. Repaired and transferred to Air Force Flight Test Center, Edwards AFB, CA. Returned to CIA in 1964 for conversion to U-2H. Converted to U-2G in August 1965. Placed in flyable storage in 1969. Transferred to NASA in 1971. Retired in April 1989 and transferred to Museum of Aviation, Robins AFB, GA.
350	56-6683	U-2A U-2F	CIA USAF	Delivered to the test site on April 24, 1956. Transferred to SAC in 1957. Used in flight-test activity in 1962. Returned to CIA in 1963 for conversion to U-2F. Loaned to SAC for Cuba reconnaissance. Crashed in the Gulf of Mexico on November 20, 1963, killing Capt. Joe Hyde, Jr.
351	56-6684	U-2A U-2C	CIA	Delivered to the test site on May 18, 1956. Converted to U-2C by 1959. Crashed at Taoyuan, Taiwan, on March 19, 1961, killing Maj. Yao-Hua Chih.
352	56-6685 N315X	U-2A U-2C	CIA Lockheed	Delivered to the test site on June 13, 1956. Converted to U-2C by September 1959. Used for test and development by Lockheed and Detachment G at Edwards in 1963. Crashed near Taiwan on October 22, 1965, killing Maj. Cheng-Wen "Pete" Wang.

Article No.	Serial No.	Model	User	History
353	56-6686	U-2A	CIA	Delivered to the test site on July 6, 1956. Moved to Detachment G in June 1957. Destroyed in crash landing at Edwards on September 14, 1961. Buster Edens escaped unharmed.
354	56-6687	U-2A	CIA	Delivered to the test site on July 27, 1956. Crashed on August 31, 1956, during a training flight, killing Frank Grace.
355	56-6688	U-2A U-2C	CIA	Delivered to the test site on August 16, 1956. Damaged in landing accident on August 30, 1956. Converted to U-2C by September 1962. Shot down over China on November 1, 1963. Maj. Chang-Di "Robin" Yeh survived.
356	56-6689	U-2A U-2F	CIA USAF	Delivered to the test site on September 5, 1956. Transferred to SAC in November 1957. Damaged by typhoon at Guam in late 1962. Transferred to CIA for conversion to U-2F in 1963. Crashed in Taiwan Straits on March 23, 1964, killing Maj. Teh-Pei "Sonny" Liang.
357	56-6690	U-2A	CIA	Delivered to the test site on September 21, 1956. Crashed in Arizona on December 19, 1956. Robert Ericson survived.

Article No.	Serial No.	Model	User	History
358	56-6691	U-2A U-2C	CIA	Delivered to the test site on October 8, 1956. Returned to Lockheed in September 1958 for conversion to U-2C and to be used in flight-test and development activity. Returned to CIA in August 1959. Shot down over China on January 10, 1965. Maj. Li-Yi "Jack" Chang survived but was captured.
359	56-6692	U-2A U-2F U-2C U-2CT	CIA USAF Lockheed	Delivered to the test site on October 22, 1956. Transferred to SAC in December 1960. Returned to CIA in July 1962 for conversion to U-2F. Loaned to SAC for Cuba reconnaissance in 1963. Used for testing in support of U-2R development from 1965 to 1967. Transferred to Air Force Flight Test Center in July 1968. Modified for Project TRIM in 1972. Converted to U-2C configuration in 1974. Returned to Lockheed in 1975 for conversion to U-2CT trainer and redelivered to SAC in January 1976. Retired in December 1987. Used as battle-damage-repair training airframe at Royal Air Force (RAF) Alconbury, England, in 1988. Restored to U-2C configuration, and transferred to Imperial War Museum, Duxford, England in 1992.

Article No.	Serial No.	Model	User	History
360	56-6693	U-2A U-2C	CIA	Delivered the test site on November 5, 1956. Used for test and development activities until May 1959. Converted to U-2C. Shot down near Sverdlovsk, Russia, on May 1, 1960. Frank Powers survived but was captured.

Second Production Batch

Article No.	Serial No.	Model	User	History
361	56-6694	U-2A	USAF	Delivered to the test site in September 1956. Moved to Laughlin AFB, TX, in June 1957. Crashed during maintenance flight on September 26, 1957. Col. Jack Nole bailed out.
362	56-6695	U-2A U-2G	USAF CIA	Delivered to the test site in November 1956. Moved to Laughlin AFB in June 1957. Transferred to CIA in 1963 for conversion to U-2G. Shot down over Fujian, China, on July 7, 1964, killing Lt. Col. Nan-Ping "Terry" Lee.
363	56-6696	U-2A	USAF	Delivered to the test site in December 1956. Moved to Laughlin AFB in June 1957. Crashed near Tucson, AZ, on March 22, 1966. Capt. Huang-Di "Andy" Fan ejected.
364	56-6697	U-2A	USAF	Delivered to the test site in January 1957. Moved to Laughlin AFB in June 1957. Crashed near Del Rio, TX, on August 6, 1958, killing Lt. Paul L. Haughland.

Article No.	Serial No.	Model	User	History
365	56-6698	U-2A	USAF	Delivered to the test site in January 1957. Moved to Laughlin AFB in June 1957. Crashed near Tucumcari, NM, on July 9, 1958, killing Capt. Al Chapin, Jr.
366	56-6699	U-2A	USAF	Delivered to the test site in February 1957. Moved to Laughlin AFB in June 1957. Crashed near Abilene, TX, on June 28, 1957, killing Lt. Leo Smith.
367	56-6700	U-2A U-2C	USAF CIA	Delivered to the test site in February 1957. Transferred to the CIA in June 1957. Returned to SAC in 1960. Converted to U-2C in October 1966. Placed in flyable storage in 1969. Returned to flight status in 1972 for the Advanced Location Strike System (ALSS) project. Crashed May 29, 1975, near Winterberg, Germany. Capt. Robert T. "Terry" Rendelman escaped unharmed.
368	56-6701	U-2A U-2C	USAF	Delivered to the test site in March 1957. Transferred to ARDC at Edwards in June 1957, and then to SAC in 1966. Converted to U-2C by November 1966. Placed in flyable storage in 1969. Returned to flight status in 1972 for ALSS project. Retired to SAC Museum, Offutt AFB, NE, in 1980.
369	56-6702	U-2A	USAF	Delivered to the test site in March 1957. Moved to Laughlin AFB in June 1957. Crashed near Abilene, TX, on June 28, 1957, killing Lt. Ford Lowcock.

Article No.	Serial No.	Model	User	History
370	56-6703	U-2A U-2E	USAF	Delivered to the test site in April 1957. Moved to Laughlin AFB in June 1957. Modified for SIGINT mission by mid-1959. Converted to U-2E in August 1962. Destroyed in crash landing at Davis-Monthan AFB, AZ, on September 18, 1964. Maj. Robert L. Primrose perished.
371	56-6704	U-2A	USAF	Delivered to the test site in April 1957. Moved to Laughlin AFB in June 1957. Crashed near Del Rio, TX, on November 28, 1957, killing Capt. Benedict A. Lacombe.
372	56-6705	U-2A U-2F	USAF CIA	Delivered to the test site in April 1957. Moved to Laughlin AFB in June 1957. First U-2 equipped for High-Altitude Sampling Program. Transferred to CIA in 1964. Converted to U-2F by May 1965 and assigned to Detachment G. Transferred to Detachment H in November 1965. Crashed at Taichung, Taiwan, on February 17, 1966, killing Capt. Tse-Shi "Charlie" Wu.
373	56-6706	U-2A U-2C	USAF CIA	Delivered to test site in May 1957. Moved to Laughlin AFB in June 1957. Transferred to CIA in August 1966 and converted to U-2C. Shot down over China on September 9, 1967, killing Maj. Jung-Bei "Denny" Hwang.

Article No.	Serial No.	Model	User	History
374	56-6707	U-2A U-2E U-2F U-2C	USAF	Delivered to test site in May 1957. Moved to Laughlin AFB in June 1957. Modified for SIGINT mission by mid-1959. Converted to U-2E in 1962. Converted to U-2F by November 1966. Placed in flyable storage in 1969. Converted back to U-2C for ALSS project in 1972. Stored at Lockheed Palmdale in 1980. Later transferred to Laughlin AFB for static display.
375	56-6708	U-2A U-2C	USAF	Delivered to Laughlin AFB in June 1957. Converted to U-2C in March 1966. Crashed near Pineville, LA, on July 1, 1967. Capt. Sam Swart ejected.
376	56-6709	U-2A	Lockheed USAF	Ready for delivery by June 1957 but retained at factory until November for SIGINT modifications. Crashed near Picayune, MS, on January 2, 1962. Capt. Charles Stratton ejected.
377	56-6710	U-2A U-2D	USAF	Delivered to ARDC in June 1957. Modified to U-2D by January 1958. Crashed at Edwards on September 11, 1958, killing Capt. Hugh P. "Pat" Hunerwadel.
378	56-6711	U-2A U-2C	CIA	Delivered to Detachment G in July 1957 and used for test and development. Converted to U-2C in 1962. Shot down over China on September 9, 1962, killing Lt. Col. Huai-Sheng Chen.

Article No.	Serial No.	Model	User	History
379	56-6712	U-2A	USAF	Delivered to Laughlin AFB in July 1957. Moved to Davis-Monthan AFB in 1963. Crashed on December 18, 1964, near Tucson after Capt. Shih-Li "Steve" Sheng ejected.
380	56-6713	U-2A	USAF	Delivered to Laughlin AFB in July 1957. Crashed July 8, 1958, near Wayside, TX, killing RAF Sq. Ldr. Christopher H. Walker.
381	56-6714	U-2A U-2G U-2C	USAF CIA	Delivered to Laughlin AFB in August 1957. Transferred to CIA in 1965 and converted to U-2G. Later transferred to SAC and eventually placed in flyable storage in 1969. Converted to U-2C in 1972. Damaged beyond repair in crash near Oroville, CA, on January 31, 1980. Capt. Edward Beaumont survived. Aircraft was later rebuilt for display at Beale AFB.
382	56-6715	U-2A U-2G	USAF CIA	Delivered to Laughlin AFB in August 1957. Transferred to CIA in 1964 and converted to U-2G in 1965. Crashed near Edwards AFB on April 26, 1965, killing Buster E. Edens.
383	56-6716 N805X	U-2A U-2C	USAF CIA	Delivered to Laughlin AFB in September 1957. Transferred to CIA in June 1965 and converted to U-2C. Transferred to SAC in 1971. Placed in storage in May 1980. Later transferred to Davis-Monthan AFB for permanent display.

Article No.	Serial No.	Model	User	History
384	56-6717	U-2A U-2C	USAF CIA	Delivered to Laughlin AFB in September 1957. Transferred to CIA in June 1964 and converted to U-2C. Crashed near Taiwan on June 21, 1966, killing Maj. Ching-Chang "Mickey" Yu.
385	56-6718	U-2A U-2G	USAF CIA	Delivered to Laughlin AFB in September 1957. Transferred to CIA in August 1964 and converted to U-2G. Crashed into Yellow Sea on January 5, 1969, killing Maj. Hseih "Billy" Chang.
386	56-6719	U-2A	USAF	Delivered to Laughlin AFB in October 1957. Crashed in Bolivia on July 28, 1966, killing Capt. Robert Hickman.
387	56-6720	U-2A	USAF	Delivered to Laughlin AFB in October 1957. Crashed near Uvalde, TX, on July 14, 1960. Maj. Raleigh B.J. Myers ejected.
388	56-6721	U-2A U-2D	USAF	Delivered to Laughlin AFB in October 1957. Damaged in forced landing at Cortez, CO, on August 5, 1959. Repaired and transferred to ARDC and modified to U-2D. Delivered to Edwards AFB in 1960. Retired in 1978 and moved to March Field Air Museum and later to Blackbird Airpark in Palmdale, CA, for display.
389	56-6722	U-2A	USAF	Delivered to USAF in November 1957. Assigned to ARDC as first aircraft to carry IR sensor. Used for numerous test and development projects. Retired in 1978 and moved to National Museum of the U.S. Air Force at Wright-Patterson AFB, OH.

Article No.	Serial No.	Model	User	History
390	56-6690	U-2A U-2C	USAF	Assigned serial number previously used for another airframe that crashed. Delivered to Laughlin AFB in December 1957. Converted to U-2C in 1966. Crashed in South Vietnam on October 8, 1966. Maj. Leo Stewart ejected.

Supplementary Production Batch

Article No.	Serial No.	Model	User	History
391	56-6951	U-2A	USAF	Delivered to Laughlin AFB in December 1957. Crashed at Davis-Monthan AFB on October 17, 1966. Capt. Leslie White survived.
392	56-6952	U-2A U-2C	USAF	Delivered to Laughlin AFB in January 1958. Converted to U-2C in 1966. Destroyed in crash landing on November 18, 1971, killing Capt. John Cunney.
393	56-6953	U-2A U-2C U-2CT	USAF	Delivered to Laughlin AFB in February 1959. Converted to U-2C in 1966. Placed in flyable storage in 1969. Reactivated in 1971 as training aircraft. Damaged in landing accident in 1972. Rebuilt as U-2CT trainer in 1973. Retired in 1987. Converted back to single-seat U-2C and displayed in Cold War Museum, Bodø, Norway, in 1994.
394	56-6954	U-2D U-2C	USAF	Delivered to Edwards AFB as U-2D in March 1959. Transferred to SAC in 1966 and converted to U-2C. Crashed near Benson, AZ, on May 31, 1968. Maj. Vic Milam ejected.

Article No.	Serial No.	Model	User	History
395	56-6955	U-2A	USAF	Delivered to Laughlin AFB in March 1959. Transferred to Davis-Monthan AFB in 1963. Crashed near Boise, ID, on August 14, 1964. Capt. Shih-Li "Steve" Sheng ejected.

Original U-2R Production

Article No.	Serial No.	Model	User	History
051	N803X 68-10329	U-2R U-2S	Lockheed CIA USAF	Prototype U-2R. First flight at Edwards AFB on August 28, 1967. Used for test and development. Configured to production standard and delivered to CIA in March 1969. Reallocated to flight testing in 1974. Transferred to Beale AFB in 1981. Converted to U-2S in 1995.
052	N809X 68-10330	U-2R	USAF Navy	First flight December 29, 1967. Delivered to Davis-Monthan AFB July 25, 1968. Test bed for Senior Lance and Navy EP-X trials. Transferred to Beale AFB in 1976. Crashed at Akrotiri, Cyprus, on December 7, 1977, killing Capt. Robert Henderson.
053	N800X 68-10331	U-2R U-2S	CIA USAF	First flight February 17, 1968. Delivered to CIA on November 22, 1968. Transferred to Davis-Monthan AFB in 1974 and to Beale AFB in 1976. Converted to U-2S in August 1996.
054	N810X 68-10332	U-2R	CIA USAF	First flight March 29, 1968, and subsequently delivered to CIA. Transferred to Davis-Monthan AFB in 1975 and to Beale AFB in 1976. Crashed off Korean coast on January 15, 1992, killing Capt. Marty McGregor.

Article No.	Serial No.	Model	User	History
055	N812X 68-10333	U-2R	CIA USAF	First flight May 8, 1968, and subsequently delivered to CIA. Transferred to Davis-Monthan AFB in 1974 and to Beale AFB in 1976. Crashed at Osan, South Korea, on May 22, 1984. Capt. David Bonsi survived.
056	N814X 68-10334	U-2R	USAF	First flight May 18, 1968. Delivered to Davis-Monthan AFB on June 10, 1968. Crashed in Gulf of Thailand on August 15, 1975. Capt. Jon Little survived.
057	N815X 68-10335	U-2R	CIA USAF	First flight July 30, 1968. Delivered to CIA on August 29, 1968. Crashed at Taoyuan, Taiwan, on November 24, 1970, killing Maj. Chi-Hsien "Denny" Huang.
058	N816X 68-10336	U-2R U-2S	USAF	First flight August 20, 1968. Delivered to Davis-Monthan AFB on August 29, 1968, and to Beale AFB in 1976. Eventually transferred to test activities at Palmdale. Converted to U-2S in 1996.
059	N817X 68-10337	U-2R U-2S	USAF	First flight on September 9, 1968. Delivered to Davis-Monthan AFB on September 21, 1968, and to Beale AFB in 1976. Converted to U-2S in June 1998.
060	N818X 68-10338	U-2R	USAF	First flight on October 2, 1968. Delivered to Davis-Monthan AFB on October 17, 1968, and to Beale AFB in 1976. Became first U-2 to reach 20,000 flight hours, in August 1994. Crashed at Fairford, England, on August 29, 1995, killing Capt. David Hawkens.

Article No.	Serial No.	Model	User	History
061	N819X 68-10339	U-2R	USAF	First flight October 22, 1968. Retained at Palmdale for testing until delivered to Davis-Monthan AFB in 1972. Transferred to Beale AFB in 1976. Crashed at Beale on December 13, 1993, killing Capt. Rich Snyder.
062	N820X 68-10340	U-2R	USAF	First flight November 26, 1968. Delivered to Davis-Monthan AFB on December 19, 1968. Transferred to Beale AFB in 1976. Crashed in Korea on October 5, 1980. Capt. Cleve Wallace survived.

Later Production

Article No.	Serial No.	Model	User	History
063	80-1063 N706NA N806NA	ER-2	NASA	First flight May 1, 1981. Delivered to NASA Ames Research Center in June 1981. Transferred to NASA Dryden Flight Research Center in 1998.
064	80-1064	TR-1B U-2RT U-2ST	USAF	Delivered to Beale AFB as TR-1B in March 1983. Redesignated U-2RT in October 1991. Converted to U-2ST in October 1994.
065	80-1065	TR-1B U-2RT U-2ST	USAF	Delivered to Beale AFB as TR-1B in May 1983. Redesignated U-2RT in October 1991. Converted to U-2ST in August 1995.

Article No.	Serial No.	Model	User	History
066	80-1066	TR-1A U-2R U-2S	USAF	First flight August 1, 1981. Delivered to Beale AFB as TR-1A in September 1981. Redesignated U-2RT in October 1991. Converted to U-2S in November 1997.
067	80-1067	TR-1A U-2R U-2S	USAF	Delivered to Beale AFB as TR-1A in July 1982. Transferred to flight test in Palmdale in 1989. Redesignated U-2R in October 1991. Converted to U-2S in 1998.
068	80-1068	TR-1A U-2R U-2S U-2ST	USAF	Delivered to Beale AFB as TR-1A in July 1982. Transferred to RAF Alconbury, England, in February 1983 and to Beale AFB in April 1987. Redesignated U-2R in October 1991. Converted to U-2S in July 1998. Converted to U-2ST in 2004.
069	80-1069 N708NA	TR-1A ER-2 U-2S	USAF NASA	Delivered to Beale AFB as TR-1A in July 1982. Transferred to Alconbury in July 1983 and damaged in ground accident 3 months later. Eventually repaired and loaned to NASA as ER-2 in March 1987. Returned to Beale AFB as U-2R in 1995. Converted to U-2S in September 1997.
070	80-1070	TR-1A U-2R U-2S	USAF	Delivered to Beale AFB as TR-1A in October 1982. Transferred to Alconbury in February 1983. Returned to Beale AFB in May 1988. Redesignated U-2R in October 1991. Converted to U-2S in February 1995.

Article No.	Serial No.	Model	User	History
071	80-1071	U-2R U-2S	USAF	Delivered to Beale AFB as U-2R in November 1983. Transferred to flight test in Palmdale in 1985. Returned to Beale AFB in 1988. Redelivered as first U-2S production conversion on October 28, 1994.
072	80-1072	TR-1A	USAF	Delivered as TR-1A to Alconbury in November 1983. Transferred to Beale AFB in March 1984. Crashed at Beale on July 18, 1984. Capt. Tom Hubbard survived.
073	80-1073	TR-1A U-2R U-2S	USAF	Delivered to Beale AFB as TR-1A in February 1984. Transferred to Alconbury in January 1991. Redesignated U-2R in October 1991. Transferred to Beale AFB in September 1992. Converted to U-2S in February 1996.
074	80-1074	TR-1A U-2R U-2S	USAF	Delivered to Beale AFB as TR-1A in February 1984. Transferred to Alconbury in December 1990. Redesignated U-2R in October 1991. Transferred to Beale AFB in October 1992. Converted to U-2S in May 1996.
075	80-1075	U-2R	USAF	Delivered to Beale AFB as U-2R in 1984. Crashed in Korea on October 8, 1984. Capt. Tom Dettmer survived.
076	80-1076	U-2R	USAF	Delivered to Beale AFB as U-2R in 1984. Converted to U-2S in August 1997.
077	80-1077	TR-1A U-2R U-2S	USAF	Delivered to Alconbury as TR-1A in March 1985. Transferred to Beale AFB in November 1989. Converted to U-2S in June 1996.

Article No.	Serial No.	Model	User	History
078	80-1078	TR-1A U-2ST	USAF	Delivered to Alconbury as TR-1A in March 1985. Damaged on April 24, 1990, and returned to Palmdale for storage. Converted to U-2ST in October 1994.
079	80-1079	TR-1A U-2R U-2S	USAF	Delivered to Alconbury as TR-1A in March 1985. Transferred to Beale AFB in January 1991. Redesignated U-2R in October 1991. Converted to U-2S in May 1997.
080	80-1080	TR-1A U-2R U-2S	USAF	Delivered to Beale AFB as TR-1A in May 1985. Redesignated U-2R in October 1991. Converted to U-2S in March 1997.
081	80-1081	TR-1A U-2R U-2S	USAF	Delivered to Alconbury as TR-1A in October 1985. Transferred to Beale AFB in August 1991. Redesignated U-2R in October 1991. Converted to U-2S in October 1996.
082	80-1082	TR-1A U-2R U-2S	USAF	Delivered to Beale AFB as TR-1A in November 1985. Redesignated U-2R in October 1991. Converted to U-2S in January 1997.
083	80-1083	TR-1A U-2R U-2S	USAF	Delivered to Alconbury as TR-1A in March 1986. Redesignated U-2R in October 1991. Transferred to Beale AFB in December 1991. Converted to U-2S in September 1996.
084	80-1084	TR-1A U-2R U-2S	USAF	Delivered to Alconbury as TR-1A in April 1986. Transferred to Beale AFB in 1988. Redesignated U-2R in October 1991. Converted to U-2S in March 1998.

Article No.	Serial No.	Model	User	History
085	80-1085	TR-1A U-2R U-2S	USAF	Delivered to Alconbury as TR-1A in August 1986. Transferred to Beale AFB in February 1991. Redesignated U-2R in October 1991. Converted to U-2S in June 1997.
086	80-1086	TR-1A U-2R U-2S	USAF	Delivered to Beale AFB as TR-1A in 1986. Transferred to Alconbury in April 1987. Returned to Beale in August 1991. Redesignated U-2R in October 1991. Converted to U-2S in December 1997.
087	80-1087	TR-1A U-2R U-2S	USAF	Delivered to Beale AFB as TR-1A in May 1987. Redesignated U-2R in October 1991. Converted to U-2S in February 1998.
088	80-1088	TR-1A U-2R	USAF	Delivered to Alconbury as TR-1A in December 1987. Transferred to Beale AFB in August 1991. Crashed near Oroville, CA, on August 7, 1996, killing Capt. Randy Roby.
089	80-1089	U-2R U-2S	USAF	Delivered to Beale AFB as U-2R in 1988. Converted to U-2S in December 1995.
090	80-1090	TR-1A U-2R U-2S	USAF	Built as TR-1A in 1988 and retained at Palmdale for test and development. Served as U-2S prototype in May 1989 and subsequently delivered to Beale AFB.
091	80-1091	U-2RT U-2ST	USAF	Delivered to Beale AFB as U-2RT in March 1988. Converted to U-2ST in December 1998.

Article No.	Serial No.	Model	User	History
092	80-1092	TR-1A U-2R U-2S	USAF	Delivered to Alconbury as TR-1A in April 1988. Redesignated U-2R in October 1991. Transferred to Beale AFB in December 1991. Converted to U-2S in September 1998.
093	80-1093	TR-1A U-2R U-2S	USAF	Delivered to Alconbury as TR-1A in June 1988. Redesignated U-2R in October 1991. Transferred to Beale AFB in April 1992. Converted to U-2S in June 1995.
094	80-1094	TR-1B U-2S	USAF	Delivered to Alconbury as TR-1B in September 1988. Redesignated U-2R in October 1991. Transferred to Beale AFB in December 1991. Converted to U-2S in June 1995.
095	80-1095	U-2R U-2S	USAF	Delivered to Beale AFB as U-2R in 1988. Converted to U-2S in January 1996. Crashed near Seoul, South Korea, on January 26, 2003. The pilot ejected.
096	80-1096	U-2R U-2S	USAF	Delivered to Beale AFB as U-2R in 1989. Converted to U-2S in April 1996.
097	80-1097 N709NA N806NA	ER-2	NASA	Delivered to NASA Ames Research Center in 1989. Transferred to NASA Dryden Flight Research Center in 1998.
098	80-1098	U-2R	USAF	Delivered to Beale AFB as U-2R in 1989. Crashed on landing at Osan, South Korea, in August 1994. Capt. Cholene Espinoza survived.

Article No.	Serial No.	Model	User	History
099	80-1099	TR-1A U-2R U-2S	USAF	Delivered to Beale AFB as TR-1A on October 3, 1989. Transferred to Alconbury in March 1990. Redesignated U-2R in October 1991. Converted to U-2S in August 1995.

U-2 Timeline

Milestone dates in the history of the U-2

Date	Milestone
May 18, 1954	Lockheed submits unsolicited proposal to Air Force for CL-282
June 7, 1954	Lockheed notified that Air Force rejected the CL-282 proposal
November 19, 1954	Kelly Johnson discusses CL-282 with CIA
November 24, 1954	U-2 project approved by President Eisenhower
December 9, 1954	Lockheed receives $54 million contract for U-2 production (first 20 airframes)
June 10, 1955	USAF and CIA sign agreement on Project Aquatone
July 1955	First U-2 (Article 341) delivered to test site
August 1, 1955	Unofficial first flight of U-2 to 35 feet altitude following inadvertent takeoff during taxi test
August 4, 1955	First planned flight of U-2 to 8,000 feet
August 8, 1955	Official first flight for VIP visitors (third planned flight)
September 1955	Second U-2 (Article 342) delivered to test site, Phase I (Contractor) testing completed
October 18, 1955	U-2 achieves design altitude of 73,000 feet
December 1955	Lockheed approved to build 30 additional airframes
May 7, 1956	NACA director Hugh L. Dryden announces existence of U-2 aircraft, same date as first operational CIA detachment deployed
June 20, 1956	First flight over Eastern Bloc countries
July 4, 1956	First flight over Russia
August 20, 1956	Second CIA detachment deployed
September 11, 1956	First U-2 flight over Middle East

Date	Milestone
February 1957	Third CIA detachment deployed
June 11, 1957	4028th Strategic Reconnaissance Squadron receives first six aircraft at Del Rio, TX
November 14, 1957	First high-altitude weather photos (Typhoon Kitt)
May 13, 1959	First flight of U-2C
May 1, 1960	Last flight over Russia, Frank Powers shot down in Article 360
October 26, 1960	First flight over Cuba
October 5, 1962	50th and final CIA U-2 flight over Cuba
May 20, 1964	First operational mission from aircraft carrier
September 1966	Lockheed receives order for 12 U-2R airframes
August 28, 1967	First flight of U-2R
December 1968	Final U-2R airframe delivered
June 3, 1971	NASA receives first U-2C for Earth Resources research
August 1, 1974	CIA U-2 program comes to an end. Remaining assets transferred to USAF
November 16, 1979	Production line reopens to build ER-2, TR-1, and additional U-2R airframes
May 11, 1981	First flight of ER-2 and delivery to NASA
August 1, 1981	First flight of TR-1
April 1989	NASA retires U-2C
October 1991	TR-1 is redesignated U-2R
August 12, 1994	First flight of U-2S (new engine)
December 2000	Reconnaissance Avionics Maintainability Program (RAMP) upgrades initiated
April 15, 2002	First RAMP U-2 delivered to Beale AFB
June 2013	Introduction of Cabin Altitude Reduction Effort (CARE)

U-2 Space Shuttle Photography

These two photos of the Space Shuttle Atlantis were among those taken from an Air Force U-2 reconnaissance aircraft flying high above Kennedy Space Center, FL, on May 4, 1989. The need for such pictures arose after the Shuttle suffered an unusual number of debris strikes during mission STS-27 in December 1988. After landing, technicians discovered more than 700 instances of damage to the orbiter's thermal protection tiles. Because this was approximately seven times the normal number of hits, NASA engineers wanted to know if the damage was unique to Atlantis or was part of a fleet-wide trend that began with STS-27. They needed to identify debris sources (ice, insulation from the external tank, ablative material falling off the solid rocket boosters, etc.), determine how much material was lost, and identify the point at which the damage occurred during flight. Residual material on the damaged tiles from STS-27 included traces of ablator and paint from the solid rocket booster (SRB) forward assemblies, but viewing the SRB nose caps during the first few minutes of flight was nearly impossible because ground-based tracking cameras were aimed only at the aft end and sides of the vehicle. In response to a NASA request, the Air Force provided a U-2 from a detachment at nearby Patrick Air Force Base to take high-resolution black-and-white photos during the first 2 minutes after liftoff. The first attempt was made during the launch of STS-29 on March 13, 1989. The pilot flew a racetrack circuit at an altitude of approximately 20,000 feet at a standoff distance of about 5 miles to keep clear of the Shuttle's flightpath. Timing was crucial because the spacecraft climbed very quickly following SRB ignition, and a wide-angle lens had to be used because there was no way for a telescopic camera to rapidly track the Shuttle. Due to a launch delay, the U-2 was not at the optimal point at liftoff and the photos were not very useful. A second attempt during STS-30 on May 4 was more successful. The U-2 pilot was able to achieve a better position and optimum slant angles for photography, but the resolution was still not sufficient to resolve enough detail to determine what was happening to the nose cones.[1]

---

1.   Glen Swanson, photo caption, *Quest: The History of Spaceflight Quarterly* 4, no. 3 (summer 1995): p. 1.

U-2 imagery of Space Shuttle Atlantis taken on May 4, 1989. The resolution was insufficient for determining the source of debris from the SRB nose caps. (U.S. Air Force)

The Skunk Works Method

Since the early 1940s, the Skunk Works (now a division of Lockheed Martin) has become synonymous with innovative aerospace design and manufacturing techniques. In the beginning, this was due in large part to Kelly Johnson's unique management approach. Designed to foster creativity and innovation, his method established principles for the development and production of highly complex aircraft in a relatively short time and at as low a cost as could be practically achieved. Johnson's successor, Ben Rich, and others who followed in their footsteps continued to use and refine the Skunk Works methods. Although not easily applied in the corporate world of the early 21st century, it is worthwhile to study this innovative business model. If implemented, it can be used to reduce development and life-cycle costs for acquisition programs involving rapid prototyping or low-rate production.

In 1975, Ben Rich, left, succeeded Kelly Johnson as head of the Advanced Development Projects division. (Lockheed Martin)

Kelly's Rules

Johnson often summed up his method in just seven words: Be quick. Be quiet. Be on time. Eventually, however, he wrote a set of 14 rules addressing program management, organization, contractor/customer relationships, documentation, customer reporting, specifications, engineering drawings, funding, cost control, subcontractor inspection, testing, security, and management compensation. These became the Basic Operating Rules of the Skunk Works:

1. The Skunk Works manager must be delegated practically complete control of his program in all aspects. He should report to a division president or higher. (It is essential that the program manager have authority to make decisions quickly regarding technical, finance, schedule, or operations matters.)

2. Strong but small project offices must be provided, both by the customer and contractor. (The customer program manager must have similar authority to that of the contractor.)

3. The number of people having any connection with the project must be restricted in an almost vicious manner. Use a small number of good people: 10 to 25 percent compared to the so-called normal systems. (Bureaucracy makes unnecessary work and must be controlled brutally.)

4. A very simple drawing and drawing release system with great flexibility for making changes must be provided. (This permits early work by manufacturing organizations, and schedule recovery if technical risks involve failures.)

5. There must be a minimum of reports required, but important work must be recorded thoroughly. (Responsible management does not require massive technical and information systems.)

6. There must be a monthly cost review covering not only what has been spent and committed, but also projected costs to the conclusion of the program. Don't have the books 90 days late and don't surprise the customer with sudden overruns. (Responsible management does require operation within the resources available.)

7. The contractor must be delegated and must assume more than normal responsibility to get good vendor bids for the subcontract on the project. Commercial bid procedures are very often better than military ones. (Essential freedom to use the best talent available and operate within the resources available.)

8. The inspection system as currently used by the Skunk Works, which has been approved by both the Air Force and Navy, meets the intent of existing military requirements and should be used on new projects. Push more basic inspection responsibility back to subcontractors and vendors. Don't duplicate so much inspection. (Even the commercial world recognizes that quality is in design and responsible operations – not inspection.)

9. The contractor must be delegated the authority to test his final product in flight. He can and must test it in the initial stages. If he doesn't, he rapidly loses his competency to design other vehicles. (Critical, if new technology and the attendant risks are to be rationally accommodated.)

10. The specification applying to the hardware must be agreed to in advance of contracting. The Skunk Works practice of having a specification section stating clearly which important military specification items will not knowingly be complied with and reasons therefore is highly recommended. (Standard specifications inhibit new technology and innovation, and are frequently obsolete.)

11. Funding a program must be timely so that the contractor doesn't have to keep running to the bank to support government projects. (Rational management requires knowledge of, and freedom to use, the resources originally committed.)

12. There must be mutual trust between the customer project organization and the contractor with very close cooperation and liaison on a day-to-day basis. This cuts down misunderstanding and correspondence to an absolute minimum. (The goals of the customer and producer should be the same – get the job done well.)

13. Access by outsiders to the project and its personnel must be strictly controlled by appropriate security measures. (This is a program manager's responsibility even if no program security demands are made – a cost avoidance measure.)

14. Because only a few people will be used in engineering and most other areas, ways must be provided to reward good performance by pay not based on the number of personnel supervised. (Responsible management must be rewarded, and responsible management does not permit the growth of bureaucracies.)[1]

This management approach offers a proven, efficient method for developing new technologies, executing engineering and manufacturing development programs, procuring limited production systems at low rates, and upgrading current systems.

Ben's Rules

Ben Rich became head of the Skunk Works in 1975. A highly capable engineer in the field of thermodynamics and propulsion, he had been with Lockheed since 1950. After joining the Skunk Works in 1954 as a senior design engineer on the U-2, he worked on the A-12 and SR-71 and oversaw pioneering development of stealth aircraft. Although Rich followed the Basic Operating Rules of the Skunk Works, he also developed his own management philosophy:[2]

1. Strong leadership. Maintain awareness of the big picture. Rely on key staff to describe the situation and alternatives. Ask appropriate questions, weigh the alternatives, and make a decision. (Be a benevolent dictator.)

2. Teamwork. Select people who can work well together Assemble the team and allow it to work with minimum interference.

1. Miller, *Lockheed Skunk Works: The First Fifty Years*, pp. 210–211.
2. Ben R. Rich, "The Skunk Works Approach," in Ben R. Rich Papers, The Huntington Library, San Marino, CA, July 25, 1990, p. 11.

3. Learn to delegate both authority and responsibility. Give people a job to do and then let them do it. (You'll be surprised at the results.)

4. Manage by charisma; be flexible, and allow people to show their capability. Provide goals and objectives, not step-by-step procedures. Let workers have a say in what is going on.

5. Be both practical and tolerant. Don't take too big a step. (Walk before you run.) Expect mistakes and learn from them when they occur. (Sometimes a mistake is just the wrong approach at the time.)

6. Maintain a tight schedule because time is money. (Give yourself less time than you think you'll need.)

7. Demand and expect results. Rely on people who know how to prioritize. Workaholics don't make the best employees. Hire people who can organize their work and communicate to subordinates how to make the most of their time. (You can't make up in time what you don't have in brains.)

8. Always be ethical. Demand integrity of yourself and those who serve under you. (No one is smart enough to lie.)

9. Always reward good performance, and never take credit for other people's work. (A boss who is not stingy with praise will have a team of loyal employees.)

10. Don't tolerate mediocrity and non-performance. Don't tolerate unprofessionalism. Tell non-performers what they are doing wrong – you owe it to the rest of the team and to them. (Mistakes happen. Give people a chance, but if they repeat their errors, get rid of them.)

11. Enjoy your work. Take satisfaction in the results of your labor. Learn not to take your work home. Take vacations to rejuvenate both mind and body. (If you work hard, play hard.)

A comparison of the management styles of the first two Skunk Works chiefs reveals distinct similarities and differences. Kelly Johnson's strong leadership molded the Skunk Works into a lean, efficient organization. As a talented engineer, he was a technical leader as well as a manager. When engineering problems arose, Johnson took personal responsibility for addressing them. He motivated his staff through the strength of his personality, but he had a legendary temper and a tendency to micromanage. He succeeded because he encouraged creativity and rewarded accomplishments.[3]

Ben Rich was careful to preserve the essential character of Johnson's operating philosophy, but since he lacked Johnson's breadth of technical expertise, Rich tended to delegate more responsibility to his subordinates. Nevertheless, he had learned many things from his mentor. "Kelly taught me that integrity was the most important thing in all my dealings with people," he said at his retirement from Lockheed in July 1991, "don't do anything or build anything that you don't believe in, and communicate with everyone from top to bottom."[4]

Wisely, none of the later Skunk Works chiefs ever tried to mimic Johnson, who was truly one of a kind. Instead, successive new leaders have integrated personal perspectives with a healthy appreciation for the Skunk Works legacy. According to Al Romig, who led the Skunk Works from June 2011 through July 2013, "The real secret to maintaining innovation is simple; it's the people." National imperatives of the Cold War spurred Kelly Johnson's genius and that of the people gathered around him to produce a unique culture that continues to resonate within the company. The unique management structure empowers engineers and fosters a willingness to take prudent risks. "By allowing that creative culture to perpetuate, the Skunks of today have been indoctrinated by the generations that have preceded them," Romig acknowledged on the occasion of the Skunk Works' 70th anniversary. "In a technical sense, our culture encourages doing things that have never been done before."[5]

Lessons Learned

The Skunk Works management approach offers a proven way to develop new technology quickly and efficiently, execute engineering and manufacturing

---

3. David C. Aronstein and Albert C. Piccirillo, *Have Blue and the F-117A: Evolution of the Stealth Fighter* (Reston, VA: American Institute of Aeronautics and Astronautics, 1997), p. 225.

4. Ben R. Rich, "B.R. Rich Retirement Speech," in Ben R. Rich Papers, The Huntington Library, San Marino, CA, January 17, 1991, p. 2.

5. "Interview with Al Romig, Chief Skunk," *Skunk Works Celebrates 70 Years of Innovation*, July 2013, *http://www.lockheedmartin.com/us/news/features/2013/roming-interview.html*, accessed July 30, 2013.

development programs, procure production systems in limited quantities, and upgrade current systems. Any manufacturer can implement a Skunk Works management philosophy providing that both corporate leadership and the customer agree to abide by the rules. Otherwise, this approach will not work.

Success of this method is dependent on establishing cost as the number one priority. Current fiscal realities demand that every acquisition dollar be spent as wisely and efficiently as possible. Program cost estimates should not be based on historical precedents. Demand for enhanced performance capabilities should not be allowed to drive costs upward as this will inevitably push the program over budget and behind schedule.[6] Expenditures should be tightly controlled, and unexpected cost overruns should not be tolerated. In order to avoid unpleasant surprises, the customer should be immediately informed of any cost growth as it is discovered. Managers should always adhere to a strict schedule but plan for some flexibility. If delays occur, it is important to identify the cause and implement corrective action expediently. Honest, open, and early communication between the contractor and the customer regarding any potential delays will provide opportunities for joint problem solving and maintain trust between both parties.[7]

According to Ben Rich, a successful engineering/production development program must have three things. First, the product must be able to perform the required mission. Second, it has to be delivered on schedule, as promised. Finally, the cost must stay within the anticipated funding. Aircraft performance requirements need to be well defined, reasonable, and stable. Constant changes can lead to failure by pushing the project behind schedule and driving up costs. Essential performance requirements must be separated from wish lists (i.e., those performance characteristics that are merely desirable, but not necessary). Any technical problems that arise should be identified as early as possible and solved quickly. Customer and contractor personnel should work together to find the best solution after examining any potential tradeoffs or alternatives.[8]

People are the most important asset. Managers should put the most qualified available personnel on the program and keep the team as small as possible. The benefits of keeping both management and total personnel at a minimum include greater individual responsibility and satisfaction, improved communications, higher productivity, and reduced costs. According to Ben Rich, "A

---

6. Leland M. Nicolai, "Skunk Works Lessons Learned," in *Strategic Management of the Cost Problem of Future Weapon Systems*, AGARD Conference Proceedings (AGARD-CP-602), September 1998, pp. 6–7.

7. Ben R. Rich, "The Skunk Works Approach," p. 8.

8. Ibid., p. 7.

large part of the success of the Skunk Works comes in the ability to develop a team and an attitude which favors getting the job done by jointly overcoming problems as they arise."[9]

In order to give designers and managers as much freedom as possible, it is important for the manufacturer to tailor mission requirements, acquisition requirements, and manufacturing specifications. Only the most critical performance parameters should be specified as requirements. Whenever possible, peripheral standards and specifications should serve only as guidelines. Documentation should be streamlined and technical and program reviews kept to a minimum. Although held regularly, formal contractor-customer program reviews should be keyed to the pace of the program. Small program offices and close, regular communications minimize the need for formal reports, documentation, and more frequent reviews.[10]

Manufacturing personnel should influence the design from the very beginning. The manufacturing group should be responsible for material and process specifications, establishing tolerances, and adopting best commercial practices. The design should be as simple as practical with a minimum part count and minimum necessity for touch labor. Assembly processes that most frequently result in rejected parts (such as drilling holes) should be minimized if possible. Components should have left-hand/right-hand interchangeability or self-locating features for ease of installation. Room-temperature processes should be used as much as possible. Use of off-the-shelf components will reduce both acquisition and development costs.[11]

An aircraft should be designed for ease of maintainability. This includes sensible installation of equipment, adequate access panels, and a minimal requirement for unique tools. Designers should give consideration to future modifications and upgrades and provide easy access, extra volume (if possible), and growth power capability.[12]

Early design development can be achieved through the use of technology demonstrators or full-scale development (FSD) prototypes. A demonstrator may be a subscale version of the proposed design or a close approximation. Its sole purpose is to prove a concept or validate a critical system feature. FSD airframes more closely match the final production structural design and may

---

9. Ibid., pp. 1–2.
10. Nicolai, "Skunk Works Lessons Learned," pp. 7–9.
11. Ibid., pp. 9–10.
12. Ibid., p. 10.

be used to validate fabrication and assembly techniques and to verify structural weight and production costs.[13]

Keys to Success

Under the Skunk Works philosophy, a project should be organized around a manager who has total control of all aspects of the program, thus giving the manager the ability to control costs and meet rational milestones and objectives. Other functional organizations within the company such as human resources, information services, facilities, environmental health and safety, legal and other specialty areas provide on-demand support to the program manager.

The program's organizational structure should be as simple as possible and contain built-in checks and balances. Overall staffing must be kept to a minimum to provide clear lines of responsibility and maintain program security. The Skunk Works approach calls for the use of a small number of skilled personnel who are given broad responsibility and a substantial, but reasonable, workload. Keeping management and total staffing to a minimum results in greater individual responsibility and job satisfaction, improved communications, higher productivity, and reduced costs.[14]

Success is dependent upon a cohesive team working closely together to achieve well-defined objectives. Tasks and responsibilities are clearly defined, and progress is measured and tracked using integrated plans and schedules. Managers of various subgroups must have a clear understanding of how their role contributes to the success of the overall program. Formal weekly program reviews track the program's progress while smaller meetings provide a forum for ironing out differences of opinion or improving operating procedures. If the program involves development of new or unique capabilities, participants must be willing to accept failures and incorporate changes based on lessons learned.

The Skunk Works approach works only if the customer is committed to working in a similar manner. This starts with a small, high-quality, highly responsive customer program office, and a small supporting organization as needed. Like the contractor program manager, the customer program manager must also be given singular authority and broad responsibilities, reporting to a senior decision-capable management level. The contractor and customer teams should maintain open communications on program issues in order to foster teamwork, rapid joint problem solving, and mutual trust, rather than adversarial

---

13. Ibid., p. 11.
14. Miller, *Lockheed Skunk Works: The First Fifty Years*, pp. 210–211.

relationships. Small program offices and regular communications minimize the need for formal reports, documentation, and frequent program reviews.[15]

If possible, contracts should be tailored to the specific procurements and eliminate restrictive and nonessential provisions while conforming to statutory and regulatory requirements. Increasing demands by Government agencies, however, for contract provisions requiring extensive reporting, prior Government approvals, and new administrative systems reduce a contractor's ability to tailor contracts in such a fashion.

Specifications should be as simple and brief as possible. Skunk Works practice emphasizes *what* is to be accomplished rather than *how* it is to be accomplished, specifying only critical performance parameters as requirements. The original U-2 specification document was just 35 pages long. The later SR-71 specification totaled 54 pages, relatively small and highly tailored compared to average procurement programs.

Manufacturing and quality assurance personnel should be involved early, working closely with design, structures, and materials engineers to ensure product criteria are met. An integrated product development process ensures the contractor will meet performance, quality, production, and affordability requirements. The engineering drawing system should readily accommodate change, and designers should be able to directly interface with manufacturers if changes are required. Modern computer-aided design techniques (not available when the U-2 was built) can reduce the need for full-scale mockups, and tooling should be kept to a minimum, especially for prototype programs. During fabrication and flight test, critical inspections verify compliance of processes with engineering requirements.[16]

Flight-testing of prototype and full-scale development aircraft is conducted under the direction of a flight-test manager reporting directly to the program manager. Duties for this position include test planning, ground and flight testing, data acquisition and analysis, flight vehicle maintenance and support, and test-data documentation. The primary objective is to get test results as quickly as possible and apply lessons learned. The contractor is entirely responsible for testing prototype vehicles. During FSD testing, the work is accomplished by an integrated team of contractor and customer personnel.

Historically, Skunk Works programs have met very stringent security requirements. Development of the Blackbirds began as a covert special-access program, and only personnel with a strict need to know were briefed in. This policy not only protected national security but also prevented interference

15. Ibid.
16. Ibid.

from outsiders and thereby increased productivity. A restrictive access policy can be similarly implemented on unclassified programs to improve efficiency and reduce costs.

By following these practices, the Skunk Works has consistently demonstrated the ability to design, develop, and produce highly advanced aircraft at low cost and in a minimal amount of time. The Skunk Works management principles allow a contractor to shorten the acquisition cycle and increase efficiency.[17]

Any organization can apply these principles, but of course applying the principles does not guarantee success. Historically, Skunk Works projects succeeded through a combination of factors including personal leadership, strong Governmental support, organizational momentum, and a solid reputation based on a long history of achievement.

Growing Pains

Implementing a classic Skunk Works management policy has become increasingly difficult. During a 1990 speech at the Air Force Academy, Ben Rich said, "I don't honestly believe that you can take the Skunk Works approach and bottle it up and sell it as a cure-all for the acquisition problems of the DoD [Department of Defense]. I do believe that you can apply these basic principles in select acquisitions where all parties agree that the conditions are right. This is not limited, in my opinion, to covert programs. But, it does require a willingness to create a small team and keep it small; to choose the right people, give them clear, stable requirements, and a job to do; and to be willing to let them alone to do that job, and to provide them with stable funding."[18]

Such conditions are not easy to achieve. When Lockheed merged with Martin Marietta in March 1995, the new Lockheed Martin Corporation retained the Skunk Works as a company within a company in order to pursue innovative design and development work, but the once fiercely independent business unit had to adjust to a new corporate culture. Within the Skunk Works, there was movement away from simple, brief specifications, particularly whenever a program transitioned from the specialized management procedures used during the prototype/demonstrator phase to conventional production management procedures. This occasionally resulted in difficulties, as with the F-22 and F-35 fighter production programs. Alan Brown, former program

---

17. Ibid.
18. Ben R. Rich, "The Skunk Works Approach," p. 12.

manager and chief engineer on the F-117A, suggested that the time it takes to get from initial design to operational use of a new airplane is directly proportional to the size of the customer oversight committee responsible for guiding the design. "For the F-117 the Air Force team was a colonel and six other experts. The corresponding team on the F-22 was 130, and if you ratio the 130 over seven, you'll get just about the ratio of the time it took from starting the airframes to getting them in service." Bob Murphy, who joined the Skunk Works in 1954, managed U-2 flight testing and was eventually promoted to deputy director of operations, laments the increased bureaucracy. "Once you get all these organizations involved, all the different Air Force bases across the country and every contractor that makes a screw for the airplane, everybody comes to every meeting and nothing ever gets settled."[19]

Despite these growing pains, the Skunk Works continues to develop some of the most innovative aircraft ever built. Lockheed Martin's Advanced Development Programs division has evolved from Kelly Johnson's small shop in Burbank to some 2,000 people working on more than 600 programs in the company's complex in Palmdale.[20] Since approximately 90 percent of all work at the facility is classified, little is known about the group's recent accomplishments, but its legacy continues.

---

19. Angus Batey, "Inside The Skunk Works," *Classic Aircraft* 45, no. 11 (November 2012).

20. William J. Hennigan, "Skunk Works: Developing top-secret weapons in SoCal for 70 years," *Los Angeles Times*, June 20, 2013.

Bibliography

Reports, Papers, Articles, and Presentations

Bailey, Susan. "Air crew radiation exposure—An overview." *Nuclear News* (January 2000).

Batey, Angus. "Inside The Skunk Works." *Classic Aircraft* 45, no. 11 (November 2012).

Broadway, Chuck. "A U-2 Dragon Lady Pilot: From interview to altitude." *Air Combat Command News.* April 3, 2009. *http://www.acc.af.mil/news/ story.asp?id=123142867.*

Bundgaard, Robert C. "The First Flyover of a Tropical Cyclone." *Weatherwise* 11, no. 3 (June 1958).

Burrows, William E. "The U-Deuce." *Air&Space/Smithsonian* (March 2005).

Cantella, Michael J. "Application of the High Resolution Return Beam Vidicon." *Optical Engineering* 16, no. 3 (June 1, 1977). *http://dx.doi. org/10.1117/12.7972141.*

Combs, Henry G. "U-2 Design and Fabrication." In *Proceedings of the U-2 Development Panel.* Washington, DC: National Reconnaissance Office, September 1998.

Dendy, John B., IV. "Crouching Airmen, Hidden Dragon." *Airman* 46, no. 7 (July 2002).

Gates, Mahlon E., et al. "Operation Morning Light: Northwest Territories, Canada, 1978: A Non-technical Summary of United States Participation." U.S. Department of Energy. NV-198 (1978).

Gentry, Bruce, Matthew McGill, Roman Machan, Daniel Reed, Ryan Cargo, David J. Wilkens, William Hart, John Yorks, Stan Scott, Shane Wake, Michael Hardesty, and Alan Brewer. "Flight Testing of the TWiLiTE Airborne Molecular Doppler Lidar." *http://ntrs.nasa.gov/archive/nasa/casi. ntrs.nasa.gov/20100026400_2010028473.pdf.*

Hennigan, William J. "Skunk Works: Developing top-secret weapons in SoCal for 70 years." *Los Angeles Times,* June 20, 2013.

Hennigan, William J. "U-2 spy plane to linger overhead a bit longer." *Los Angeles Times*, January 28, 2012.

Holm, Skip. "Article Airborne." *Air Progress Aviation Review*, June 1986.

Hotz, Robert. "Lockheed U-2 Over Sverdlovsk: A Study in Fabrication." Reprinted in *Congressional Record, Proceedings and Debates of the 86th Congress, Second Session*, vol. 106, part 9. Washington, DC: U.S. Government Printing Office, June 16, 1960.

Joiner, Ernie L. "Testing the U-2." In *Proceedings of the U-2 Development Panel*. Washington, DC: National Reconnaissance Office, September 1998.

King, Michael D., and Paul Menzel. "First ISCCP Regional Experiment (FIRE) NASA ER-2 Moderate Resolution Imaging Spectroradiometer (MODIS) Airborne Simulator (MAS) Langley DAAC Data Set Document." Atmospheric Data Science Center. October 1996. *https://eosweb.larc.nasa. gov/sites/default/files/project/fire/guide/base_fire_ci2_er2_mas_dataset.pdf.*

Kinkead, E.R., C.L. Gaworski, C.D. Flemming et al. "Tumorigenic Evaluation of Jet Fuels JP-TS and JP-7." Armstrong Laboratory. AL-TR-1991-0020 (April 1991).

Klinger, Robert T. "Flight Test Development of the Lockheed U-2 Airplane." Lockheed Aircraft Corp. SP-109 (November 4, 1958).

Koziol, Benedict J. "The U-2 Aircraft Engine." In *Proceedings of the U-2 Development Panel*. Washington, DC: National Reconnaissance Office, September 1998.

MacGill, Markus. "'Mental-decline brain lesions' found in high-flying military pilots." *Medical News Today.* August 21, 2013. *http://www.medicalnewsto-day.com/articles/265036.php.*

Majumdar, Dave. "Global Hawk to Replace U-2 in 2015." *Defense News*, Digital Edition. August 10, 2011. *http://www.defensenews.com/article/20110810/ DEFSECT01/108100302/Global-Hawk-Replace-U-2-2015.*

Majumdar, Dave. "Notebook: Plans for Reinvigorated U-2 Include Hyperspectral Sensor." *Defense News*, Digital Edition. March 22, 2012. *http://www.defensenews.com/article/20120322/C4ISR02/303220012/ Notebook-Plans-Reinvigorated-U-2-Include-Hyperspectral-Sensor.*

Nickel, Shawn. "Fueling the high flyers—U-2 tube food calms cravings in the cockpit." *Air Combat Command News.* February 8, 2013. *http://www.acc. af.mil/news/story.asp?id=123335478.*

Nicolai, Leland M. "Skunk Works Lessons Learned." In *Strategic Management of the Cost Problem of Future Weapon Systems.* AGARD Conference Proceedings. AGARD-CP-602, September 1998.

O'Leary, Jeremiah A. "NASA Issued U-2 Cover Story on CIA Advice." *Washington Star*, June 1, 1960.

Passon, Ray. "The Early Days of the U-2: How They Did It." *Star Dusters Newsletter*, September 2003.

Pocock, Chris. "Early History of the U-2 Dragon Lady." *Code One Online.* February 2002. *http://www.codeonemagazine.com/article.html?item_id=103.*

Polmar, Norman. "When the U-2 Went to Sea." *Air Force Magazine* 84, no. 2 (February 2001).

Reade, David. "U-2 Spyplanes: What You Didn't Know About Them!" *http:// www.roadrunnersinternationale.com/u-2/u-2_science_3.html.*

Reinert, Bob. "Natick tube foods keep U-2 pilots flying high." *Army News Archives.* January 18, 2013. *http://www.army.mil/article/94301/ Natick_tube_foods_keep_U_2_pilots_flying_high.*

Schogol, Jeff. "Air Force re-pressurizes U-2 cabin to prevent brain lesions in pilots." *Air Force Times*. August 28, 2013. *http://www.airforcetimes.com/article/20130828/NEWS04/308280019/Air-Force-re-pressurizes-U-2-cabin-prevent-brain-lesions-pilots*.

Townsend, Lawrence W. "Radiation exposures of aircrew in high altitude flight." *Journal of Radiological Protection* 21, no. 1 (March 2001).

Van Atta, Richard H., Sidney G. Reed, and Seymour J. Deitchman. "IR Surveillance: Teal Ruby/Hi-CAMP." In *DARPA Technical Accomplishments Vol. II: An Historical Review of Selected DARPA Projects*. Alexandria, VA: Institute for Defense Analyses, April 1991.

Books and Monographs

Aronstein, David C., and Albert C. Piccirillo. *Have Blue and the F-117A: Evolution of the Stealth Fighter*. Reston, VA: American Institute of Aeronautics and Astronautics, 1997.

Bissell, Richard M., Jr., Jonathan E. Lewis, and Frances T. Pudlo. *Reflections of a Cold Warrior: From Yalta to the Bay of Pigs*. New Haven, CT: Yale University Press, 1996.

Churchill, Winston. *Maxims and Reflections*. Boston: Houghton Mifflin Company, 1949.

Jenkins, Dennis R. *Dressing for Altitude: U.S. Aviation Pressure Suits—Wiley Post to Space Shuttle*. Washington, DC: NASA SP-2011-595, 2012.

Merlin, Peter W., and Tony Moore. *X-Plane Crashes*. North Branch, MN: Specialty Press, 2008.

Miller, Jay. *Lockheed Skunk Works: The First Fifty Years*. Arlington, TX: Aerofax, 1993.

Miller, Jay. *Lockheed U-2*. Austin, TX: Aerofax, 1983.

Miller, Jay. *The X-Planes: X-1 to X-45*. Hinckley, U.K.: Midland Publishing, 2001.

Pedlow, Gregory W., and Donald E. Welzenbach. *The CIA and the U-2 Program, 1954–1974*. Washington, DC: Central Intelligence Agency, 1998.

Polmar, Norman. *Spyplane: The U-2 History Declassified*. Osceola, WI: MBI Publishing Company, 2001.

Pocock, Chris. *50 Years of the U-2*. Atglen, PA: Schiffer Military History, 2005.

Pocock, Chris. *The U-2 Spyplane: Toward The Unknown*. Atglen, PA: Schiffer, 2000.

Powers, Francis Gary, and Curt Gentry. *Operation Overflight*. New York: Holt Rinehart and Winston, 1970.

Sóbester, András. *Stratospheric Flight: Aeronautics at the Limit*. New York: Springer-Praxis, 2011.

Other Resources

Alexander, Michael A. "TR-1A/TR-1B/U-2R/ER-2 Handbook." U.S. Air Force, April 1986.

Bailey, Bernard L. Draft memo to NASA from John L. McLucas, Director, National Reconnaissance Office. "Subject: U-2C/G Aircraft." May 16, 1970. *http://www.nro.gov/foia/declass/NROStaffRecords/1055.pdf*.

Bissell, Richard M., Jr. Memorandum for Deputy Project Director. "Arrangements with NACA and Kelly Johnson re Release of U-2 Photographs." CIA SAPC-12313, CIA-RDP33-02415A000200390023-1. January 26, 1957. Declassified and released by the CIA April 11, 2000.

Bissell, Richard M., Jr. Memorandum for Project Cover Officer. "Release of NACA Top Secret Research Data to Select Contractors." CIA SAPC-25666, CIA-RDP33-02415A000200390014-1. March 25, 1958. Declassified and released by the CIA April 11, 2000.

Brown, Alan, and Beth Hagenauer. "NASA's ER-2 Completes MABEL Validation Deployment." May 1, 2012. *http://www.nasa.gov/topics/earth/features/ER-2_completes_MABEL_deployment.html*.

CIA. "Aircraft Accident Investigation, U-2F N800X (342), 25 February 1966." CIA-RDP74B00447R000100010064-1. March 1966. Approved for Release June 18, 2002.

CIA. Chairman of the Planning Group. Memorandum for Project Director. "Planning Group Report." CIA-RDP33-02415A000400040001-9. July 15, 1957.

CIA. Memo from Acting Deputy Director of Plans. "Chronological Account of Handling of U-2 Incident, August 10, 1960." CIA-RDP33-02415A000300300007-7. Declassified and released by the CIA August 21, 2000.

CIA. Memorandum for Project Director. "Cover Research Releases (NACA)." SAPC-8675, CIA-RDP33-02415A000200390031-2. August 22, 1956. Declassified and released by the CIA April 11, 2000.

CIA. Memorandum for Project Security Officer. "Cover Meeting with AWS and NACA." CIA-RDP33-02415A000200390051-1. March 20, 1956. Declassified and released by the CIA April 11, 2000.

CIA. Memorandum. "Proposed NACA Press Release." CIA-RDP33-02415A000200390018-7. April 24, 1957. Declassified and released by the CIA April 11, 2000.

CIA. Memorandum for the Record. "Cover Discussions with NACA." CIA-RDP33-02415A000200390025-9. November 19, 1956. Declassified and released by the CIA April 11, 2000.

CIA. "U-2 Aircraft Carrier Operation: Project Whale Tale." CIA-RDP75B00446R000100210015-3. December 1964. Approved for release September 30, 2003.

CIA. "U-2 Utility Flight Handbook." March 1, 1959.

Coleman, Thomas L., and Emilie C. Coe. "Airplane Measurements of Atmospheric Turbulence for Altitudes Between 20,000 and 50,000 Feet Over the Western Part of the United States." NACA Research Memorandum No. L57G02, August 1957.

Coleman, Thomas L., and Jack Funk. "Preliminary Measurements of Atmospheric Turbulence at High Altitude as Determined from Acceleration Measurements on Lockheed U-2 Airplane." NACA Research Memorandum No. L57A11, March 1957.

Coleman, Thomas L., and May T. Meadows. "Airplane Measurements of Atmospheric Turbulence for Altitudes Between 20,000 and 55,000 Feet for Four Geographic Areas." NASA Memorandum No. 4-17-59L, June 1959.

Cunningham, James A. Memorandum for Project Director. "Proposed Cover Modifications." CIA SAPC-18216, CIA-RDP33-02415A000200390016-9. August 6, 1957. Declassified and released by the CIA April 11, 2000.

Downie, Don, and Jim Jarboe. *The Inquisitive Angel*. A 16-millimeter film documentary produced by Hycon Mfg. Co. for the CIA. April 1957. Declassified in 2006. Roadrunners Internationale collection.

Dryden, Hugh L. "NACA Announces Start of New Research Program." NASA Historical Reference Collection, May 7, 1956.

Dulles, Allen W., Director of Central Intelligence. "Statement to the Senate Foreign Relations Committee." May 31, 1960. *http://www.foia.cia.gov/sites/default/files/document_conversions/89801/DOC_0000009190.pdf.*

Hansen, Kathryn. "PODEX Experiment to Reshape Future of Atmospheric Science." January 16, 2013. *http://www.nasa.gov/topics/earth/features/qa-starr.html.*

Hartley, Frank W., Jr. Draft of memo to John L. McLucas, Director, National Reconnaissance Office. "Subject: U-2C/G Storage Costs." February 26, 1970. *http://www.nro.gov/foia/declass/NROStaffRecords/1056.pdf.*

Johnson, Kelly. "Log for Project X." Lockheed California Company, Advanced Development Projects Division.

Land, Edwin H. Project 3, Technological Capabilities Panel, Office of Defense Mobilization, Executive Office of the President. Memorandum to Allen W. Dulles, Central Intelligence Agency. November 5, 1954. *http://www.gwu.edu/~nsarchiv/NSAEBB/NSAEBB74/U2-03.pdf.*

Lockheed Martin. "Interview with Al Romig, Chief Skunk." July 2013. *http:// www.lockheedmartin.com/us/news/features/2013/roming-interview.html.*

Lockheed Martin. "U-2 Reconnaissance/Surveillance/Earth Resources System Description." Lockheed Advanced Development Company, March 27, 1991.

Merlin, Peter W. "U-2 Cover Story Timeline." NASA Armstrong Flight Research Center historical reference collection, July 2004.

NASA. "ER-2 Airborne Laboratory Experimenter Handbook." August 2002.

NASA. "ER-2 Program History." NASA Fact Sheet. Rich, Ben R. "B.R. Rich Retirement Speech." Ben R. Rich Papers. The Huntington Library, San Marino, CA, January 17, 1991.

NASA. Memorandum describing Project Rainbow cover story. Walter Bonney files. NASA Headquarters Historical Reference Collection. June 21, 1957.

NASA. "NASA Aircraft Sets New World Altitude Record." *Science Daily.* November 24, 1998. *http://www.sciencedaily.com/releases/1998/11/981124064046.htm.*

NASA Ames Research Center staff. *High Altitude Perspective.* NASA SP-427, 1978.

NASA. "NASA ER-2 Flies Over Russia on Ozone research Mission." News Release 00-14. January 27, 2000. *http://www.nasa.gov/centers/dryden/news/ NewsReleases/2000/00-14.html.*

NASA. "ER-2 High Altitude Airborne Science Aircraft." Fact Sheet FS-2007-4-046-DFRC, 2007. *http://www.nasa.gov/centers/dryden/pdf/171831main_ FS-2007-04-046-ER-2.pdf.*

NASA. "NASA SEAC4RS Mission Targets How Pollution, Storms And Climate Mix." June 6, 2013. *http://www.nasa.gov/topics/earth/features/ seac4rs_2013.html.*

Nevada Aerospace Hall of Fame. "Original U-2 Flight Test Crews—1955." Nevada Aerospace Hall of Fame historical collection.

North American Newspaper Alliance. "U.S. Mapping World for Missile War." NASA Headquarters Historical Reference Collection. May 19, 1957.

Rich, Ben R. "The Skunk Works Approach." Ben R. Rich Papers. The Huntington Library, San Marino, CA, July 25, 1990.

U.S. Air Force. "Flight Manual, Models U-2C and U-2F Aircraft." U.S. Air Force AF(C)-1-1, May 10, 1967.

U.S. Air Force. "U-2 Pilot Application." June 14, 2012. *http://www.beale. af.mil/library/factsheets/factsheet.asp?id=5077*.

Yancey, William R. Undated letter (circa 2007) to Hank Meierdierck regarding early U-2 training operations. Roadrunners Internationale historical reference collection. *http://www.nasa.gov/centers/dryden/research/AirSci/ ER-2/history.html*.

"Research Plane Explodes; Altitude Pilot Bails Out," *The Washington Post and Times Herald*, December 20, 1956, p. A2. Clotaire Wood files. NASA Headquarters Historical Reference Collection.

Acknowledgments

The author would like to thank the many people who helped us make this book possible. First of all, thanks to Tony Springer, NASA Aeronautics Research Mission Directorate, Office of Education and Communications, for sponsoring this project. I am grateful for the efforts of many people at NASA Armstrong Flight Research Center including Jim Sokolik, Steve Parcel, and others. Thanks to Barbara Bullock and Ben Weinstein at Media Fusion for preparing the manuscript for publication. Special thanks to the subject matter experts who reviewed the material for technical accuracy—and, especially, to Sarah Merlin for copyediting the final manuscript.

About the Author

Peter W. Merlin has been an aerospace historian under contract to NASA at Armstrong Flight Research Center, Edwards, CA, since 1997. He has authored a variety of books, including several NASA Special Publications on aeronautical research projects, as well as two volumes on aerospace safety. He served as co-author of research pilot Donald Mallick's autobiography, *The Smell of Kerosene: A Test Pilot's Odyssey*, and with Tony Moore co-wrote *X-Plane Crashes—Exploring Experimental, Rocket Plane and Spycraft Incidents, Accidents and Crash Sites*. He has also authored several technical papers for the American Institute of Aeronautics and Astronautics as well as numerous journal articles on aerospace history and technology. In addition, he serves as a contributing editor for historical publications at Armstrong and has appeared in more than a dozen documentary television programs for Discovery, the History Channel, National Geographic, and others. He holds a bachelor of science degree in aviation management from Embry-Riddle Aeronautical University.

Index

Page numbers in **bold** indicate pages with illustrations.

G

H

Q